Lecture Notes in Mathematics

A collection of informal reports and seminars
Edited by A. Dold, Heidelberg and B. Eckmann, Zürich

160

Contributions to Ergodic Theory and Probability

Proceedings of the First Midwestern Conference on Ergodic Theory
held at the Ohio State University, March 27–30, 1970

Organized by
Louis Sucheston, Ohio State University, Columbus, OH/USA

Springer-Verlag
Berlin · Heidelberg · New York 1970

Title No. 3317

Offsetdruck: Julius Beltz, Weinheim/Bergstr.

Lecture Notes in Mathematics

A collection of informal reports and seminars
Edited by A. Dold, Heidelberg and B. Eckmann, Zürich

160

Contributions to Ergodic Theory and Probability

Springer-Verlag
Berlin · Heidelberg · New York

This series aims to report new developments in mathematical research and teaching – quickly, informally and at a high level. The type of material considered for publication includes:

1. Preliminary drafts of original papers and monographs
2. Lectures on a new field, or presenting a new angle on a classical field
3. Seminar work-outs
4. Reports of meetings

Texts which are out of print but still in demand may also be considered if they fall within these categories.

The timeliness of a manuscript is more important than its form, which may be unfinished or tentative. Thus, in some instances, proofs may be merely outlined and results presented which have been or will later be published elsewhere.

Publication of *Lecture Notes* is intended as a service to the international mathematical community, in that a commercial publisher, Springer-Verlag, can offer a wider distribution to documents which would otherwise have a restricted readership. Once published and copyrighted, they can be documented in the scientific literature.

Manuscripts

Manuscripts are reproduced by a photographic process; they must therefore be typed with extreme care. Symbols not on the typewriter should be inserted by hand in indelible black ink. Corrections to the typescript should be made by sticking the amended text over the old one, or by obliterating errors with white correcting fluid. Should the text, or any part of it, have to be retyped, the author will be reimbursed upon publication of the volume. Authors receive 75 free copies.

The typescript is reduced slightly in size during reproduction; best results will not be obtained unless the text on any one page is kept within the overall limit of 18 x 26.5 cm (7 x 10 ½ inches). **The publishers will be pleased to supply on request special stationery with the typing area outlined.**

Manuscripts in English, German or French should be sent to Prof. Dr. A. Dold, Mathematisches Institut der Universität Heidelberg, Tiergartenstraße or Prof. Dr. B. Eckmann, Eidgenössische Technische Hochschule, Zürich.

Die „*Lecture Notes*" sollen rasch und informell, aber auf hohem Niveau, über neue Entwicklungen der mathematischen Forschung und Lehre berichten. Zur Veröffentlichung kommen:

1. Vorläufige Fassungen von Originalarbeiten und Monographien.
2. Spezielle Vorlesungen über ein neues Gebiet oder ein klassisches Gebiet in neuer Betrachtungsweise.
3. Seminarausarbeitungen.
4. Vorträge von Tagungen.

Ferner kommen auch ältere vergriffene spezielle Vorlesungen, Seminare und Berichte in Frage, wenn nach ihnen eine anhaltende Nachfrage besteht.

Die Beiträge dürfen im Interesse einer größeren Aktualität durchaus den Charakter des Unfertigen und Vorläufigen haben. Sie brauchen Beweise unter Umständen nur zu skizzieren und dürfen auch Ergebnisse enthalten, die in ähnlicher Form schon erschienen sind oder später erscheinen sollen.

Die Herausgabe der „*Lecture Notes*" Serie durch den Springer-Verlag stellt eine Dienstleistung an die mathematischen Institute dar, indem der Springer-Verlag für ausreichende Lagerhaltung sorgt und einen großen internationalen Kreis von Interessenten erfassen kann. Durch Anzeigen in Fachzeitschriften, Aufnahme in Kataloge und durch Anmeldung zum Copyright sowie durch die Versendung von Besprechungsexemplaren wird eine lückenlose Dokumentation in den wissenschaftlichen Bibliotheken ermöglicht.

MIDWESTERN CONFERENCE ON ERGODIC THEORY

at the Ohio State University

PROGRAM

FRIDAY, March 27 — Afternoon Session — Room 031 Hitchcock Hall

Chairman: Professor E. Hopf, Indiana University

1:30 PM to 2:20 PM

Professor A. Ionescu Tulcea, Northwestern University
"Super-mean-valued Functions and Semipolar Sets"

2:40 PM to 3:30 PM

Professor P. Erdős, Hungarian Academy of Sciences
"Some Number-theoretic Applications of Probabilistic Methods"

3:50 PM to 4:10 PM

Mr. T. Terrell, Ohio State University
"An n-parameter Local Ergodic Theorem"

4:30 PM to 4:50 PM

Professor H. Fong, University of Michigan
"On Ergodic Theorems for Semi-groups of Positive Operators"

5:10 PM to 5:30 PM

Professor T. Schwartzbauer, Ohio State University
"Approximation and Invariance"

- -

SATURDAY, March 28 — Morning Session — Room 031 Hitchcock Hall

Chairman: Professor R. V. Chacon, University of Minnesota
Visiting Ohio State University

10:30 AM

Welcoming addresses by the representatives of the University: Provost James A. Robinson and Mathematics Department Chairman, Arnold E. Ross.

11:00 AM to 11:50 AM

Professor D. S. Ornstein, Stanford University
"The Isomorphy Theorem"

SATURDAY, March 28 — Afternoon Session — Room 031 Hitchcock Hall

Chairman: Professor P. R. Halmos, Indiana University

2:00 PM to 2:20 PM

Professor E. M. Klimko, Purdue University
"Ratio Theorems for Weak Convergence"

2:40 PM to 3:30 PM

Professor D. L. Hanson, University of Missouri
"On Convergence Rates in Limit Laws"

3:50 PM to 4:20 PM

Professor U. Krengel, Ohio State University
"Transformations Without Finite Invariant Measure Have Finite Strong Generators"

4:50 PM to 5:20 PM

Professor W. Krieger, Ohio State University
"Non-singular Transformations"

- -

SUNDAY, March 29 — Afternoon Session — Room 250 Mathematics Building

Chairman: Professor S. Kakutani, Yale University

1:00 PM to 1:50 PM

Professor K. Jacobs, Erlangen University,
Visiting the Ohio State University
"Strict Ergodicity"

2:10 PM to 2:30 PM

Professor S. Horowitz, University of Minnesota
"On σ-finite Invariant Measures"

2:50 PM to 3:40 PM

Professor A. Brunel, University of Rennes,
Visiting the University of Minnesota
"New Conditions for Existence of Invariant Measures"

4:00 PM to 4:50 PM

Professor M. M. Rao, Carnegie-Mellon University
"Generalized Martingales"

5:10 PM to 5:40 PM

Professor F. Papangelou, Ohio State University
"The Ambrose-Kakutani Theorem and the Poisson Process"

MONDAY, March 30 — Morning Session — Room 031 Hitchcock Hall

Chairman: Professor A. Brunel, University of Rennes,
Visiting the University of Minnesota

9:00 AM to 9:50 AM

Professor Anatole Beck, University of Wisconsin
"Continuous Flows in the Plane"

10:10 AM to 11:00 AM

Professor C. Ionescu Tulcea, Northwestern University
"Liftings and Derivation Bases"

11:20 AM to 12:10 PM

Professor S. Kakutani, Yale University
"Examples of Ergodic Transformations"

- -

MONDAY, March 30 — Afternoon Session — Room 031 Hitchcock Hall

Chairman: Professor A. Ionescu Tulcea, Northwestern University

1:30 PM to 1:50 PM

Professor L. Sucheston, Ohio State University
"Zero-Two Processes"

2:00 PM to 2:50 PM

Professor R. V. Chacon, University of Minnesota
Visiting the Ohio State University
"Finite Spectral Multiplicity"

3:10 PM to 4:00 PM

Professor D. S. Ornstein, Stanford University
"The Isomorphy Theorem, II"

- -

Besides those appearing on the program the following mathematicians attended the conference:

Mustafa A. Akcoglu, University of Toronto
Robert E. Atalla, Ohio University
Joseph Auslander, University of Maryland
Kenneth R. Berg, University of Maryland
Jürgen Bliedtner, Erlangen University
L. W. Goodwyn, University of Kentucky
D. J. Hebert, Jr., University of Pittsburgh
Choo-Whan Kim, Simon Fraser University
Larry Klimko, Pennsylvania State University
S. Natarajan, Florida State University
Michael Weiss, Wayne State University

- -

Louis Sucheston

CONTENTS

CONTINUOUS FLOWS IN THE PLANE

by Anatole Beck
University of Wisconsin

Topological Dynamics has its roots deep in the theory of differential equations, specifically in that portion called the "qualitative theory". The most notable early work was that of Poincaré and Bendixson, regarding stability of solutions of differential equations, and the subject has grown around this nucleus. It has developed now to a point where it is fully capable of standing on its own feet as a branch of Mathematics studied for its intrinsic interest and beauty, and since the publication of *Topological Dynamics* by Gottschalk and Hedlund, it has been the subject of widespread study in its own right, as well as for the light it sheds on differential equations. The *Bibliography for Topological Dynamics* by Gottschalk contains 690 entries in the 1966 edition, and progress in the field since then has been even more prodigious.

The study of dynamical systems is an idealization of the physical studies bearing such names as aerodynamics, hydrodynamics, electrodynamics, etc. We begin with some space (call it X) and we imagine in this space some sort of idealized particles which change position as time passes. This change of position is in accordance with some rule or principle or formula φ. Without inquiring into the nature of the idealized particles, we simply state that after a time t, the particle which was at x will be transposed to the position $\varphi(t,x)$. Both x and $\varphi(t,x)$, being positions, or "space variables" are elements of the underlying space X. If our study were abstract aerodynamics, then certain physical considerations, such as compressability, pressure gradients, inertia, *etc*. would be reflected in specific laws concerning $\varphi(t,x)$ as a function of t and x. If it were hydrodynamics, different restraints on φ would apply. In the study of abstract dynamical systems, we replace these physical laws with mathematical considerations.

The most important mathematical constraint is the *flow equation*, also known as the *group property*: $\varphi(t_1,\varphi(t_2,x)) = \varphi(t_1+t_2,x)$. What this says basically is that as the particles move, the behavior at each point does not change with the passage of time. Various special disciplines have their own names for this phenomenon.

Stochastic processes which obey the flow equation are called stationary; differential equations which obey it are called autonomous. But they are special cases of this general principle of consistency of action at each location as time passes. If the flow equation is satisfied for all real values of t_1 and t_2, then it is a semi-flow.

In addition to the flow equation itself, we usually impose another condition on φ, and the nature of this other condition defines for us which of the several categories of dynamics we are studying. In our forthcoming book*, we will study continuous flows, i.e. those in which φ is a continuous function of t and x together. To do this, we must suppose that X is a topological space. Alternatively, we might have taken X to be a probability space and φ to be measurable. In that case, our study would have become that of stationary stochastic processes. We might have gone further and required that φ be measure-preserving, or ergodic, and each of these conditions would put us in one of the special categories of dynamics, many of which are venerable studies with their own vocabularies and histories. Especially important are the cases in which X is a topological linear space or an analytic manifold and in which the function

$$\dot{\varphi}(x) = \lim_{t \to 0} \frac{\varphi(t,x) - x}{t}$$

exists at each point. These are the autonomous differential equations, which we see from the vantage point of dynamical theory as differential flows. There are important subclasses of the differential flows, in which the function $\dot{\varphi}(x)$ is continuous, or Lipschitzian, or differentiable in x, or even multiply differentiable in x. These are called continuous, or Lipschitzian, or C_1 differential equations, or, in the other cases, C_2, C_∞ or even analytic differential equations.

The study in our book concerns itself with continuous flows in $\mathbb{R}^2$, the Euclidean plane. The plane is an especially simple space, fully available to our visual intuition, and abundantly studied. Amont its special properties in the Jordan

---

* Continuous Flows In The Plane, by Anatole Beck with the assistance of Jonathan and Myrtle Lewin. To be published in the series Grundlehren der Mathematischen Wissenschaften (Springer-Verlag, Heidelberg).

Curve Theorem. Together with its corollary, the Theta Curve Theorem, it enables us to prove a basic result, the Gate Theorem, which simplifies the analysis of the orbits of any flow in the plane. It is interesting to see how the orbits of flows fit into the classical concepts of the theory of differential equations.

We might note that the differential equation $\frac{dy}{dx} = f(x,y)$ can be thought of as assigning to each point (x,y) of the plane a specific direction. Some treatments of differential equations do in fact think of the plane as being filled with tiny "lineal elements", one at each point, and directed according to the required slope. This concept is not far from the autonomous differential equation $= f(\ )$, where and are two-dimensional vectors. In this latter situation, the lineal element is replaced by a vector. In the first case, a solution of the differential equation is a curve which has at each point the slope specified by the equation. In the second case, a solution is such a curve, given in parametric form with time as a parameter. If we imagine a particle moving so that its position at time t is (t), then the velocity of that particle at that time will be $f(\ (t))$. In a certain sense, we could imagine the whole set of solution curves to be the solution in the first case. In the same way, we could think of the whole set of motions as constituting the solution of the second equation. This last construction is a motion of the whole plane, and it is something very like a flow. Conversely, if a flow φ is a differential flow and the velocity $\dot{\varphi}(\ )$ satisfies $\dot{\varphi}(\ ) = f(\ )$, then we can think of φ as a solution of the differential equation $= f(\ )$.

However, the theory of differential equations usually focuses on the individual solution curves, raising the question of which curve passes through a given (initial) point. In the corresponding flow, the place of this curve is taken by the focus of points traversed by a particle which at some time is located at this initial point. If the system is a semi-flow, we are only interested in its path for positive time; if a flow, for positive and negative time. These curves are called the positive semi-orbit and the orbit respectively, and "trajectory" is sometimes used as a synonym for "orbit". The collection of solution curves is often called the phase diagram of a flow.

One of our major efforts will be to delineate, as well as we can, the possible orbit diagrams of continuous flows in the plane. In keeping with a topological approach to this problem, we will consider our question answered when we have obtained a solution up to a homeomorphic equivalence. By this we mean that if φ and ψ are flows in $\mathbb{R}^2$ (or in any topological space) which are related by a homeomorphism h in such a way that $\varphi(t,h(x)) = h(\psi(t,x))$, for all t and x, then for most purposes, we will not distinguish between φ and ψ. In such a situation, for example, the orbit diagrams will be homeomorphic.

As with any study, we will attack first the easy cases, in the hope that the tools acquired there will aid us in the more difficult ones. This raises immediately the question of which added conditions will yield a simple and understandable structure. It is especially in this area that our work brings forth a new insight. The theory of differential equations has classically considered that complexity of structure attends those points where the derivative vanishes, and has approached such points with elaborate care, using for them frightening names, such as critical point and singular point, which suggest that order and regularity end wherever such points are found. Indeed, if we stay away from such points, we find that the orbit diagrams consist locally of more or less "parallel" curves, and it is from such considerations that much of the qualitative theory of differential equations derives. These critical points are represented in the theory of flows as fixed points, and indeed if a flow has a Lipschitzian derivative, then every critical point is indeed a fixed point. But not all fixed points are equally difficult to manage; some are rather easy and some are quite complex. We have learned to be especially wary of what we call stagnation points, fixed points which are limit points of other orbits. Whenever a flow divides to avoid an obstacle, or changes direction, or shows any other signs of what we intuitively understand as "turbulence", stagnation points must come into the picture. And when a flow proceeds without stagnation points, things are rather simple, even though other fixed points might abound. It is thus these stagnation points, and other points clovely associated with them (details of this must be sought in the body of the book) that we designate as singular points, and they include both fixed and moving points.

As an example of the difference created by this insight, we might consider the classic paper *Global structure of ordinary differential equations in the plane*, by Lawrence Markus, in which he discusses continuous differential equations (*i.e.* differential flows) in $\mathbb{R}^2$ with no critical (*i.e.* fixed) points. The analysis is quite difficult and is based in turn on some very subtle work of Wilfred Kaplan. This difficulty and complexity arises, from our point of view, from the fact that ∞ is a stagnation point, and a limit point of every orbit. Thus, in our concept, every point in the plane is a singular (moving) point, and it is not surprising that the results are so hard to obtain. This singularity of the flow is made manifest only in the neighbourhood of ∞; in any bounded portion of the plane, it is not possible to distinguish it from a translation flow (up to a homemorphism). Such observations as these convince us that any fruitful approach to flows in $\mathbb{R}^2$, which will reveal the true complexities, must consider them rather as flows in S^2, the two-dimensional sphere, considered as the one-point compactification of $\mathbb{R}^2$. Every flow in the plane can be considered as a flow in the sphere which has ∞ as a fixed point; every flow in S^2 having a fixed point at ∞ can be thought of as a flow in $\mathbb{R}^2$. Since every (continuous) flow in S^2 has a least one fixed point, the theory of flows in the plane and that of flows in the sphere are equivalent.

Returning now to our concentration on stagnation points, we take for our simplest flows those with no stagnation points in S^2 (not even at ∞). There is actually a simpler category, namely flows having only periodic orbits (including fixed points in this class), and we deal with these as well. But the flows without any stagnation points are the largest class for which we know essentially everything; not only the orbit diagrams but even the time structures on those diagrams. In the case of flows with only finitely many stagnation points, we have discovered much, but not the same sort of coverage as the "no-stagnation points" case. For flows whose stagnation points have countable closure, we are almost equally well informed. In each of these cases, for example, we can characterize completely the set $\mathfrak{F}(\varphi)$ of fixed points by intrinsic topological properties without reference to flows, over and above the condition satisfied by the fixed set of any flow (*i.e.* that $\mathfrak{F}(\varphi)$ be closed).

The most useful general tool in all these characterizations is this: that in the case of each flow φ, we can describe completely the structure of $_r(\varphi)$ is revealed as a result of a major theorem called the Gate Theorem, which tells us roughly that if a moving point y belongs to the closure of another orbit $\mathcal{O}(x)$, then $\mathcal{O}(x)$ divides S^2, in some sense, just as a periodic orbit (Jordan curve) does. Thus, the Gate Theorem is a generalization, in a sense, of the Jordan Curve Theorem, and it is this generalization which is the clue to the structure of continuous flows in the plane.

In addition to the principle thrust outlined above, our book contains studies based on some of the major techniques used to obtain the central theorems. Inter alia, it contains the entire texts of the doctoral dissertations of Jonathan Lewis and Myrtle Lewin on, respectively, reparametrization of flows and algebraic combinations of flows. Together, we have presented an introduction to a vital area of study, somewhat neglected in recent years, which offers to be a gateway to the study of Topological Dynamics and of Ordinary Differential Equations.

Among the results of special interest to specialists in Ergodic Theory is the following, which comes directly from our methods:

THEOREM: If φ is any continuous flow in S^2, then we can find disjoint open sets U_1 and U_2 which are invariant under φ. Furthermore, S^2 is the only compact, orientable 2-manifold with this property.

NEW CONDITIONS FOR EXISTENCE OF INVARIANT
MEASURES IN ERGODIC THEORY.

by A. Brunel

0. Introduction - In this note we consider the following situation: let be T a positive contraction on a space $\mathcal{L}^1(X,\mathfrak{F},\mu)$ where $(X,\mathfrak{F},\mu)$ is a σ-finite measure space. The first problem, denoted by $\mathcal{P}$, is

$\mathcal{P}$ - Does there exist in $\mathcal{L}^1_+(X,\mathfrak{F},\mu)$ an element f satisfying

(i) $Tf = f$ (a.e.),

(ii) $\mu(\{f = 0\}) = 0$.

In the following, as is customary in ergodic theory, we will not distinguish between functions in the same equivalence class (mod μ) and we will denote by L^1 (and L^∞) the quotient space $\mathcal{L}^1(X,\mathfrak{F},\mu)/\mathfrak{n}$ (and $\mathcal{L}^\infty(X,\mathfrak{F},\mu)/\mathfrak{n}$), $\mathfrak{n}$ being the space of null functions. If f is a solution of $\mathcal{P}$, then $\nu = f\cdot\mu$ is a finite invariant measure, $\mu \sim \nu$, because

$$(1)\ \forall h \in L^\infty \int T^*h\, d\nu = \int T^*h\, f\, d\mu = \int h\, Tf\, d\mu = \int h\, d\nu .$$

It is known that it is possible to extend T and T* to the space $\mathcal{M}^+$ of all $\mathfrak{F}$-measurable, non negative functions, or more accurately to the quotient space $M_+ = \mathcal{M}_+/\mathfrak{n}$. Then (1) is also true for every $h \in M_+$.

The last section of the present work is devoted to the case of σ-finite invariant measures, that is to say, to the problem $\mathcal{P}'$:

$\mathcal{P}'$ - Does there exist $f \in M_+$ satisfying

(i') $Tf = f$

(i'i') $\mu(\{f=0\} \cup \{f = +\infty\}) = 0$,

but we will consider only conservative operators. Without loss of generality we can also suppose that μ is a probability measure. Let us briefly see why.

Let $\mu' = f_0\mu \sim \mu$ be a probability measure and define T' as follows:

$$\varphi \in M_+ \quad T'\varphi = \frac{1}{f_0} T(f_0\varphi) .$$

It is easy to check that T' is a contraction on $L^1(X,\mathfrak{F},\mu')$ and $T'^* = T^*$. Now if f is a solution of $\mathcal{P}$ (or $\mathcal{P}'$), $\frac{f}{f_0}$ is a solution of $\mathcal{P}$ (or $\mathcal{P}'$) for T'.

The theorems we will prove deal with the concept of derived contractions. First, we define what is meant by the term.

Definition 1 - A derived contraction of T is an operator U defined by

$$U = \sum_{j\geq 0} a_j T^j \quad \text{with} \quad a_j \geq 0, \ \sum_{j\geq 0} a_j = 1.$$

We will denote by $\mathcal{S}(T)$ the set of these operators.

The main result of this work is

Theorem 1 - Problem $\mathcal{P}$ has a solution if and only if all derived contractions of T are conservative.

In section 1 some results of Neveu [1] and Dean and Sucheston [2] are recalled and a lemma that is an immediate consequence of these results is proved. Section 2 contains two technical lemmas of elementary analysis - In section 3, theorem 1 is proved and, by the same method, a proposition giving a characterization of the strongly closed sub-space $\overline{(1-T)(L^1)}$. In section 4 we extend theorem 1 to the case of the problem $\mathcal{P}'$ when T is markovian. The method of proof of theorem 2 is very close to that we applied in our thesis [3] for reducing $\mathcal{P}'$ to $\mathcal{P}$ when T is conservative, combined with an argument like that in the proof of Theorem 1.

1. - Neveu [1] and Dean and Sucheston [2] proved that $\mathcal{P}$ has a solution if and only if T^* satisfies the condition:

(2) $\forall\ h \in L^\infty_+ \quad \liminf_n \int T^{*n}h \cdot d\mu = 0 \Rightarrow h = 0$.

From (2) J. Neveu deduced a condition like the one given by Hajian and Kakutani in the case of point transformations. We will use an equivalent form of that condition, namely

(3) $\quad L^\infty_+ \cap \overline{(1-T^*)L^\infty} = \{0\}$. ([3] and S. Horowitz [4]).

Now let be $V = \frac{1}{e}\exp(T) = \sum_{j\geq 0} \frac{1}{e \cdot j!} T^j \in \mathcal{S}(T)$.

<u>Lemma 1</u> - $\mathcal{P}$ has no solutions if and only if there exists

$$h \in L^\infty_+ \text{ , } h \neq 0, \text{ such that } \lim_n \|V^{*n} h\|_\infty = 0 \text{ .}$$

<u>Proof</u> - Let us write $V^n = \sum_{j\geq 0} \alpha_{j,n} T^j$ with $\alpha_{j,n} = \frac{n^j}{e^n j!}$; $j, n \in N$.

We have $\quad \alpha_{j,n} \leq \alpha_{j+1,n}$ if $j < n$

$$\alpha_{j,n} > \alpha_{j+1,n} \quad \text{if } j \geq n$$

$$\max_{j\geq 0} (\alpha_{j,n}) = \alpha_{n,n} = O(n^{-\frac{1}{2}}) \text{ .}$$

Then,

$$(1-T)V^n = \sum_{j\geq 0} (\alpha_{j,n} - \alpha_{j-1,n}) T^n, \ (\alpha_{-1,n} = 0),$$

which gives,

$$(4) \qquad \|(1-T^*)V^{*n}\|_\infty = \|(1-T)V^n\| \leq \sum_{j\geq 0} |\alpha_{j,n} - \alpha_{j-1,n}| = 2\alpha_{n,n} \text{ .}$$

Now if $\mathcal{P}$ has no solution there exists $h \in L^\infty_+ \cap \overline{(1-T^*)L^\infty}$, $h \neq 0$ and this together with (4) shows that $\lim_n \|V^{*n} h\|_\infty = 0$. On the other **hand** , if $g = Tg \in L^1_+$, $g = Vg$ too and the condition of the lemma implies that $\int g\, h\, d\mu = 0$ so that (ii) cannot be satisfied.

2. Let be $\mathcal{D}$ the set of real sequences $(c_j)_{j\in N}$ satisfying,

D_1 $\quad c_o \geq 1, \quad j \in N, \ c_j > 0$.

D_2 $\quad \left(\frac{c_j + 1}{c_j}\right)_{j\in N}$ is a non decreasing sequence and $\lim_j \left(\frac{c_{j+1}}{c_j}\right) = 1$.

D_3 $\quad \sum_{j\geq 0} c_j = +\infty$.

The sequences of $\mathcal{D}$ satisfy the following lemma:

<u>Lemma 2</u> - With each $(c_j) \in \mathcal{D}$, there exists a real sequence (a_j), non negative, $\sum_{j\geq 0} a_j = 1$, such that

$$\frac{1}{1 - \sum_{j\geq 0} a_j z^j} = \sum_{j\geq 0} c_j z^j \quad \text{when } |z| < 1.$$

Proof - We have to establish that the following system of equations on the a_n,

$$c_o(1-a_o) = 1$$

$$c_1(1-a_o) - c_o a_1 = 0$$

$$c_n(1-a_o) - c_{n-1}a_1 \cdots - c_o a_n = 0$$

has a solution satisfying the conditions of the lemma. We have $a_o = 1 - \frac{1}{c_o} \geq 0$. Suppose that $a_1, a_2, \cdots a_n \geq 0$ and let us set $\frac{c_{n+1}}{c_n} = t$. D2 implies that

$$c_n a_1 + c_{n-1}a_2 + \cdots c_1 a_n \leq t(c_{n-1}a_1 + \cdots + c_o a_n) = tc_n(1-a_o) = c_{n+1}(1-a_o),$$

then $a_{n+1} \geq 0$. The radius of convergence of $\sum_{j\geq 0} c_j z^j$ is 1, according to D2. Then $\sum_{j\geq 0} a_j \leq 1$ and D3 implies the equality.

Lemma 3 - If $(b_j)_{j\in N}$ is a real non negative sequence and $\lim_n (b_n) = 0$, there exist $(c_j) \in \mathcal{D}$ such that $\sum_{j\geq 0} b_j c_j < +\infty$.

Proof - Let us choose a decreasing positive sequence $(\alpha_j)_{j\in N}$ such that $\sum_{j\geq 0} \alpha_j < +\infty$ and a real number ρ_o, $0 < \rho_o < 1$. Now we define the integers $(m_k)_{k\in N}$ in the following way:

Suppose that (b_n) is not increasing and let

(5) $m_o = \text{card}(\{j \in N \mid b_j \geq \alpha_o\}), \cdots, m_k = \text{card}(\{j \in N \mid \alpha_{k-1} > b_j \geq \alpha_k\}), \cdots$

Let be n_o the least integer such that

$$n_o \geq m_o \quad \text{and} \quad \rho_o^{n_o} \leq \min(1-\rho_o, \tfrac{1}{2}).$$

Now, if $\rho_1, n_1, \cdots \rho_k, n_k$ have been chosen, let

(6) $$\rho_{k+1} = 1 - \rho_o^{n_o} \rho_1^{n_1} \cdots \rho_k^{n_k},$$

and let be n_{k+1} the least integer such that

(7) $$n_{k+1} \geq m_{k+1} \quad \text{and} \quad \rho_{k+1}^{n_{k+1}} \leq \min\left(\frac{1-\rho_{k+1}}{1-\rho_k}, \frac{1}{2}\right).$$

We are going to show that the sequence

$$(c_j)_{j \in \mathbb{N}}: 1, \rho_o, \dots, \rho_o^{n_o}, \rho_o^{n_o}\rho_1, \dots, \rho_o^{n_o}\rho_1^{n_1}, \rho_o^{n_o}\rho_1^{n_1}\rho_2, \dots$$

is an element of $\mathcal{D}$ and satisfies the conditions of the lemma. First, (6) implies $1-\rho_{k+1} < 1-\rho_K$ for every $K \geq 0$. Then $(\rho_j)_{j \in \mathbb{N}}$ is an increasing sequence and (6) and (7) imply $\lim_n(\rho_n) = 1$, so that (c_j) satisfies D1 and D2.

Then we have

$$\sum_{j \geq 0} c_j = \frac{1-\rho_o^{n_o}}{1-\rho_o} + \rho_o^{n_o} \frac{1-\rho_1^{n_1}}{1-\rho_1} + \dots + \rho_o^{n_o} \dots \rho_{k-1}^{n_{k-1}} \frac{1-\rho_k^{n_k}}{1-\rho_k} + \dots$$

and taking into account (6) and (7),

$$\sum_{j \geq 0} c_j \geq \sum_{k \geq 1} (1-\rho_k^{n_k}) = +\infty, \text{ because } 1-\rho_k^{n_k} \geq \frac{1}{2} .$$

To complete the proof we write

$$\sum_{j \geq 0} b_j c_j \leq \sum_{k \geq 0} a_k \rho_o^{n_o} \dots \rho_{k-1}^{n_{k-1}} \frac{1-\rho_k^{n_k}}{1-\rho_k} \leq \sum_{k \geq 0} a_k < +\infty ,$$

using (5), (6), and (7).

If (b_n) is not monotone we have only to replace (b_n) by (b'_n), $b'_n = \sup_{j \geq n} (b_j)$ and notice that $\lim_n(b'_n) = 0$.

3. <u>Proof of Theorem 1</u>

Suppose that the problem $\mathcal{P}$ has no solutions. By Lemma 1, there exists $h \in L^\infty_+$, $h \neq 0$ such that $\lim_n \|V^{*n}h\| = 0$. Lemma 3 guarantees the existence of a sequence $(c_j) \in \mathcal{D}$ such that

(8) $$\sum_{j \geq 0} c_j \|V^{*j}h\|_\infty < +\infty ,$$

and (8) implies:

$$h' = \sum_{j \geq 0} c_j V^{*j} h \in L^\infty .$$

Now let (a_j) be the sequence associated with (c_j) as in lemma 2 and let

$U = \sum_{n \geq 0} a_n V^n$. $U \in \mathscr{D}(V)$, then $U \in \mathscr{D}(T)$.

Lemma 2 shows that $1 + \sum_{k \geq 0} (\sum_{j \geq 0} a_j z^j)^k = \sum_{j \geq 0} c_j z^j$ if $|z| < 1$.

Let be $a_j^{(k)}$ the real numbers defined by

(9) $\sum_{j \geq 0} a_j^{(k)} z^j = (\sum_{j \geq 0} a_j z^j)^k$ so that $c_j = \sum_{k \geq 0} a_j^{(k)}$,

and $c_{n,p} = \sum_{k=0}^{p} a_n^{(k)}$. It is clear that

$$\sum_{k=0}^{p} U^{*k} h = \sum_{n=0}^{\infty} c_{n,p} V^{*n} h \leq h' ,$$

then $\sum_{k \geq 0} U^{*k} h \in L^\infty$ and U is not conservative. The converse is obvious, because if $Tf = f \in L^1$, $Wf = f$ for every $W \in \mathscr{D}(T)$ so that if the problem $\mathscr{P}$ has a solution each derived contraction W of T is conservative.

Using the same methods as the preceding ones we want to prove now a theorem giving the nature of the space $\overline{(1 - T)L^1}$.

<u>Theorem 1'</u> - For every $g \in \overline{(1 - T)L^1}$ (or $g \in \overline{(1 - T^*)L^\infty}$), there exists $g' \in L^1$ (or $g' \in L^\infty$) and $U \in \mathscr{D}(T)$ (or $\mathscr{D}(T^*)$), such that $g = g' - Ug'$.

<u>Proof</u> - As in lemma 1, we have $\lim_n \|V^n g\| = 0$. (We do not write $\|\cdot\|_1$ because the following proof works also for V^*, $g \in L^\infty$ and $\|\cdot\|_\infty$). We can find $(c_j) \in \mathscr{D}$ such that

$$\sum_{j \geq 0} c_j \|V^j g\| < +\infty .$$

Let be $U = \sum_{j \geq 0} a_j V^j$, where (a_j) is related to (c_j) as in lemma 2. We are going to prove the convergence in L^1 (or L^∞) of the series $\sum_{k \geq 0} U^k g$ and it is sufficient to prove that the sequence $S_n = \sum_{k=0}^{n} U^k g$ is a Cauchy sequence. Let be p,q integers, $p < q$. An estimate of $\|S_q - S_p\|$ is obtained as follows:

$$S_q - S_p = \sum_{k=p+1}^{q} U^k g = \sum_{n \geq 0} (c_{n,q} - c_{n,p+1}) V^n g, \text{ and}$$

$$\|S_q - S_p\| \leq \sum_{n\geq 0} (c_n - c_{n,p+1})\|V^n g\| .$$

Because $\lim_p \sum_{n\geq 0} c_{n,p}\|V^n g\| = \sum_{n\geq 0} c_n\|V^n g\|$, we have too,

$$\lim_{\substack{p\to+\infty \\ p<q}} \|S_q - S_p\| = 0 .$$

Let $g' = \lim_p S_p = \lim_p \sum_{k=0}^{p} U^k g$ which gives

$$g' - Ug' = \lim_p (g - U^{p+1} g) = g .$$

4. The problem $\mathcal{P}'$ of σ-finite invariant measures.

We want to give a statement similar to Theorem 1. First we have to replace the notion of conservativity by a new concept. That will be as follows,

Definition 2 - To each $u \in L^\infty$, $u > 0$, is associated a vector subspace L_u of L^∞ defined by

$$L_u = \{\varphi \in L^\infty \mid \exists \varphi \in \mathbb{R}_+ \exists W \in \mathscr{D}(T),\ |\varphi| \leq \varphi W^*(u)\},$$

and let

$$\{\varphi\}_u = \inf\{\lambda \in \mathbb{R}_+ \mid \exists\, W \in \mathscr{D}(T),\ |\varphi| \leq \lambda W^*(u)\}.$$

It is obvious from this definition that $\|\varphi\|_\infty \leq \{\varphi\}_u \cdot \|u\|_\infty$, so that $\{\cdot\}_u$ is a norm on the real vector space L_u. It is clear too that $T^*(L_u) \subset L_u$ and $\{T^*\varphi\}_u \leq \{\varphi\}_u$. If u is the constant function 1, $L_u = L^\infty$ and $\{\varphi\}_u = \|\varphi\|_\infty$.

Definition 3 - T is called u-conservative if

$$\varphi \in L_u^+ \quad \sum_{j\geq 0} T^{*j}\varphi \in L_u \Rightarrow \varphi = 0 .$$

The goal of this section is to prove

Theorem 2 - If T is a conservative operator, the problem $\mathcal{P}'$ has a solution if and only if there exists $u \in L^\infty$, $u > 0$ such that every derived contraction of T is u-conservative.

Our conjecture is that theorem 2 is valid without the restriction of T being conservative.

A - The condition is necessary - Let be f a solution of $\mathcal{P}'$. Then $Uf = f$ for every $U \in \mathcal{S}(T)$. Let us choose $u \in L^\infty$, $u > 0$ such that $\int u f d\mu < +\infty$. If $\sum_{j\geq 0} U^{*j} \varphi \in L_u$, and $\varphi \in L_u^+$, $\int (\sum_{j\geq 0} U^{*j}\varphi) f d\mu < +\infty$ that implies $\varphi = 0$ so that U is u-conservative.

B - The condition is sufficient. We will prove that if u is given and $\mathcal{P}'$ has no solution, there exist $U \in \mathcal{S}(T)$ and $h \in L_u^+$, $h \neq 0$, such that $\sum_{k\geq 0} U^{*k} h \in L_u$.

First notice that if f is a solution of $\mathcal{P}'$ and u is chosen as in A with $0 < u \leq 1$, we can write $f = T(uf) + T((1-u)f) = T(uf) + T_u(f)$, letting $T_u(\varphi) = T[(1-u)\varphi]$. More generally,

$$f = \sum_{j=0}^{n-1} T_u^j(Tuf) + T_u^n(f) \quad \text{for every integer } n \geq 1.$$

But $T_u^n(f)$ is a non increasing sequence in M_+ with limit 0. Because if $g = \lim_n T_u^n(f)$, we have $f \geq g = T_u(g) = Tg - T(ug)$, $Tg - g = T(ug)$. Let $g' = Tg - g$. Then, for every integer n,

$$\sum_{k=0}^{n-1} T^k g' = T^n g - g \leq f - g; \; g' \in L_+^1 ,$$

and taking into account the property of conservativity of T,

$$g' = 0 \text{ that implies } u g = 0, \text{ then } g = 0.$$

Now letting $R_u = \sum_{k\geq 0} T_u^k$, we can write

(10) $f = R_u(Tuf)$ and $uf = \mathcal{J}(uf)$ where $\mathcal{J} = uR_uT$.

The operator $\mathcal{J}$ is a positive contraction on L^1 because

$$(1 - T_u^*)(1) = 1 - (1-u)T^*\mathbf{1} = u, \; R_u^*(u) = 1 - \lim_n T_u^{*n}(1) \leq 1,$$

so that $\mathcal{J}^*(1) = T^*(R_u^*(u)) \leq 1$.

Now (10) proves that uf is a solution of $\mathcal{P}$ for $\mathcal{J}$. Then $\mathcal{J}$ is conservative and $R^*_u(u) = 1$.

Conversely if g is a solution of the problem $\mathcal{P}$ for $\mathcal{J}$, let be $f = \frac{1}{u} g$. Then $uf = uR_u T f u$, $f = R_u Tfu$, and

$$(I - T_u)(f) = f - T(1-u) = T(uf) \Rightarrow Tf = f,$$

and f also satisfies the condition (i'i') of $\mathcal{P}'$.

Now let be u, $0 < u \leq 1$, and consider the space L_u.

<u>Lemma</u> 4 - L_u equipped with $\{\cdot\}_u$ is a Banach space.

<u>Proof</u> - Let be (φ_n) a Cauchy sequence in L_u. We extract a subsequence (φ_{n_k}) such that

$$\{\varphi_{n_{k+1}} - \varphi_{n_k}\}_u < 2^{-k} \ ; \ k = 0,1,2,\cdots$$

According the definition 2 this implies the existence of real non negative numbers $\lambda_j^{(k)}$ satisfying the conditions

$$(11) \quad \sum_{j \geq 0} \lambda_j^{(k)} \leq 2^{-k}, \ |\varphi_{n_{k+1}} - \varphi_{n_k}| \leq \sum_{j \geq 0} \lambda_j^{(k)} T^{*j}(u).$$

Then $\psi = |\varphi_{n_0}| + \sum_{k \geq 0} |\varphi_{n_{k+1}} - \varphi_{n_k}| \in L_u$. On the other hand, (φ_n) is a Cauchy sequence in L^∞. Let be $\varphi = \lim_n \varphi_n$. φ is in L_u because $|\varphi| \leq \psi$ and (11) implies $\{\varphi - \varphi_{n_k}\}_u \leq 2^{-k+1}$ so that $\varphi_{n_k} \xrightarrow{L_u} \varphi$ and also $\varphi_n \xrightarrow{L_u} \varphi$.

We will use the operator $\mathcal{J}$ defined by (10) and $\mathcal{S} = TuR_u$ that is a contraction of L^1 too. We have

$$(12) \quad \forall \varphi \in L^\infty \ (1 - T^*)\mathcal{S}^*(\varphi) = u[(1 - \mathcal{J}^*)T^*(\varphi)],$$

that is proved as follows,

$$(1 - T^*)\mathcal{S}^*(\varphi) = (1 - T_u^*)\mathcal{S}^*(\varphi) - uT^*\mathcal{S}^*(\varphi) = (1 - T_u^*)R_u^* uT^*\varphi - uT^*R_u^* uT^*(\varphi)$$

$$= uT^*(\varphi) - u\mathcal{J}^*T^*(\varphi) = u[(1 - \mathcal{J}^*)T^*(\varphi)].$$

The mapping $\Theta : \varphi \to (1 - T^*)\mathcal{S}^*(\varphi)$ sends L^∞ into L_u and Θ is continuous because

$$\{(1 - T^*)\mathcal{S}^*(\varphi)\}_u \leq \|(1 - \mathcal{J}^*)T^*(\varphi)\|_\infty \leq 2\|\varphi\|_\infty \text{ by (12).}$$

The adjoint $\Theta^* : L_u^* \to (L^\infty)^*$ can be written $\Theta^* = \mathcal{S}(1 - T)$ and

$$\mathcal{J} = \ker(1 - T) \subset \ker(\Theta^*).$$

According to the duality between L_u and L_u^*,

$$(1 - T^*)\mathcal{S}^*(L^\infty) \subset \mathcal{J}^\perp .$$

But it is known that $\mathcal{J}^\perp = \overline{(1 - T^*)L_u}$ (strong closure under $\{\cdot\}_u$), and taking into account the results of section 1 about $V = \frac{1}{e}\exp(T)$,

$$\forall\ \varphi \in L^\infty \quad \lim_n \left\{V^{*n}(1 - T^*)\mathcal{S}^*(\varphi)\right\}_u = 0 .$$

The problem $\mathcal{P}$ having no solution for $\mathfrak{J}$, there exists $h_1 \in L_+^\infty$, $h_1 \neq 0$, in the L^∞ - closure of $(1 - \mathfrak{J}^*)(L^\infty)$, so that for every $\epsilon > 0$ there exists $\varphi \in L^\infty$ such that $\|T^*h_1 + (1 - \mathfrak{J}^*)T^*\varphi\|_\infty \leq \epsilon$, then letting $h = uT^*h_1$,

$$\lim_n \left\{ V^{*n}(h) \right\}_u = 0 .$$

As it was done in the proof of theorem 1, we can find $(c_j) \in \mathcal{D}$ such that,

$$\sum_{j \geq 0} c_j \left\{ V^{*j}(h) \right\}_u < +\infty$$

and the proof is concluded in the same way as it was done for theorem 1.

Bibliography

1 J. Neveu C.R. Acad. Sc. Paris, t. 260(11 Jan v. 1965).

2 D. Dean and L. Sucheston On invariant measures for operators. Z. Wahrscheinlichkeits-theorie verw. Geb. 6, 1-9 (1966).

3 A. Brunel Thesis.

4 S. Horowitz A note on σ-finite invariant measures. (To appear)

APPROXIMATION AND SPECTRAL MULTIPLICITY

by

R. V. Chacon
University of Minnesota

0. Introduction. In the theory of functions a powerful tool has been the method of approximation. A familiar result which deals with this sort of problem is, for example, the Weierstrass approximation theorem. The general idea is to use certain simple functions to approximate an arbitrary function of a class, and then to use the properties of the simple functions to obtain results for the class in question.

Several recent papers [1] - [8], [9], [10] have been concerned in a general way with this approach in the context of ergodic theory, but have been limited by an apparent defect in the methods thus far considered. It had turned out that the transformations which could be approximated have simple spectrum. In the present paper we extend the results so that they apply to transformations having finite (and, by a small extension, infinite) spectral multiplicity and show that the degree of finiteness of the spectral multiplicity limits precisely the type of approximation which is possible. These methods are very well suited to the construction of wide classes of transformations. In a forthcoming paper we have applied some of the ideas outlined here to solve the problem of the existence of a strongly mixing transformation which has roots only of certain specified orders.

1. Preliminaries. As usual, we let $(X, \mathfrak{F}, \mu)$ be the unit interval, the Lebesgue sets and Lebesgue measure. By a transformation (automorphism) τ we mean a one-to-one mapping of X onto itself such that $A \in \mathfrak{F}$ implies that $\tau(A), \tau^{-1}(A) \in \mathfrak{F}$ and $\mu(A) = \mu(\tau(A)) = \mu(\tau^{-1}(A))$, where $\tau(A) = \{y: y = \tau x, x \in A\}$. The transformation τ induces a unitary transformation U_τ on $L_2(X, \mathfrak{F}, \mu)$ obtained by setting $U_\tau f(x) = f(\tau x)$. By the spectral properties of τ we mean the spectral properties of U_τ restricted to the orthogonal complement of the constant functions. There are some well-known results from spectral theory which we shall use and for the sake of convenience we'll list them here.

If U is a unitary operator of a separable Hilbert space H then for each

$f \in H$ there is a unique measure μ_f on the unit circle C of the complex plane such that

$$(1) \qquad (U^n f, U^m f) = \int_C z^{n-m} \mu_f (dz),$$

$n, m = 0, \pm 1, \ldots$. For each $f \in H$ we let $H(f) = \overline{\{\ldots, U^{-1}f, f, Uf, \ldots\}}$ and if $H(f) = H$ then f is said to be a generator of U . Operators having generators are called cyclic and if f and g are generators then $\mu_f \overset{\sim}{=} \mu_g$.

If U is unitary, then U can be written as the orthogonal sum of cyclic unitary operators $U = U_1 \oplus U_2 \oplus \ldots$, with $H = H_1 \oplus H_2 \oplus \ldots$, U_i acting on H_i, and with the corresponding measures being restrictions of the preceeding ones, i.e. there exist Borel subsets $\{E_n\}$, $C \supset E_n \supset E_{n+1}$, such that $\mu_i (A) = \mu_1(A \cap E_i)$, where $\mu_i = \mu_{f_i}$, and we have also that the sequence is unique up to equivalence. We say that the spectrum has multiplicity k if $\mu_1 \neq 0, \ldots, \mu_k \neq 0, \mu_{k+1} = 0$.

2. Definition of Approximability.

Definition 2.1. A partition $\xi = \{C_0, \ldots, C_q\}$ is a collection of pairwise disjoint measurable sets. If $A \in \mathfrak{F}$, by $A(\xi)$ we mean the set made up of sets of ξ with the property that $\mu(A \,\Delta\, A(\xi))$ is a minimum.

Definition 2.2. A sequence $\{\xi(n)\}$ of partitions converges to the unit partition, and we write $\xi(n) \to \epsilon$, provided that for each measurable set A, $\mu(A \,\Delta\, A(\xi(n))) \to 0$.

We are interested in a more general type of approximation, but for the sake of clarity we first give a restricted definition.

Definition 2.3. The transformation τ admits of simple approximation with multiplicity N if there exists a sequence $\{\xi(n)\}$ of partitions such that the sets of $\xi(n)$ may be indexed as follows

$$\xi(n) = \{C_{ij}(n),\ i = 1,\ldots,q_j(n);\ j = 1,\ldots,N\}$$

and

$$\text{i)} \quad \xi(n) \to \epsilon,\ n \to \infty,$$

$$\text{ii)} \quad \tau C_{ij}(n) = C_{i+1j}(n),\ i = 1,\ldots,q_j(n) - 1;\ j = 1,\ldots,N.$$

Intiutively, we may regard $\xi(m)$ in the following way. The sets $C_{i1}(m)$,

$i = 1,\dots, q_1(m)$, are arranged in a stack, with $C_{11}(m)$ at the bottom $C_{21}(m)$ above it, and so on, with $C_{q_1(m)1}(m)$ at the top. The same procedure is followed with $C_{i2}(m)$, $i = 1,\dots,q_2(m)$, with $C_{i3}(m)$, $i = 1,\dots,q_3$, and so on, yielding N stacks of heights $q_1(m),\dots,q_N(m)$. The action of τ is then, by ii), to map each point of each stack to the one directly above (actually, we should say that the sets can be so arranged), except for those points on the top layers, where the transformation τ is not restricted by $\xi(m)$, although ultimately it is by some $\xi(n)$, $n \geq m$, as we see by i).

We also will discuss a second type of approximation. It is, of course, possible to give a difinition which includes both of these as special cases. Unfortunately it is somewhat involved so that we prefer instead to treat these cases separately. The second type is the following:

Definition 2.4. The transformation τ admits of approximation with multiplicity N and speed $(f_1(n),\dots,f_N(n))$ if there exists a sequence $\{\xi(n)\}$ of partitions with $\xi(n) = \{C_{ij}(n),\ i = 1,\dots,q_j(n);\ j = 1,\dots,N\}$ such that

i) $\xi(n) \to \varepsilon,\ n \to \infty$,

ii) $\mu(C_{ij}(n)) = \delta_j(n),\ i = 1,\dots,q_j(n),\ j = 1,\dots, N$.

iii) $$\sum_{i=1}^{q_j(n)-1} \mu(\tau C_{ij}(n) \,\Delta\, C_{i+1j}(n)) < f_j(1/\delta_j(n))\quad j = 1,\dots,N.$$

Although we shall not construct examples in this paper, we note that it is possible to give examples, for each N, of transformations which admit of simple approximation with multiplicity N which do not admit of simple approximation with multiplicity N-1.

3. Principal Results. We start with a simple result for operators in Hilbert space which generalizes results given in [9] and [6].

Theorem 3.1. If U is a unitary operator on a separable Hilbert space H and if the spectral multiplicity of U is at least k, then there exist k orthonormal vectors $u_1,u_2,\dots,u_k$ in H such that

$$\sum_{i=1}^{k} d^2 (u_i, H(w)) \geq k - 1$$

for any $w \in H$, $H(w) = \overline{\{\ldots, U^{-1}w, w, Uw, \ldots\}}$.

Proof: Since the spectral multiplicity of U is at least k, $U = U_1 \oplus \ldots \oplus U_k \oplus \ldots$ where $\mu_1 \neq 0, \mu_2 \neq 0, \ldots, \mu_k \neq 0$ and since μ_{i+1} is a restriction of μ_i, $i = 1,\ldots,k-1$, there exists a Borel set E such that $\mu_1(E) = \mu_2(E) = \ldots = \mu_k(E)$. We let $\hat{u}_1,\ldots,\hat{u}_k$, be the vectors in $H_1,\ldots,H_k$ which correspond to the characteristic function of E under the spectral isomorphism, and then define

$$u_i = \hat{u}_i / \|\hat{u}_i\|, \quad i = 1,\ldots,k .$$

We note that w can be approximated arbitrarily closely by an expression of the form

$$\sum_{j=1}^{M} Q_j(U,U^{-1})f_j , \quad M \geq k,$$

where f_j is a generator of H_j. We have therefore, that for $\epsilon > 0$,

$$d^2(u_i,H(w)) > \inf\,(u_i,g) - \epsilon, \quad i = 1,\ldots,k, \tag{3.1}$$

where g is of the form

$$g = P(U,U^{-1}) \left(\sum_{j=1}^{k} Q_j(U,U^{-1})\, f_j \right) ,$$

(we have dropped the terms from $k+1$ on since we are interested in an inequality, and since u_i, $i = 1,\ldots,k$ is perpendicular to H_j, $j \geq k+1$). We have by (3.1) and by the spectral isomorphism that

$$d^2(u_i,H(w)) > \int |\alpha \chi_E - P_i Q_i|^2 + \sum_{\substack{j=1 \\ j\neq i}}^{k} \int |P_i Q_j|^2 - \epsilon, \quad i = 1,\ldots,k, \text{ and}$$

which implies that

$$d^2(u_i,H(w)) > \int_E |\alpha \chi_E - P_i Q_i|^2 + \sum_{j=1, j\neq i}^{k} |P_i Q_j|^2 - \epsilon, \; i = 1,\ldots,k, \text{ and}$$

$\alpha^2 = 1/\mu/E)$. The theorem follows, then, if we show that at each point of E

$$\sum_{i=1}^{k} \{ |1 - (1/\alpha)P_i Q_i|^2 + \sum_{j=1, j\neq i}^{k} |(1/\alpha)P_i Q_j|^2 \} \geq (k-1) .$$

This is, however, a simple consequence of the Cauchy-Schwartz inequality, as we can see by letting $A_i = (1/\alpha)\ P_i$, and rearranging terms to obtain that it is sufficient to show that

$$1 - 2 \sum_{i=1}^{k} |A_i||Q_i| + \sum_{i=1}^{k} \sum_{j=1}^{k} |A_i|^2\ |Q_j|^2 \geq 0 .$$

We note that it is clear from the definition that if τ admits of simple approximation with multiplicity N, then it also admits of simple approximation with multiplicity M, $M \geq N$, and therefore we can only expect to bound the spectral multiplicity in terms of the multiplicity of simple approximation. The theorem which yields this bound is the following:

Theorem 3.2. If τ admits of simple approximation with multiplicity N, then the spectral multiplicity of τ is at most N.

Proof: Suppose that the spectral multiplicity is greater than N. Then by Theorem 3.1 there exist $N + 1$ orthonormal vectors $u_1, u_2, \ldots, u_{N+1}$ such that for any $w \in H$

$$\sum_{i=1}^{N+1} d^2\ (u_i, H(w)) \geq N .$$

If τ admits of simple approximation with multiplicity N, then exists a sequence $\{\xi(n)\}$ of partition with $\xi(n) = \{C_{ij}(n),\ i = 1,\ldots,q_j(n);\ j = 1,\ldots,N\}$. We let

$$W_j(n) = \chi_{C_{ij}}(n) .$$

For $j = 1,\ldots,N$ we have by Theorem 3.1 that

$$(3.2) \qquad \sum_{i=1}^{N+1} d^2(u_i, H(w_j(n))) \geq N .$$

We have also that each u_i, $i=1,\ldots,N+1$, can be written

$$u_i(n) = u_{i\,1}(n) + \ldots + u_{iN}(n) + h_i(n)$$

where

i) $\|h_i(n)\| \to 0$,

ii) $d^2(u_{ik}(n), H(w_k(n))) = 0$, $k = 1,\ldots,N$,

and

iii) $u_{ik}(n)$, $k = 1,\ldots,N$, have disjoint support.

This follows easily by taking $u_{ij}(n)$ as the linear combination of the functions $\chi_{C_{ij}(n)},\ldots,\chi_{C_{q_j(n)j}(n)}$ closest to u_i. Next, we have that

$$d^2(u_i, H(w_j(n))) = d^2(u_{i1}(n) + \ldots + u_{iN}(n) + h_i(n), H(w_j(n))$$

$$\leq \sum_{k=1}^{N} d^2(u_{ik}(n), H(w_j(n))) + \epsilon_i(n) ,$$

where $\epsilon_i(n) \to 0$ as $n \to \infty$. Combining this with (3.2) we obtain that

$$\sum_{k=1}^{N} \sum_{i=1}^{N+1} d^2(u_{ik}(n), H(w_j(n))) \geq N + \epsilon(n) \tag{3.3}$$

where $\epsilon(n) = \epsilon_1(n) + \ldots + \epsilon_{N+1}(n)$. Finally, summing over j, we have that

$$\lim_{n\to\infty} \sum_{\substack{i=1,\ldots,N+1 \\ j,k=1,\ldots,N}} d^2(u_{ik}(n), H(w_j(n))) \geq N^2 . \tag{3.4}$$

We have by (ii) that

$$d^2(u_{ik}(n), H(w_k(n))) = 0 , \; k = 1,\ldots,N . \tag{3.5}$$

It is clear that

$$\|u_{ik}(n)\|^2 \geq d^2(u_{ik}(n), H(w_j(n))) \; k = 1,\ldots,N, \tag{3.6}$$

and since the $u_{ik}(n)$, $k=1,\ldots,N$ have disjoint support and $\|h_i(n)\| \to 0$,

$$\|u_i\|^2 = \lim_{n\to\infty} \sum_{k=1}^{N} \|u_{ik}(n)\|^2. \tag{3.7}$$

Substituting (3.5) and (3.6) into (3.4) yields

$$\lim_{n\to\infty} (N-1) \sum_{\substack{i=1,\ldots,N+1 \\ k=1,\ldots,N}} \|u_{ik}(n)\|^2 \geq N^2$$

from which we obtain, with (3.7), that

$$\lim_{n\to\infty} (N-1) \sum_{i=1,\ldots,N+1} \|u_i(n)\|^2 \geq N^2$$

which is impossible since $u_i(n)$, $i = 1,\dots,N+1$ have unit length.

An analogous result can be obtained for the second type of approximability as well, and it may be stated in the following way, extending, even for $N = 1$, a result given in [9].

<u>Theorem 3.3</u>. If τ admits of approximation with multiplicity N and speed $(\theta_1/n,\dots,\theta_N/n)$, $\theta_i < 2/N+1$, $i = 1,\dots,N$, then the spectral multiplicity of τ is at most N.

<u>Proof</u>: The proof is similar to that of theorem 3.2. We again suppose that the spectral multiplicity is greater than N and hence that there exist $N + 1$ orthonormal vectors $u_1,u_2,\dots,u_{N+1}$ such that for any $w \in H$

$$(3.8) \qquad \sum_{i=1}^{N+1} d^2(u_i, H(w)) \geq N .$$

If τ admits of approximation with multiplicity N and speed $(\theta_1/n,\dots,\theta_N/n)$, $\theta_i < 1$, then there exists a sequence $\{\xi(n)\}$ of partitions with $\xi(n) = \{C_{ij}(n)$, $i = 1,\dots,q_j(n);\ j = 1,\dots,N\}$ and speed $(\theta_1/n,\dots,\theta_N/n)$, $\theta_i < 1$. We let

$$A_j(n) = \bigcap_{i=1}^{q_j(n)} \tau^{1-i}\, C_{ij}(n),\ j = 1,\dots,N,$$

so that

$$\tau^{i-1} A_j(n) \subset C_{ij}(n),\ i = 1,\dots,q_j(n);\ j = 1,\dots,N .$$

We also have that

$$(3.9) \qquad \mu(A_j) > \delta_j(n) - \frac{1}{2} \sum_{i=1}^{q_j(n)-1} \mu(\tau C_{ij}(n) \,\Delta\, C_{i+1j}(n))$$

$$> \delta_j(n)\,(1 - \theta_j/2) .$$

We then let

$$w_j(n) = \chi_{A_j(n)} .$$

For $j = 1,\dots,N$ we have by theorem 3.1, as in the proof of theorem 3.2, that

$$(3.10) \qquad \sum_{i=1}^{N+1} d^2(u_i, H(w_j(n))) \geq N .$$

We have also that each u_i, $i = 1,\dots,N+1$, can be written

$$u_i(n) = u_{i1}(n) + \dots + u_{iN}(n) + h_i(n)$$

where

$$\text{i)} \quad \|h_i(n)\| \to 0,$$

$$\text{ii)} \quad d^2(u_{ik}(n), H(w_k(n))) \le \|u_{ik}(n)\|^2 \ \theta_k/2,$$

and

$$\text{iii)} \quad u_{ik}(n),\ k = 1,\dots,N \ \text{have disjoint support.}$$

This follows easily, as in the previous theorem, by taking $u_{ij}(n)$ as the linear combination of the functions $\chi_{C_{1j}(n)},\dots \chi_{C_{q_j(n)j}}(n)$ closest to u_i. Part ii) follows from the inequality (3.9).

We also have that

$$d^2(u_i, H(w_j(n))) = d^2(u_{i1}(n) + \dots + u_{iN}(n) + h_i(n), H(w_j(n)))$$

$$\le \sum_{k=1}^{N} d^2(u_{ik}(n), H(w_j(n))) + \epsilon_i(n),$$

where $\epsilon_i(n) \to 0$ as $n \to \infty$. Combining this with (3.8) we have that

$$\text{(3.11)} \qquad \sum_{k=1}^{N} \sum_{i=1}^{N+1} d^2(u_{ik}(n), H(w_j(n))) \ge N + \epsilon(n)$$

where $\epsilon(n) = \epsilon_1(n) + \dots + \epsilon_{N+1}(n)$. Summing over j we have that

$$\text{(3.12)} \qquad \lim_{n\to\infty} \sum_{\substack{i=1,\dots,N+1 \\ j,k=1,\dots,N}} d^2(u_{ik}(n), H(w_j(n))) \ge N^2.$$

We have by ii) that

$$\text{(3.13)} \qquad d^2(u_{ik}(n), H(w_k(n))) \le \|u_{ik}(n)\|^2 \ \theta_k/2,\ k = 1,\dots, N .$$

It is again clear that

$$\text{(3.14)} \qquad \|u_{ik}(n)\|^2 \ge d^2(u_{ik}, H(w_j(n))),\ \ k = 1,\dots, N,$$

and since the $u_{ik}(n)$, $k = 1,\dots,N$ have disjoint support and $\|h_i(n)\| \to 0$,

$$\text{(3.15)} \qquad \|u_i\|^2 = \lim_{n\to\infty} \sum_{k=1}^{N} \|u_{ik}(n)\|^2 .$$

Substituting (3.13), (3.14) and (3.15) into (3.12) yields

$$\lim_{n\to\infty} \left\{ \sum_{\substack{i=1,\ldots,N+1\\ k=1,\ldots,N}} (N-1)\ \|u_{ik}(n)\|^2 + \|u_{ik}(n)\|^2\ \theta_k/2 \right\} \geq N^2$$

from which we obtain, with (3.15), that

$$\lim_{n\to\infty} \sum_{i=1,\ldots,N+1} [N-1 + (1/2) \max_{1\leq k\leq N} \theta_k]\ \|u_i(n)\|^2 \geq N^2$$

and since the $u_i(n)$ are orthonormal, that

$$N^2 - 1 + (N+1)/2 \max_{1\leq k\leq N} \theta_k \geq N^2$$

or that

$$\max_{1\leq k\leq N} \theta_k \geq 2/N+1,$$

which is impossible.

BIBLIOGRAPHY

[1] Akcoglu, M. A., Chacon, R. V., and Schwartzbauer, T., Commuting transformations and mixing, to appear, Proc. Amer. Math. Soc.

[2] Baxter, J., A class of ergodic automorphisms, Thesis, University of Toronto, 1969.

[3] Chacon, R. V., A geometric construction of measure preserving transformations, Fifth Berkeley Symposium on Probability and Statistics, (2) 2, pp. 335-360, (1967).

[4] Chacon, R. V., Weakly mixing transformations which are not strongly mixing, to appear.

[5] Chacon, R. V., Approximation of transformations with continuous spectrum, to appear.

[6] Chacon, R. V., Spectral properties of measure preserving transformations, to appear.

[7] Chacon, R. V. and Schwartzbauer, T., Commuting point transformations, to appear.

[8] Halmos, P. R., Lectures on ergodic theory, Math. Soc. of Japan, (1956), Chelsea.

[9] Katok, A. B. and Stepin, A. M., Approximation of ergodic dynamical systems by periodic transformations (Russian), Dokl, Akad. Nauk SSSR, 171, pp. 1268-1271 (1966) (Soviet Math. Dokl., 7, pp. 1638-1641, (1966)).

[10] Katok, A. B. and Stepin, A. M., Approximations in ergodic theory (Russian), Uspekhi Math. Nauk, (5) 22, pp. 81-106 (1967) (Russian Math. Surveys (5) 22, pp. 77-1-2, (1967)).

[11] Ornstein, D. S., A mixing transformation that commutes only with its powers, to appear.

[12] Rokhlin, V. A., On the fundamental ideas of measure theory (Russian), Math Sbor. 67, pp. 107-150, (1949) (Amer. Math. Soc. Translation No. 71, (1952)).

[13] Rokhlin, V. A. Lectures on the entropy theory of measure-preserving transformations (Russian), Uspekhi Math. Nauk, (5) 22, pp. 3-56, (1967) (Russian Math. Surveys, (5) 22, pp. 1-52, (1967)).

APPROXIMATION AND INVARIANCE

by

R.V. Chacon and T. Schwartzbauer

1. Introduction. The method of approximation by periodic transformations has proved to be an effective means of investigating the properties of measure perserving transformations. References [1] through [4], for example, deal with such properties as ergodicity, weak mixing, and strong mixing. The present paper concerns itself with the following question. If a transformation T can be approximated by periodic transformations at a certain rate of speed and if E is a set which is invariant under T, with what speed can T restricted to E be approximated? The methods of approximation used in the above references are too inflexible to deal with this question and so we make use of the more general method of approximation introduced in [5].

2. Definitions. Let $(X,\mathfrak{F},\mu)$ denote the unit interval, the Lebesque measurable sets, and Lebesque measure. An invertible transformation T of X onto X will be called an automorphism if and only if $TA \in \mathfrak{F}$ whenever $A \in \mathfrak{F}$ and if $\mu(A) = \mu(T^{-1}A) = \mu(TA)$ for any $A \in \mathfrak{F}$. If $TA = A$ we say that A is invariant under T.

If $E \in \mathfrak{F}$ and $\mu(E) > 0$ then $(E,\mathfrak{F}_E,\mu_E)$ denotes the measure space consisting of the set E, the Lebesque measurable subsets of E, and the measure μ_E where $\mu_E(A) = \mu(A)/\mu(E)$ for all $A \in \mathfrak{F}_E$.

Definition 2.1. If $\xi = \{C_i, i=1,\cdots q\}$ is a collection of pairwise disjoint measurable sets such that $\bigcup_{i=1}^{q} C_i \subset X$, we say that ξ is a partition. If in addition $\bigcup_{i=1}^{q} C_i = X$, we say that ξ is a partition of X.

If ξ is a partition and $A \in \mathfrak{F}$ then among those sets which are unions of the elements of ξ there is at least one whose symmetric difference with A has minimal measure. We denote any one of these sets by $A(\xi)$.

Definition 2.2. If $\xi(n) = \{C_i(n),\ i = 1,2,\cdots,q(n)\}$ is a sequence of partitions such that $\lim_{n\to\infty} \mu(A \Delta A(n)) = 0$ for each $A \in \mathfrak{F}$, we write $\xi(n) \to \epsilon$ as $n \to \infty$. If $E \in \mathfrak{F}$ and $\xi(n)$ is a sequence of partitions whose elements are subsets of E, then we write $\xi(n) \to \epsilon_E$ as $n \to \infty$ if $\lim_{n\to\infty} \mu(A \Delta A(n)) = 0$ for each measurable subset A of E.

Definition 2.3. Let $\{f(n)\}$ be a monotonic sequence of positive numbers such that $\lim_{n\to\infty} f(n) = 0$. We say that the automorphism T admits an approximation with speed $f(n)$ if for each positive integer n there exists a partition $\xi(n) = \{C_i(n),\ i = 1,2,\cdots q(n)\}$ such that

1. $\xi(n) \to \epsilon$ as $n \to \infty$

2. $\lim_{n=\infty} \sum_{i=1}^{q(n)} \left| \mu(C_i(n)) - \frac{1}{q(n)} \right| = 0$,

3. $\sum_{i=1}^{q(n)} \mu(T C_i(n) \cap C'_{i+1}(n)) < f(q(n))$,

where $C'_{i+1}(n)$ indicates the complement of the set $C_{i+1}(n)$ with respect to the whole space and where $C_{q(n)+1}(n)$ is understood to be $C_1(n)$.

Definition 2.4. If T is an automorphism and $E \in \mathfrak{F}$ such that $TE = E$, then we say that T restricted to E admits an approximation with speed $f(n)$ if T considered as an automorphism on the measure space $(E, \mathfrak{F}_E, \mu_E)$ admits an approximation with speed $f(n)$.

3. Properties of the Method of Approximation.

The following lemmas, stated and proved in [5], exhibit certain properties of the partitions $\xi(n)$ which will be used in proving the results of §4.

Lemma 3.1. Let $\xi(n) = \{C_i(n),\ i = 1,\cdots,q(n)\}$ be a sequence of partitions such that $\lim_{n\to\infty} \sum_{i=1}^{q(n)} \left| \mu(C_i(n)) - \frac{1}{q(n)} \right| = 0$. Fix a number η, $0 < \eta < 1$, and define the set

$$I_\eta(n) = \{i, \left|\mu(C_i(n)) - \frac{1}{q(n)}\right| > \frac{\eta}{q(n)}\}$$

then

$$\lim_{n\to\infty} \sum_{i\in I_\eta(n)} \mu(C_i(n)) = 0 .$$

Proof. It is easily seen that $\sum_{i\in I_\eta(n)} \mu(C_i(n))$ is majorized by

$$\left(\frac{1}{\eta}+1\right) \sum_{i=1}^{q(n)} \left| \mu(C_i(n)) - \frac{1}{q(n)} \right| .$$

Lemma 3.2. Let $\xi(n) = \{C_i(n), i = 1,2,\cdots q(n)\}$ be a sequence of partitions such that $\xi(n) \to \epsilon$ as $n \to \infty$. Fix a number η, $0 < \eta < 1$, and define for $E \in \mathfrak{F}$,

$$I_{\eta,E}(n) = \{ i \mid \mu(E \cap C_i(n)) < (1-\eta)\mu(C_i(n))\}.$$

Let $G(n)$ be the set determined by

$$E(\xi(n)) = \sum_{i\in G(n)} C_i(n),$$

then $$\lim_{n\to\infty} \sum_{i\in G(n)\cap I_{\eta,E}(n)} \mu(C_i(n)) = 0 .$$

Proof. Under the given hypotheses we have

$$\sum_{i\in G(n)\cap I_{\eta,E}(n)} \mu(C_i(n)) \le \frac{1}{\eta}\, \mu(E \,\Delta\, E(\xi(n))) .$$

In the following lemma $G(n)$, $I_\eta(n)$, and $I_{\eta,E}(n)$ refer to the sets defined in lemma 3.1 and lemma 3.2.

Lemma 3.3. Let $\xi(n) = \{C_i(n), i = 1,\cdots q(n)\}$ be a sequence of partitions such that $\xi(n) \to \epsilon$ as $n \to \infty$ and $\lim_{n\to\infty} \sum_{i=1}^{q(n)} \left| \mu(C_i(n)) - \frac{1}{q(n)} \right| = 0$. Then if $E \in \mathfrak{F}$ there exists a sequence $\{\eta_n\}$ of positive numbers such that $\lim_{n\to\infty} \eta_n = 0$ and such that if $H(n) = G(n) \cap I'_{\eta_n}(n) \cap I'_{\eta_n,E}(n)$ then

$\lim_{n\to\infty} \frac{N(H(n))}{q(n)} = \mu(E)$ **where** $N(H(n))$ denotes the number of elements in $H(n)$.

Proof. If the sequence $\{\eta_n\}$ is chosen properly we can assume, by choosing a subsequence of the partitions $\xi(n)$ if necessary, that

$$\lim_{n\to\infty} \sum_{i\in I_{\eta_n}(n)} \mu(C_i(n)) = \lim_{n\to\infty} \sum_{i\in I_{\eta_n,E}(n)} \mu(C_i(n)) = 0$$

so that

$$\sum_{i\in H(n)} \mu(E\cap C_i(n)) \le \mu(E) \le \sum_{i\in H(n)} \mu(C_i(n)) + \sum_{i\in H'(n)} \mu(E\cap C_i(n))$$

which implies that

$$\overline{\lim_{n\to\infty}}\, N(H(n)) \frac{(1-\eta_n)^2}{q(n)} \le \mu(E) \le \underline{\lim}_{n\to\infty} N(H(n)) \frac{(1+\eta_n)}{q(n)}$$

which gives us $\lim_{n\to\infty} \frac{N(H(n))}{q(n)} = \mu(E)$.

4. Approximation and Invariance.

Theorem 4.1. If T admits an approximation with speed $f(n)$ and if $E_1, E_2, \cdots E_K$ are pairwise disjoint sets which are invariant under T, then T restricted to E_k admits an approximation with speed $f_k(n) + \delta_n$ where

$$\delta_{q_k(n)} = o(f(q(n))) \text{ and } \sum_{k=1}^{K} \mu(E_k) f_k(q_k(n)) \le f(q(n))$$

where $q_k(n)$ denotes the number of elements in the n-th partition in the approximation of T restricted to E_k.

Proof. Let $\{\eta_n\}$ be the sequence of positive numbers defined in lemma 3.3. Let the set $H_k(n)$ be determined by $i \in H_k(n)$ if

$$\left| \mu(C_i(n)) - \frac{1}{q(n)} \right| < \frac{\eta_n}{q(n)} \text{ and } \mu(E_k \cap C_i(n)) \ge (1-\eta_n)\mu(C_i(n)) .$$

Define $D_1^{(k)}(n) = E_k \cap C_{i(1)}(n)$ where $i(1)$ is the least integer in $H_k(n)$. We will define a sequence of sets $D_1^{(k)}(n), D_2^{(k)}(n), \cdots D^{k}_{q_k(n)}(n)$ inductively. Assume that $D_1^{k}(n), \cdots D_j^{(k)}(n)$ have been defined and that $D_j^{(k)}(n) = E_k \cap C_{i(j)}(n)$ for some $i(j) \in H_k(n)$. Let $i(j+1)$ denote the least element in $H_k(n)$ greater than $i(j)$. If for some integer i, $i(j) < i < i(j+1)$ we have

$$\left| \mu(C_i(n)) - \frac{1}{q(n)} \right| < \frac{\eta_n}{q(n)} \text{ and } \mu(E_k' \cap C_i(n)) > (1-\eta_n)\mu(C_i(n))$$

we define $D^{(k)}_{j+1}(n) = E_k \cap C_{i(j+1)}(n)$. Otherwise we define

$$D^{(k)}_{j+\ell}(n) = E_k \cap C_{i(j)+\ell}(n) \quad \text{for} \quad \ell = 1,2,\cdots,i(j+1) - i(j).$$

Since $H_k(n)$ is a finite set, the process will terminate with $j = q_k(n)$, for some integer $q_k(n)$, where $D^{(k)}_{q_k(n)+1}(n) = D^{(k)}_1(n)$.

Clearly $\lim_{n\to\infty} \mu\left(\bigcup_{j=1}^{q_k(n)} D^{(k)}_j(n)\right) = \lim_{n\to\infty} \frac{q_k(n)}{q(n)} = \mu(E_k)$

and if $\xi_k(n) = \{D^{(k)}_j(n),\ j = 1,\cdots q_k(n)\}$ then $\xi_k(n) \to \epsilon_{E_k}$ as $n \to \infty$.

There are now two cases to consider:

(1) Suppose that $D^{(k)}_j(n) = E_k \cap C_{i(j)}(n)$ and $D^{(k)}_{j+1}(n) = E_k \cap C_{i(j)+1}(n)$, then

$$\mu(T D^{(k)}_j(n) \cap D^{(k)}_{j+1}(n)) = \mu(T E_k \cap T C_{i(j)}(n) \cap (E_k \cap C_{i(j)+1}(n))')$$

$$= \mu(E_k \cap T C_{i(j)}(n) \cap (E'_k \cup C'_{i(j)+1}(n)) = \mu(E_k \cap T C_{i(j)}(n) \cap C'_{i(j)+1}(n))$$

$$\leq \mu(T C_{i(j)}(n) \cap C'_{i(j)+1}(n)).$$

(2) If on the other hand $D^{(k)}_j(n) = E_k \cap C_{i(j)}(n)$ and $D^{(k)}_{j+1}(n) = E_k \cap C_{i(j)+N}(n)$ for $N > 1$ then for some ℓ, $1 \leq \ell < N$ we have

$$\left| \mu(C_{i(j)+\ell}(n)) - \frac{1}{q(n)} \right| < \frac{\eta_n}{q(n)} \quad \text{and}$$

$$\mu(E'_k \cap C_{i(j)+\ell}(n)) \geq (1-\eta_n)\mu(C_{i(j)+\ell}(n)) \geq \frac{(1-\eta_n)^2}{q(n)},$$

so that $\sum_{m=i(j)}^{i(j)+\ell-1} \mu(T C_m(n) \cap C'_{m+1}(n)) \geq \frac{(1-\eta_n)^2}{q(n)} - \frac{\eta_n(1+\eta_n)}{q(n)} = \frac{1-3\eta_n}{q(n)}$

Therefore

$$\mu(T D^{(k)}_j(n) \cap D^{(k)}_{j+1}{}'(n) \leq \mu(D^{(k)}_j(n))$$

$$\leq \frac{1+\eta_n}{q(n)} \leq \sum_{m=i(j)}^{i(j)+\ell-1} \mu(T C_m(n) \cap C'_{m+1}(n)) + \frac{4\eta_n}{q(n)},$$

Let $M_k(n)$ denote the number of times that this second case occurs. We then have

$$\sum_{j=1}^{q_k(n)} \mu_{E_k}(T D_j^{(k)}(n) \cap D_{j+1}^{(k)'}(n)) \le f_k(q_k(n)) + \frac{4M_k(n)\eta_n}{\mu(E_k)q(n)}$$

where

$$\sum_{k=1}^{K} \mu(E_k) f_k(q_k(n)) \le \sum_{i=1}^{q(n)} \mu(T C_i(n) \cap C'_{i+1}(n)) < f(q(n)).$$

Since $M_k(n)\frac{(1-3\eta_n)}{q(n)} \le f(q(n))$, if we define $\delta_{q_k(n)} = \frac{4M(n)\eta_n}{\mu(E_k)q(n)}$ it is immediately clear that $\delta_{q_k(n)} = o(f(q(n)))$.

Let $\epsilon_n^{(k)} = \left| \frac{q_k(n)}{q(n)} - \mu(E_k) \right|$ then $\lim_{n\to\infty} \epsilon_n(k) = 0$ and we have

$$\sum_{j=1}^{q_k(n)} \left| \mu_{E_k}(D_j^{(k)}(n)) - \frac{1}{q_k(n)} \right| = \frac{1}{\mu(E_k)} \sum_{j=1}^{q_k(n)} \left| \mu(D_j^{(k)}(n) - \frac{\mu(E_k)}{q_k(n)} \right|$$

$$\le \frac{1}{\mu(E_k)} \left(\sum_{j=1}^{q_k(n)} \left|(\mu(D_j^{(k)}(n) - \frac{1}{q(n)} \right| + \sum_{j=1}^{q_k(n)} \left|\frac{1}{q(n)} - \frac{\mu(E_k)}{q_k(n)} \right|\right)$$

$$\le \frac{1}{\mu(E_k)} \left(\eta_n \frac{q_k(n)}{q(n)} + \frac{1}{q_k(n)} \sum_{j=1}^{q_k(n)} \left|\frac{q_k(n)}{q(n)} - \mu(E_k)\right|\right)$$

$$\le \frac{1}{\mu(E_k)} (\eta_n + \epsilon_n(k)) \quad \text{so that} \quad \lim_{n\to\infty} \sum_{j=1}^{q_k(n)} \left| \mu_{E_k}(D_j^{(k)}(n)) - \frac{1}{q_k(n)} \right| = 0 .$$

<u>Corollary</u> 4.1. If T admits an approximation with speed $f(n)$ and if $E_1, E_2, \cdots$ is a countable collection of pairwise disjoint invariant sets then T restricted to E_k admits an approximation with speed $f_k(n) + \delta_n$ where $\delta_{q_k(n)} = o(f(q(n)))$ and $\sum_{k=1}^{\infty} \mu(E_k) f_k(q_k(n)) < f(q(n))$.

<u>Theorem</u> 4.2. If T admits an approximation with speed $f(n) = \frac{\theta}{n^s(\ln n)^r}$ where s and r are chosen so that $\lim_{n\to\infty} f(n) = 0$ and if $E_1, E_2, \cdots$ is a countable collection of pairwise disjoint invariant sets then T restricted to E_k admits an approximation with speed $\mu(E_k)^{s-1} \frac{\theta_k + \delta}{n^s(\ln n)^r}$ for every $\delta > 0$ where $\sum_{k=1}^{\infty} \theta_k \le \theta$.

<u>Proof</u>. From corollary 4.1 it follows that T restricted to E_k admits an

approximation with speed $f_k(n) + \delta_n$ and that $\sum_{k=1}^{\infty} \mu(E_k) f_k(q_k(n)) < f(q(n))$.

Define $\theta_k(n) = q_k(n)^s (\ln q_k(n))^r \mu(E_k)^{1-s} f_k(q_k(n))$, then we have

$$\theta_k(n) \leq q_k(n)^s (\ln q_k(n))^r \mu(E_k)^{-s} f(q(n)) \leq \left(\frac{q_k(n)}{q(n)}\right)^s \left(\frac{\ln q_k(n)}{\ln q(n)}\right)^r \mu(E_k)^{-s} \theta .$$

Since $\lim_{n\to\infty} \frac{q_k(n)}{q(n)} = \mu(E_k)$ it follows that $\lim_{n\to\infty} \frac{\ln q_k(n)}{\ln q(n)} = 1$ so that

$\theta_k = \underline{\lim}_{n\to\infty} \theta_k(n) < \theta$.

It follows immediately that T restricted to E_k admits an approximation with speed (1) $\mu(E_k)^{s-1} \frac{\theta_k + \epsilon}{n^s (\ln n)^r} + \delta_n$ for every $\epsilon > 0$ and where

$\delta_{q_k(n)} = o(f(q(n)))$. We may, therefore, write

$$\delta_{q_k(n)} = \epsilon_k(n) \frac{\theta}{q(n)^s (\ln q(n))^r}$$

where $\lim_{n\to\infty} \epsilon_k(n) = 0$,

so that

$$\delta_{q_k(n)} = \epsilon_k(n) \left(\frac{q_k(n)}{q(n)}\right)^s \left(\frac{\ln q_k(n)}{\ln q(n)}\right)^r \frac{\theta}{q_k(n)^s (\ln q_k(n))^r} .$$

Therefore, given $\delta > 0$ we can assume that for n sufficiently large

$$\delta_{q_k(n)} < \mu(E_k)^{s-1} \frac{\delta/2}{q_k(n)^s (\ln q_k(n))^r} .$$

Letting $\epsilon = \delta/2$ in (1) we have that T restricted to E_k admits an approximation with speed $\mu(E_k)^{s-1} \frac{\theta_k + \delta}{n^s (\ln n)^r}$ for every $\delta > 0$.

Finally, for any positive integer N we have

$$\sum_{k=1}^{N} \theta_k \leq \underline{\lim}_{n\to\infty} \sum_{k=1}^{N} \theta_k(n) \leq \underline{\lim}_{n\to\infty} \sum_{k=1}^{N} q_k(n)^s (\ln q_k(n))^r \mu(E_k)^{1-s} f_k(q_k(n))$$

$$\leq \underline{\lim}_{n\to\infty} q(n)^s (\ln q(n))^r \sum_{k=1}^{N} \left(\frac{q_k(n)}{q(n)}\right)^s \left(\frac{\ln q_k(n)}{\ln q(n)}\right)^r \mu(E_n)^{1-s} f_k(q_k(n))$$

$$\leq \underline{\lim}_{n\to\infty} q(n)^s (\ln q(n))^r \sum_{k=1}^{N} \mu(E_k) f_k(q_k(n)) \leq \underline{\lim}_{n\to\infty} q(n)^s (\ln q(n))^r f(q(n)) = \theta ,$$

which implies that $\sum_{k=1}^{\infty} \theta_k \leq \theta$.

In view of the fact that if T is not ergodic and admits an approximation with speed $\frac{\theta}{n}$ then the number of ergodic components of T can not be greater than θ (see [5]), some restriction must be made on the numbers r and s to prevent the above theorem from becoming vacuous. We must in particular restrict s so that $0 \leq s \leq 1$. In the case that $s = 1$ we must have $r \leq 0$, and if $s = 0$ we must have $r > 0$.

Corollary 4.2. If T admits an approximation with speed $\frac{\theta}{n}$ and if $E_1, E_2, \cdots, E_m$ is a collection of pairwise disjoint invariant sets then T restricted to E_k admits an approximation with speed $\frac{\theta_k + \delta}{n}$ for every $\delta > 0$ where $\sum_{k=1}^{M} \theta_k \leq \theta$.

Corollary 4.3. If T admits an approximation with speed $\frac{\theta}{(\ln n)^r}$ where r is a positive number and if $E_1, E_2, \cdots$ is a countable collection of pairwise disjoint invariant sets then T restricted to E_k admits an approximation with speed $\frac{\theta_k + \delta}{\mu(E_k)(\ln n)^r}$ for every $\delta > 0$ where $\sum_{k=1}^{\infty} \theta_k \leq \theta$.

Bibliography

[1] Chacon, R.V. Weakly mixing transformations which are not strongly mixing, to appear.

[2] Chacon, R.V. Approximation of transformations with continuous spectrum, to appear.

[3] Katok, A.B. and Stepin, A.M., Approximations in ergodic theory, Uspelshi Math. Nauk, (5) 22 (1967), pp. 81-106. Translation: Russian Math. Surveys (5) 22, 1967, pp. 77-102.

[4] Schwartzbauer, T. Automorphisms that admit an approximation by periodic transformations, to appear in Zeitschrift der Wahrscheinlichkeitstheorie.

[5] Schwartzbauer, T. A general method for approximating measure preserving transformations, Proc. Amer. Math. Soc. 24 (1970), pp. 643-648.

ON SOME APPLICATIONS OF PROBABILITY METHODS TO ADDITIVE NUMBER THEORETIC PROBLEMS

P. Erdős and A. Rényi

UNIVERSITY OF COLORADO AND MATHEMATICAL INSTITUTE
HUNGARIAN ACADEMY OF SCIENCES

Throughout this paper A and B will denote infinite sequences of integers, B_k denotes a sequence of integers having k terms. A + B denotes the set of integers of the form $a_i + b_j$, $a_i \in A$, $b_j \in B$.

B is called a basis of order r if every sufficiently large integer is the sum of r or fewer b's, B is a basis if it is a basis of order r for some r.

$\bar{A}$ will denote the complementary sequence of A, in other words n is in $\bar{A}$ if and only if it is not in A.

Put $A(x) = \sum_{a_i \leq x} 1$, $A(u,v) = A(u) - A(v)$, $\lim_{x=\infty} \frac{A(x)}{x}$ <u>if it exists</u> is the density of A, $\liminf_{x=\infty} \frac{A(x)}{x}$ is the lower density.

R. Blum asked us the following question: Does there exist for every $0 < \alpha < 1$ a sequence A of density α so that for every B the density of A + B is 1? We shall prove this by probabilistic methods, in fact we prove the following, (in the meantime Blum solved his original problem by different methods).

<u>Theorem 1</u>. <u>To every</u> α, $0 < \alpha < 1$ <u>there is a sequence</u> A <u>of density</u> α <u>so that for every</u> B_k, $k = 1,2,\cdots$ <u>the density of</u> $A + B_k$ <u>is</u> $1 - (1 - \alpha)^k$.

Theorem 1 clearly implies that for every B the density of A + B is 1, thus the answer to Blum's question is affirmative.

Next we show that Theorem 1 is, in a certain sense, best possible. We prove

<u>Theorem 2</u>. <u>Let</u> A <u>be any sequence of density</u> α. <u>Then to every</u> $\epsilon > 0$ <u>and to every</u> k <u>there is a</u> B_k <u>so that the lower density of</u> $A + B_k$ <u>is less than</u> $1 - (1 - \alpha)^k + \epsilon$.

There is a slight gap between Theorems 1 and 2. It seems certain that

Theorem 1 can be slightly strengthened and that the following result holds:

<u>To every</u> α <u>there is a sequence</u> A <u>of density</u> α <u>so that for every</u> B_k <u>the density of</u> $A + B_k$ <u>is greater than</u> $1 - (1 - \alpha)^k$.

We did not carry out the details of the construction of such a sequence A.

We observe that in Theorem 2 lower density cannot be replaced by density or upper density. To see this let $n_1 < n_2 < \cdots$ be a sequence of integers satisfying $n_{k+1}/n_k \to \infty$. For every j, $j = 1,2,\cdots$ and $k = 2^{j-1}(2r + 1)$, $r = 0,1,\cdots$, U is in A if $n_k < U \leq n_{k+1}$ and $U \equiv \ell (\text{mod } 2j)$, $\ell = 0,\cdots,j-1$. Clearly A has density 1/2, but for every B_2, $A + B_2$ has upper density 1 (to see this let b_1 and $b_1 + j$ be the elements of B_2 then for every $k = 2^{j-1}(2r + 1)$ all but $o(n_{k+1})$ of the integers not exceeding n_{k+1} are in $A + B_2$).

Finally we settle an old question of Stöhr. Stöhr [4] asked if there is a sequence A of density 0 so that for every basis B, A + B has density 1 ? He also asked if the primes have the above property? Erdös [1] proved that the answer to the latter is negative. We shall outline the proof of the following:

<u>Theorem 3. Let</u> $f(n)$ <u>be an increasing function tending to infinity as slowly as we please. There always is a sequence</u> A <u>of density</u> 0 <u>so that for every</u> B <u>satisfying, for all sufficiently large</u> n, $B(n) > f(n)$, $A + B$ <u>has density</u> 1.

It is well known and easy to see that for every basis B of order r we have $B(n) > cn^{1/r}$, thus Theorem 3 affirmatively answers Stöhr's first question.

Before we prove our Theorems we make a few remarks and state some problems. First of all it is obvious that for every A of density 0 there is a B so that A + B also has density 0. On the other hand it is known [5] that there are sequences A of density 0 so that for every B of positive density A + B has density 1. It seems very likely that such a sequence A of density 0 cannot be too lacunary. We conjecture that if A is such that $n_{k+1}/n_k > c > 1$ holds for every k then there is a B of positive density so that the density of A + B is not 1.

We once considered sequences A which have the property P that for every B $A + B$ contains all sufficiently large integers [2]. We observed that then there is a subsequence B_k of B so that $A + B_k$ also contains all sufficiently large integers (k depends on B).

It is easy to see that the necessary and sufficient condition that A does not have property P is that there is an infinite sequence $t_1 < t_2 < \cdots$ so that for infinitely many n and for every $t_i < n$

$$\bar{A}(n - t_i, n) \geq i . \tag{1}$$

(1) easily implies that if A has property P then the density of A is 1 (the converse is of course false).

It is not difficult to construct a sequence A which has property P and for which there is an increasing sequence $t_1 < t_2 < \cdots$ so that for every i there are infinitely many values of n for which

$$\bar{A}(n - t_i, n) > i . \tag{2}$$

(2) of course does not imply (1). Also we can construct a sequence A having property P so that for every k there is a $B^{(k)}$ so that for every subsequence $B_k^{(k)}$ of $B^{(k)}$ infinitely many integers should not be of the form $A + B_k^{(k)}$.

Now we prove our Theorems. The proof of Theorem 1 will use the method used in [3]; thus it will be sufficient to outline it. Define a measure in the space of all sequences of integers. The measure of the set of sequences which contain n is α and the measure of the set of sequences of n which does not contain n is $1 - \alpha$. It easily follows from the law of large numbers that in this measure almost all sequences have density α. We now show that almost all of them satisfy the requirement of our theorem.

For the sake of simplicity assume $\alpha = 1/2$. Then our measure is simply the Lebesgue measure in (0,1) (we make correspond to the sequence $A = \{a_1 < \cdots\}$ the real number $\sum_{i=1}^{\infty} \frac{1}{2^{a_i}}$). Our theorem is then an immediate consequence of the following theorem (which is just a restatement of the classical theorem of Borel that almost all real numbers are normal). Almost all real numbers $X = \sum_{i=1}^{\infty} \frac{1}{2^{a_i}}$ have the following property: Let $b_1 < \cdots < b_k$ be any k integers. Then the density of integers n for which $n - b_j$ is one of the a's for some $j = 1, \cdots, k$ is $1 - \frac{1}{2^k}$. For $\alpha \neq \frac{1}{2}$ the proof is the same.

Next we prove Theorem 2. Here we give all the details. Let $T = T(k, \epsilon)$ be sufficiently large, we shall show that there is a sequence B_k in $(1,T)$ (i.e. $1 \leq b_1 < \cdots < b_k \leq T$) so that the lower density of $A + B_k$ is less than $1 - \frac{1}{2^k} + \epsilon$.

First we show

$$(3) \qquad \sum_{n=T}^{x} \bar{A}(n - T, n) = (1 + o(1))\frac{Tx}{2} .$$

Let $\bar{a}_1 < \bar{a}_2 < \cdots$ be the elements of $\bar{A}$. To prove (3) observe that with a number (at most T) of exceptions, independent of x, every $\bar{a}_i \leq x - T$ occurs in exactly T of the intervals $(n - T, n)$, $T \leq n \leq x$ and each a_i satisfying $x - T < \bar{a}_i \leq x$ occurs in fewer than T of these intervals. Thus the $a_i \leq x - T$ each contribute T to the sum on the left of (3). Hence

$$o(x) + T\bar{A}(x - T) \leq \sum_{n=T}^{x} \bar{A}(n - T, n) \leq T\,\bar{A}(x)$$

which by $\bar{A}(x) = (1 + o(1))\frac{x}{2}$ proves (3).

Let now $T \leq n \leq x$. Clearly we can choose in

$$\binom{\bar{A}(n - t, n)}{k}$$

ways k integers $1 \leq b_1 < \cdots < b_k \leq T$ so that $A + B_k$ should not contain n. Thus by a simple averaging argument there is a choice of a B_k in $(1,T)$ so that there are at least

$$(4) \qquad \frac{1}{\binom{T}{k}} \sum_{n=T}^{x} \binom{\bar{A}(n - T, n)}{k}$$

values of $n \leq x$ not in $A + B_k$. Now it follows from (3) that

$$(5) \qquad \sum_{n=T}^{x} \binom{\bar{A}(n - T, n)}{k} \geq (1 + o(1))\, x \binom{[\frac{T}{2}]}{k}$$

since it is well known and easy to see that if $\Sigma\, w_i$ is given then $\Sigma\binom{w_i}{k}$ is a minimum if the w_i's are as equal as possible. Finally observe that for $T > T(k, \epsilon)$

$$(6) \qquad \binom{[\frac{T}{2}]}{k} > \left(1 - \frac{\epsilon}{2}\right)2^{-k}\binom{T}{k} .$$

Thus from (4), (5) and (6) it follows that there is a B_k in $(1,T)$ so that more than $x\left(\frac{1}{2^k} - \frac{\epsilon}{2}\right)$ integers $n \leq x$ are not in $A + B_k$. This B_k may depend on x, but there are at most $\binom{T}{k}$ possible choices of B_k and infinitely many values of x. Thus the same B_k occurs for infinitely many different choices of the integer X.

In other words for this B_k the lower density of $A + B_k$ is less than $1 - \frac{1}{2^k} + \epsilon$ as stated.

It is easy to see that Theorem 2 remains true for all sequences A of lower density α. The only change in the proof is the remark that (3) does not hold for all X but only for the subsequence x_i, $x_i \to \infty$ for which $\lim_{x_i = \infty} A(X_i)/X_i = \alpha$.

Now we outline the proof of Theorem 3. The proof is similar but more complicated than the proof of Theorem 1. We can assume without loss of generality that $f(x) = o(x^{\eta})$ for every $\eta > 0$, but $g(x) = [f(\log x)^{1/2}]$. Define a measure in the space of sequences of integers so that the set of sequences containing n has measure $\frac{1}{g(n)}$ and the measure of the set of sequences not containing n has measure $1 - \frac{1}{g(n)}$. It easily follows from the law of large numbers that for almost all sequences

$$A(x) = (1 + o(1))\frac{x}{g(x)} .$$

We outline the proof that for almost all sequences A, $A + B$ has density 1 for all B satisfying $B(x) > f(x)$ for all sufficiently large x. In fact we prove the following statement:

For every $\epsilon > 0$ there is an $n_o(\epsilon)$ so that for every $n > n_o(\epsilon)$ the measure of the set of sequences A for which there is a sequence B_k, $k > [f(\log n)]$ in $(1, \log n)$ so that the number of integers $m \leq n$ not of the form $A + B_k$ is greater than ϵn, is less than $\frac{1}{n^2}$.

Theorem 3 easily follows from our statement by the Borel-Cantelli lemma.

Thus we only have to prove our statement. Let $1 \leq b_1 < \cdots < b_k < \log n$ be one of our sequences B_k. If m is not in $A + B_k$ then none of the numbers $m - b_i$, $i = 1, \cdots, k$, $k \geq f(\log n)$, are in A. Thus the measure of the set of sequences for which $A + B_k$ does not contain m equals

$$(7) \qquad \prod_{i=1}^{k} \left(1 - \frac{1}{g(m - b_i)}\right) < \left(1 - \frac{1}{g(n)}\right)^k = \left(1 - \frac{1}{\sqrt{k}}\right)^k < \frac{\epsilon}{4} .$$

Let now $m_1, \cdots, m_r$ be any r integers which are pairwise congruent mod $[\log n]$. A simple argument shows that the r events: m_i does not belong to $A + B_k$ are independent. Then by a well known argument it follows from (7) that the measure of the set of sequences A for which these are more than $\frac{\epsilon n}{2}$ integers $m \equiv u(\text{mod } [\log n])$, $m < n$ which are not in $A + B_k$ is less than $(\exp 2 = e^2)$

$$(8) \qquad \exp(-c_\epsilon n/\log n) < \exp(-n^{1/2}) .$$

From (8) and from the fact that there are only log n choices for u it follows that the measure of the set of sequences A so that for a given B_k there should be more than ϵn integers $m \leq n$ not in $A + B_k$ in less than

$$(9) \qquad \log n . \quad \exp(-n^{1/2}).$$

There are clearly fewer than $2^{\log n} < n$ possible choices for B_k, thus by (9) the measure of the set of sequences A for which there is a B_k in $(1, \log n)$ so that there should be more than ϵn integers not in $A + B_k$ is less than

$$n \log n \exp(-n^{1/2}) < 1/n^2$$

for $n > n_o$, which proves our statement, and also Theorem 3.

References

1. Erdős, Einige Bemerkungen zur Arbeit von A. Stöhr: Gelöste und ungelöste Fragen uber Basen der naturlichen Zahlenreihe J. reine u. angew. Math 197 (1957), 216-219.

2. P. Erdős and A. Rényi: Remarks on a problem of Obreanu, Canad. Math. Bull. 6 (1963), 267-274.

3. P. Erdős and A. Rényi: Additive properties of random sequences of positive integers, Acta Arith. 6 (1960-61), 83-110. See also the book H. Halberstam - K. F. Roth, Sequences, Oxford 1966.

4. A. Stöhr: Gelöste and ungelöste Fragen uber Basen der naturlichen Zahlenreihe J. reine u. angew. Math. 197 (1957), 216-219.

5. A. Stöhr und E. Wirsing: Beispiele von Wesentlichen Komponenten die keine Basen sind, J. reine u. angew. Math 196 (1956), 96-98. See also J. u. V. Linnik, On Erdős' theorem on the addition of numerical sequences, Mat. Sbornik N.S. 10 (52) (1942), 67-78.

Example of an Ergodic Measure Preserving Transformation on an Infinite Measure Space

by

Arshag B. Hajian and Shizuo Kakutani

Northeastern University and Yale University

Let φ be an ergodic measure preserving transformation defined on an infinite measure space $(X, \mathcal{B}, m)$. A measurable subset A of X of positive measure is said to be a <u>weakly wandering set</u> for φ under a sequence $\{n_i \mid i = 0,1,2,\ldots\}$ of integers if $\varphi^{n_i}(A)$, $i = 0,1,2,\ldots$, are mutually disjoint. In this case, $\{n_i \mid i = 0,1,2,\ldots\}$ is called a <u>weakly wandering sequence</u> for φ. A sequence $\{r_i \mid i = 0,1,2,\ldots\}$ of integers is said to be a <u>recurrent sequence</u> for φ if there exists a measurable set A of finite measure such that $\underline{\lim}_{i \to \infty} m(\varphi^{r_i}(A) \cap A) > 0$. The main purpose of this note is to construct an ergodic measure preserving transformation defined on an infinite measure space $(X, \mathcal{B}, m)$ for which there exist a weakly wandering set X_0 with $m(X_0) = 1$ and a weakly wandering sequence $\{n_i \mid i = 0,1,2,\ldots\}$ such that $X = \bigcup_{i=0}^{\infty} \varphi^{n_i}(X_0)$ (disj). This transformation φ has other interesting properties (Theorem 1 and its Corollary). Although it is difficult to determine all weakly wandering sequences for this transformation φ, we can give a complete description of all recurrent sequences for φ (Theorem 2).

Let $(X_0, \mathcal{B}_0, m)$ be a measure space, where

(1) $X_0 = \{x \mid x \in \mathbb{R},\ 0 < x < 1,\ x \neq \text{dyadic rational}\}$,

$\mathcal{B}_0$ is the σ-field of all Lebesgue measurable subsets of X_0, and m is the ordinary Lebesgue measure on $\mathcal{B}_0$ with $m(X_0) = 1$. For $n = 0,1,2,\ldots$, let

(2) $A_n = \{x \mid x \in X_0,\ 1 - 1/2^n < x < 1 - 1/2^{n+1}\}$

be the dyadic interval of length $1/2^{n+1}$. We define the transformation ψ on X_0 onto itself as follows:

(3) $\psi(x) = x - (1 - 3/2^{n+1})$ if $x \in A_n$, $n = 0,1,2,\ldots$

ψ is an ergodic measure preserving transformation defined on the measure space $(X_0, \mathcal{B}_0, m)$ with $m(X_0) = 1$.

Let us put $f(0) = 0$, and

(4) $f(n) = 2 + 2^3 + \ldots + 2^{2n-1}$, $n = 1,2,\ldots$

For $n = 1,2,\ldots$, consider $f(n) + 1$ mutually disjoint copies of A_n, namely, $A_n^0 = A_n, A_n^1, \ldots, A_n^{f(n)}$. We denote by the same letter χ all the following isomorphisms:

(5) $\chi(A_n^i) = A_n^{i+1}$, $i = 0,1,\ldots,f(n)-1$; $n = 1,2,\ldots$

We next consider the measure space $(X, \mathcal{B}, m)$, where

(6) $X = \bigcup_{n=0}^{\infty} \bigcup_{i=0}^{f(n)} A_n^i$ (disj),

$\mathcal{B}$ is the σ-field of all "Lebesgue measurable" subsets of X, and m is the corresponding measure on $\mathcal{B}$.

We now define the transformation φ on X onto itself as follows:

$$(7) \qquad \varphi(x) = \begin{cases} \chi(x) & \text{if } x \in A_n^i,\ i = 0,1,\dots,f(n)-1;\ n = 1,2,\dots \\ \psi(\chi^{-f(n)}(x)) & \text{if } x \in A_n^{f(n)},\ n = 0,1,2,\dots \end{cases}$$

It is clear that φ is an ergodic measure preserving transformation defined on the measure space $(X, \mathcal{B}, m)$ with $m(X) = \infty$.

We introduce the following subsets of X: $B_o = X_o$, and

$$(8) \qquad B_j = \bigcup_{n=j}^{\infty} \bigcup_{i=f(j-1)+1}^{f(j)} A_n^i \ \text{(disj)}, \quad j = 1,2,\dots$$

$$(9) \qquad C_k = \bigcup_{j=0}^{k} B_j \ \text{(disj)}, \quad k = 0,1,2,\dots,$$

and observe that B_j's and C_k's have the following properties:

$$(10) \qquad m(B_j) = [f(j) - f(j-1)] \sum_{n=j}^{\infty} 1/2^{n+1} = 2^{j-1}, \quad j = 1,2,\dots,$$

$$(11) \qquad m(C_k) = 1 + \sum_{j=1}^{k} m(B_j) = 2^k, \quad k = 0,1,2,\dots,$$

$$(12) \qquad X = \bigcup_{j=0}^{\infty} B_j \ \text{(disj)},$$

$$(13) \qquad C_o \subset C_1 \subset C_2 \subset \dots \subset C_k \subset \dots \to X.$$

Also, from the definition (7) of φ follows:

$$(14) \qquad \varphi^n(C_k) \subset C_{k+\ell} \quad \text{for} \quad n = 0,1,\dots, f(k+\ell) - f(k);$$
$$k = 0,1,2,\dots; \quad \ell = 0,1,2,\dots$$

We put $n_o = 0$, and define, for $i = 1,2,\dots,$

$$(15) \qquad n_i = \varepsilon_0 2^1 + \varepsilon_1 2^3 + \dots + \varepsilon_k 2^{2k+1}$$

if

(16) $\quad i = \varepsilon_0 2^0 + \varepsilon_1 2^1 + \dots + \varepsilon_k 2^k ,$

where $\varepsilon_j = 0$ or 1 for $j = 0,1,\dots,k$. We observe that the following important relation holds:

(17) $\quad B_j = \bigcup_{i=2^{j-1}}^{2^j - 1} \varphi^{n_i}(X_0) \ (\text{disj}), \quad j = 1,2,\dots,$

and hence

(18) $\quad C_k = \bigcup_{i=0}^{2^k - 1} \varphi^{n_i}(X_0) \ (\text{disj}), \quad k = 0,1,2,\dots,$

(19) $\quad X = \bigcup_{i=0}^{\infty} \varphi^{n_i}(X_0) \ (\text{disj}).$

Theorem 1. *The ergodic measure preserving transformation* φ *defined by* (7) *on the infinite measure space* $(X, \mathcal{B}, m)$ *has a weakly wandering set* X_0 *with* $m(X_0) = 1$ *and a weakly wandering sequence* $\{n_i \mid i = 0,1,2,\dots\}$ *for which the relation* (19) *holds. Further, if* W *is any weakly wandering set for* φ *under the same sequence* $\{n_i \mid i = 0,1,2,\dots\}$, *then* $m(W) \leqq 1$.

Proof. It suffices to prove the last statement. Assume that W is a measurable subset of X such that $\varphi^{n_i}(W)$, $i = 0,1,2,\dots$, are mutually disjoint. For $k = 1,2,\dots$, put $W_k = W \cap C_k$. Then

(20) $\quad \bigcup_{i=1}^{2^k(2^\ell - 1)} \varphi^{n_i}(W_k) \ (\text{disj}) \subset \bigcup_{n=1}^{f(k+\ell)-f(k)} \varphi^{n}(W_k) \subset C_{k+\ell},$

for $\ell = 1,2,\dots$, where the last inclusion is an immediate consequence of (14) and the first inclusion follows from the fact that

(21) $$n_{2^k(2^\ell-1)} = n_{2^k+2^{k+1}+\cdots+2^{k+\ell-1}}$$
$$= 2^{2k+1} + 2^{2k+3} + \ldots + 2^{2k+2\ell-1}$$
$$= f(k+\ell) - f(k).$$

Since the first term of (20) is a disjoint union, it follows

(22) $$2^k(2^\ell - 1)\ m(W_k) \leqq m(C_{k+\ell}) = 2^{k+\ell},$$

or, equivalently,

(23) $$m(W_k) \leqq 2^\ell/(2^\ell - 1).$$

Since this is true for $\ell = 1,2,\ldots$, we have (by letting $\ell \to \infty$) $m(W_k) \leqq 1$. Since this is true for $k = 1,2,\ldots$, we have (by letting $k \to \infty$) $m(W) \leqq 1$ by using (13).

<u>Corollary</u>. <u>If τ is any non-singular measurable transformation on the measure space</u> $(X, \mathcal{B}, m)$ <u>onto itself such that</u> $\tau\varphi(x) = \varphi\tau(x)$ <u>for all</u> $x \in X$, <u>then</u> τ <u>is a measure preserving transformation</u>.

<u>Proof</u>. Since φ is an ergodic measure preserving transformation, it follows that there exists a positive constant $\alpha > 0$ such that $m(\tau(B)) = \alpha\, m(B)$ for all $B \in \mathcal{B}$. We consider the weakly wandering set X_0 and the weakly wandering sequence $\{n_i \mid i = 0,1,2,\ldots\}$ of Theorem 1. It is easy to see that the sets $\tau(X_0)$ and $\tau^{-1}(X_0)$ are again weakly wandering

sets for φ under the same sequence $\{n_i \mid i = 0,1,2,\dots\}$ If $\alpha \neq 1$, then this yields a contradiction to the last statement of Theorem 1, and this completes the proof of the Corollary.

We note that the transformation ψ on $(X_o, \mathcal{B}_o, m)$ from which φ was constructed has a pure point spectrum and hence has entropy zero. In case φ is constructed from a transformation ψ of positive entropy, it is possible to prove the Corollary in a different way by using the techniques of the theory of entropy.

We next proceed to give a complete description of all the recurrent sequences for φ. Let $N_o = \{0\}$, and

(24) $$N_k = \{n \mid n = \pm 2^{2p_1} \pm 2^{2p_2} \pm \dots \pm 2^{2p_k}\},$$

where $p_1, p_2, \dots, p_k$ are integers satisfying $0 \leqq p_1 < p_2 \dots < p_k$. It is not difficult to show that the set X_o satisfies

(25) $$m(\varphi^n(X_o) \cap X_o) = \begin{cases} 1/2^k & \text{if } n \in N_k, \ k = 0,1,2,\dots \\ 0 & \text{if } n \in \mathbb{Z} - \bigcup_{k=0}^{\infty} N_k . \end{cases}$$

Let now $\{r_i \mid i = 0,1,2,\dots\}$ be a recurrent sequence for φ. Let A be a measurable set of finite measure such that

(26) $$\varliminf_{i \to \infty} m(\varphi^{r_i}(A) \cap A) > 3\delta > 0.$$

From (13) follows that there exists a positive integer k such that $m(A - A \cap C_k) < \delta$. Then we have

(27) $$\lim_{i \to \infty} m(\varphi^{r_i}(C_k) \cap C_k) > \delta > 0.$$

From (18) follows

(28) $$\lim_{i \to \infty} \sum_{p=0}^{2^k-1} \sum_{q=0}^{2^k-1} m(\varphi^{r_i+n_p-n_q}(X_0) \cap X_0) > \delta > 0.$$

Let ℓ be a positive integer such that $1/2^{\ell} < \delta/2^{2k}$.
Then there exists a positive integer i_0 such that for any integer $i > i_0$ there exist two integers p and q ($0 \leqq p, q \leqq 2^k-1$) such that

(29) $$m(\varphi^{r_i+n_p-n_q}(X_0) \cap X_0) \geqq 1/2^{\ell}.$$

We note that (29) is equivalent to saying that

(30) $$r_i + n_p - n_q \in \bigcup_{k=0}^{\ell} N_k \quad \text{or} \quad r_i \in \bigcup_{k=0}^{\ell} (N_k - n_p + n_q).$$

<u>Theorem 2.</u> $\{r_i \mid i = 0,1,2,\dots\}$ <u>is a recurrent sequence for</u> φ <u>if and only if there exist two positive integers</u> ℓ <u>and</u> s <u>such that</u>

(31) $$\{r_i \mid i = 0,1,2,\dots\} \subset \bigcup_{n=-s}^{s} \bigcup_{k=0}^{\ell} (N_k + n).$$

<u>Proof.</u> The necessity follows from the above argument. The sufficiency is obvious.

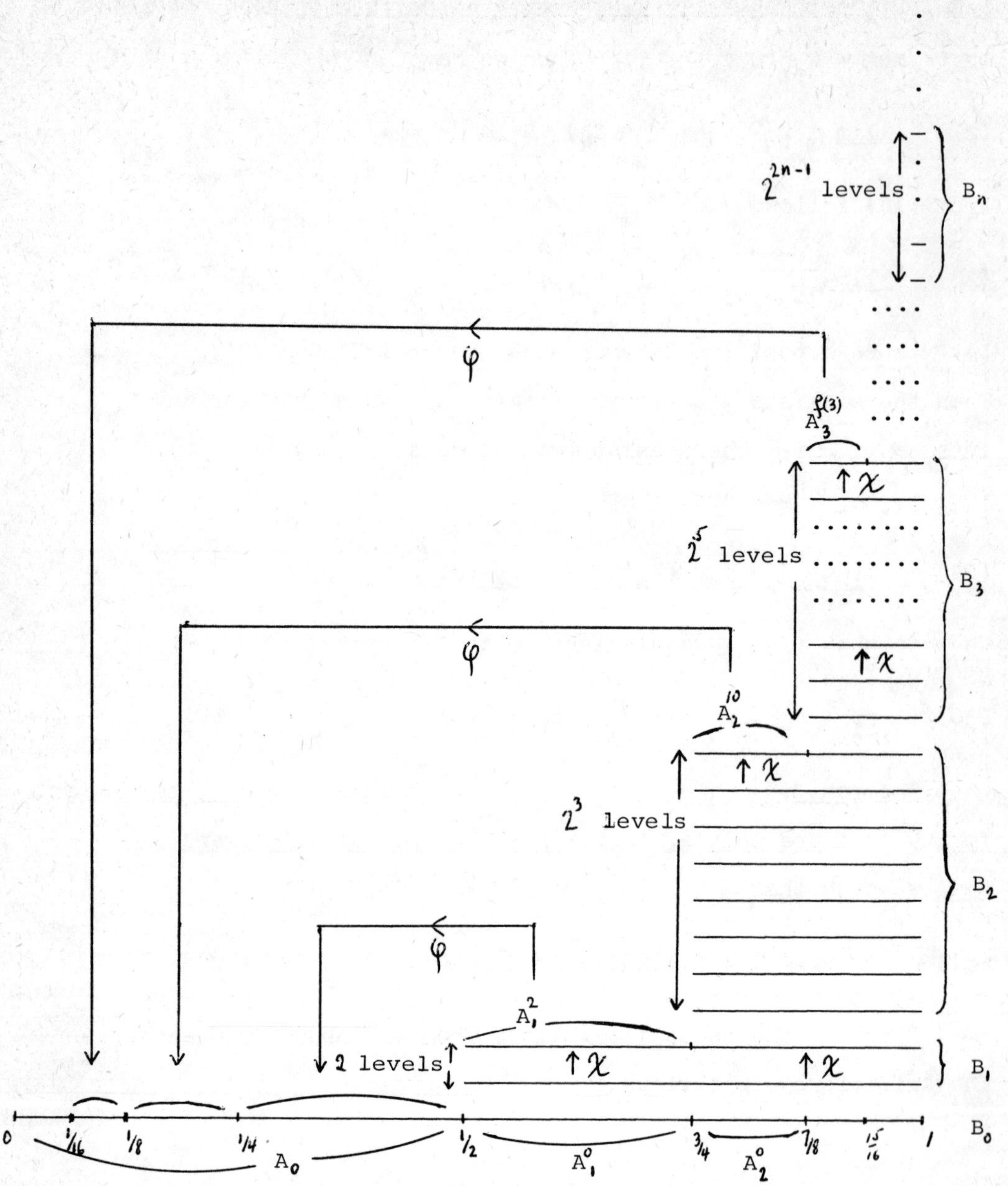

2^{2n-1} levels
B_n
φ
A_3^{f(3)}
χ
2^5 levels
B_3
φ
A_2^{10}
χ
2^3 levels
B_2
φ
A_1^2
2 levels
χ
χ
B_1
0
1/16
1/8
1/4
1/2
3/4
7/8
15/16
1
B_0
A_0
A_1^0
A_2^0

SOME RESULTS ON CONVERGENCE RATES FOR WEIGHTED AVERAGES

by

D. L. Hanson

University of Missouri-Columbia

1. Introduction

Let X_k be random variables on some probability space and let $a_{N,k}$ be real numbers. Define

$$A_N = \frac{1}{N} \sum_{k=1}^{N} X_k$$

and

$$(1) \qquad S_N = \sum_k a_{N,k} X_k \qquad \text{or} \qquad \sum_k a_{N,k} (X_k - EX_k)$$

depending on whether $E|X_k|$ is infinite or finite respectively. (When dealing with S_N we will always have made enough assumptions to guarantee that the sum makes sense.)

This paper treats the rates at which $P\{|A_N - \mu| \geq \varepsilon\}$ and $P\{|S_N| \geq \varepsilon\}$ converge to zero. If the random variables X_k are i.i.d. with $EX_k = \mu$ then the probabilities $P\{|A_N - \mu| \geq \varepsilon\}$ and the rate at which they converge to zero are of interest when estimating μ. In some practical problems models have been set up in which

$$Y_N = \sum_k a_k X_{N-k}$$

where the X's are i.i.d. and the range of summation is finite, infinite, or doubly infinite. In all three cases successive averages of the Y's are of the form (1) and arise, for example, in estimating the mean of the Y_N process.

So much for rationalization. I believe the main reason for considering the S_N's is that the mathematical problems involved are hard and interesting.

Intuitively, when one has convergence he would expect its rate to improve with increased averaging. "Clearly" there is more averaging in the sum $\frac{X_1}{2} + \frac{X_2}{4} + \frac{X_3}{4}$ than in the sum $\frac{X_1}{2} + \frac{X_2}{2}$, but how does the averaging in the first sum compare with the averaging in the sum $\frac{X_1}{3} + \frac{X_2}{3} + \frac{X_3}{3}$? Also intuitively again, success in getting good convergence rates for $P\{|S_N| \geq \varepsilon\}$ would seem to depend on how well one can measure the averaging due to the coefficients $a_{N,k}$ in the sum S_N.

2. Exponential Rates

Suppose the X_k's are i.i.d. and that $E\,e^{\theta|X_i|} < \infty$ for some $\theta > 0$. Then (See the work of Chernoff [6], and also of Cramér [8].) there exists $0 \leq \rho_\varepsilon < 1$ such that $P\{|A_N - \mu| \geq \varepsilon\} \leq 2\rho_\varepsilon^N$; an optimal ρ_ε may be obtained from $E\,e^{\theta X_i}$. The above results have been asymptotically sharpened (See [8], [4], and [1].) by multiplying by an appropriate factor which goes to zero less than exponentially fast.

The exponential bounds obtained above have been extended in [13] and [11] to cover the probabilities $P\{|S_N| \geq \varepsilon\}$. The current "best" theorem along these lines seems to be the following.

Theorem 1. *If* $X_1, X_2, \ldots$ *are independent random variables having finite means and satisfying* $P\{|X_k - EX_k| \geq x\} \leq \int_x^\infty Me^{-\gamma t^p}dt$ *for some*

$M > 0$, $\gamma > 0$, $1 \leq p \leq 2$, and all $x > 0$, then there exist constants C_1 and C_2 depending only on M, γ, and p such that for every $\varepsilon > 0$

$$P\{|S_N| \geq \varepsilon\} \leq 2 \exp\left\{-\min\left[C_1\left(\frac{\varepsilon}{\|a_N\|_2}\right)^2, \; C_2\left(\frac{\varepsilon}{\|a_N\|_q}\right)^p\right]\right\}$$

where $\|a_N\|_q$ is the ℓ_q-norm of the sequence $a_N = \{a_{N,i}\}$ and $\frac{1}{p} + \frac{1}{q} = 1$.

Note that $\|a_N\|_2$ and $\|a_N\|_q$ can be thought of as measuring a combination of the overall coefficient weight and of the amount of averaging which the coefficients provide.

Unfortunately the bounds in this theorem are not sharp; no bounds with optimality properties have yet been obtained. Higgins [19] has obtained expansions similar to those in [1], [4], and [8] but until the exponential term can be obtained accurately these won't be very useful.

3. Rates Related to Moments

Now let X_k be i.i.d. random variables. Results of Katz [22], [23] and of Baum and Katz [2] provide three theorems giving convergence rates under conditions related to moments.

Theorem 2. If $t > 1$ then the following are equivalent.

(a) $n^t P\{|X_k| > n\}$ is bounded and $EX_k = \mu$.

(b) $n^{t-1} P\{|A_n - \mu| > \varepsilon\}$ is bounded for all $\varepsilon > 0$.

(c) $n^{t-1} P\{\sup_{k \geq n}|A_k - \mu| > \varepsilon\}$ is bounded for all $\varepsilon > 0$.

Theorem 3. If $t > 1$ then the following are equivalent.

(a) $n^t P\{|X_k| > n\} \longrightarrow 0$ and $EX_k = \mu$.

(b) $n^{t-1} P\{|A_n - \mu| > \varepsilon\} \longrightarrow 0$ for all $\varepsilon > 0$.

(c) $n^{t-1} P\{\sup_{k\geq n}|A_k - \mu| > \varepsilon\} \longrightarrow 0$ <u>for all</u> $\varepsilon > 0$.

<u>Theorem 4</u>. <u>If</u> $t > 1$ <u>then the following are equivalent</u>.

(a) $E|X_k|^t < \infty$ <u>and</u> $EX_k = \mu$.

(b) $\sum_{n=1}^{\infty} n^{t-2} P\{|A_n - \mu| > \varepsilon\} < \infty$ <u>for all</u> $\varepsilon > 0$.

(c) $\sum_{n=1}^{\infty} n^{t-2} P\{\sup_{k\geq n}|A_k - \mu| > \varepsilon\} < \infty$ <u>for all</u> $\varepsilon > 0$.

Baum and Katz have other results. These three are listed for comparison with results involving S_N. They also consider $0 < t \leq 1$. The case $t = 1$ is a "boundary case." (Heyde and Rohatgi [18] have results similar to those in Theorems 2 and 3.)

Now suppose the X_k are independent but not identically distributed, that

$$F(x) = \sup_k P\{|X_k| \geq x\}$$

and

$$F'(x) = \sup_k P\{|X_k - EX_k| \geq x\} ,$$

that

$$\sum_k |a_{N,k}|^2 \leq \gamma_N \quad \text{or} \quad CN^{-\gamma} ,$$

and that

$$\sum_k |a_{N,k}|^t \leq \rho_N \quad \text{or} \quad CN^{-\rho} .$$

Work similar to that of Baum and Katz, except for S_N instead of A_N, is contained in [10], [16], and [17]. Representative theorems are

Theorem 2'. *If* $1 < t < 2$ *and* $y^t F'(y) \le M < \infty$ *for all* $y > 0$, *then* $P\{|S_N| > \varepsilon\} = O(\rho_N)$ *for every* $\varepsilon > 0$.

Theorem 3'. *If* $1 < t < 2$ *and* $y^t F'(y) \longrightarrow 0$ *as* $y \longrightarrow \infty$, *then* $P\{|S_N| > \varepsilon\} = o(\rho_N)$ *for every* $\varepsilon > 0$.

Theorem 4'. *If* $1 \le t < 2$, $0 < \rho$, *and there exists a non-increasing real valued function* G *such that* $\lim_{y\to\infty} G(y) = 0$, $G(y) \ge F(y)$ *for all* y, $\int_0^\infty y^t |dG(y)| < \infty$, *and*

$$\sup_{x\ge 1} \sup_{y\ge x} \frac{y^t F(y)}{x^t G(x)} < \infty ,$$

then for every $\varepsilon > 0$

$$\sum_N N^{\rho-1} P\{|S_N| > \varepsilon\} < \infty . \tag{2}$$

Variants of the above theorems are available when $0 < t \le 1$ and when $2 \le t$. (See [16] and [17].) The cases $t = 1$ and $t = 2$ are both exceptional. We note that there is no interesting analog for S_N to the (c) part of Theorems 2, 3, and 4. This should be expected since it is possible for the sets $\{k|\ a_{N,k} \ne 0\}$ to be disjoint for different N's so the sequence $\{S_N\}$ could be independent.

Sharpness results for these last three theorems are available in [16] and [17]. We note that Theorems 2' and 3' are quite similar to Theorems 2 and 3 but that Theorem 4' does not bear as much resemblance to Theorem 4. It turns out that Theorem 4' is quite sharp, that the weakest moment conditions one can put on F in order to get (2) are

$$\lim_{y\to\infty} F(y) = 0 \quad \text{and} \quad \int_0^\infty y^t \log^+ y |dF(y)| < \infty ,$$

and that these moment conditions on F imply the existence of a G satisfying the conditions of Theorem 4'. The conditions $\lim_{y\to\infty} F(y) = 0$ and $\int_0^\infty y^t \, |dF(Y)| < \infty$ are insufficient for (2) unless some additional restrictions are put on the $a_{N,k}$'s or on the regularity with which $F(y)$ decreases to zero; Theorem 4' is thus about as close an analog to Theorem 4 as is available.

Early work of Hsu and Robbins [20] and of Erdös [9] shows that if the X_k's are i.i.d. then

$$\sum_{N=1}^{\infty} P\{|A_N| > 1\} < \infty$$

if and only if $E|X_i|^2 < \infty$ and $|EX_i| < 1$. This is the same as the equivalence of (a) and (b) in Theorem 4 when $t = 2$. If $\sum_{k=1}^{\infty} P\{|A_N-\mu| > \varepsilon\} < \infty$ for every $\varepsilon > 0$, then $P\{|A_N-\mu| > \varepsilon \text{ i.o.}\} = 0$ for every $\varepsilon > 0$, and thus $A_N \longrightarrow \mu$ a.e. It seems likely that this was the stimulus for the original series work.

The proofs of most results of this type involve a "double truncation" used by Erdös [9]. The method of proof has been improved and extended by Katz [22] and Pruit [24], and in [10], [16], and [17]. The proofs "essentially" involve part or all of the following. We note that

$$\text{(3)} \quad P\{|S_N| > 3\varepsilon\} \le \sum_k P\{|a_{N,k}(X_k - EX_k)| > \varepsilon\}$$
$$+ \sum_{j\neq k} P\{|a_{N,k}(X_k - EX_k)| > \delta_N\} P\{|a_{N,j}(X_j - EX_j)| > \delta_N\}$$
$$+ P\{|\sum_k a_{N,k} EY_{N,k}| > \varepsilon\}$$
$$+ P\{|\sum_k a_{N,k}(Y_{N,k} - EY_{N,k})| > \varepsilon\}$$

where $\{\delta_N\}$ is an appropriately chosen sequence of positive numbers and

$$Y_{N,k} = \begin{cases} X_k - EX_k & \text{if } |a_{N,k}(X_k - EX_k)| \le \delta_N \\ 0 & \text{otherwise.} \end{cases}$$

Proofs consist of showing that each of the four terms on the right hand side of (3) goes to zero at the appropriate rate, or that an appropriately weighted sum of them converges. Markov's inequality is used to bound each of the probabilities in the first term (on the right hand side of (3)); in some cases the number of $a_{N,k}$'s of various sizes must be counted. The size of this first term is very closely related to the moment (or moment-like) condition imposed on the X_k's. Markov's inequality is used to bound each of the probabilities in the second term also. Because a product is involved and because of the choice of $\{\delta_N\}$ this term causes no trouble. The third term is either zero or one and, for large enough N, it can be shown to be zero. Markov's inequality is used again to bound the last term; the problem arises in then bounding $E[\sum_k a_{N,k} (Y_{N,k} - EY_{N,k})]^{2\nu}$ where ν is a positive integer, usually large; the bounding of this moment is tedious and intricate. The rates are most closely related to the first term, but the last term is, in a sense, the hardest to handle. The right hand side of (3) varies somewhat from theorem to theorem. EX_k is omitted, for example, when $t < 1$.

4. Dependence.

As can be seen from the proofs in [17], independence is not required in the analogs for $0 < t < 1$ of Theorems 2' and 3'. Wright [27] has shown that it is not required in Theorem 4' when $0 < t < 1$.

Is independence needed in any or all of these theorems when $t = 1$?

Let $\mathcal{B}\{\cdots\}$ stand for the σ-algebra generated by the random variables $\{\cdots\}$, let $\mathcal{B}_N = \mathcal{B}\{X_k : k \leq N\}$ and $\mathcal{B}^N = \mathcal{B}\{X_k : k \geq N\}$. If there exists a real value function f such that $f(N) \longrightarrow 0$ as $N \longrightarrow \infty$ and such that if $A \in \mathcal{B}_N$ and $B \in \mathcal{B}^{N+n}$ then

$$|P(AB) - P(A)P(B)| \leq f(n)\, P(A)P(B),$$

then [19] all rates results holding for independence hold for the sequence $\{X_k\}$ with the possible exception of various constants being different. The method of proof follows that used in [5] and [14]. Can one get any rates results using any weaker mixing condition(s)? An example of Baum and Katz [2] in which $\{X_k\}$ is strictly stationary and ergodic, $EX_k = 0$, $|X_k| = 1$, but $\sum_{N=1}^{\infty} N^{-1} P\{S_N = 1\} = \infty$ shows that some sort of mixing is necessary. Higgins [19] has shown that if $\{X_k\}$ in a stationary Gaussian process with $EX_k = 0$, $EX_k^2 = 1$, and $EX_k X_{n+k} = \rho_n$ then

(a) if $\sum_{n=1}^{\infty} |\rho_n| < \infty$ one gets exponential convergence rates

(b) if $\rho_N > 0$ and ρ_N converges monotonically to zero slowly enough then $NP\{|A_N| > \varepsilon\} \longrightarrow \infty$.

Since $\rho_N \longrightarrow 0$ implies mixing of all orders for Gaussian processes, (b) above shows that in fact a very strong form of mixing is necessary to get general rates of convergence.

5. An Unsolved Problem.

Using the fact that $P\{\sup_{k \geq n} |A_k - \mu| > \varepsilon\}$ is non-increasing Baum and Katz [2] were able to show that the series

$$\sum_{N=1}^{\infty} (-1)^N N^{t-1} P\{\sup_{k \geq N} |A_k - \mu| > \varepsilon\}$$

converges for every $\varepsilon > 0$ if the X_k's are i.i.d., $EX_k = \mu$, and $E|X_k|^t < \infty$. Does the series

$$\sum_{N=1}^{\infty} (-1)^N N^{t-1} P\{|A_N - \mu| > \varepsilon\}$$

converge? It is known [12] that when $t = 0$ (i.e. under no moment restriction whatever on the X_k's with $N^{t-1} = \frac{1}{N}$) this series converges.

REFERENCES

[1] R.R. Bahadur and R. Ranga Rao, On Deviations of the Sample Mean, Ann. Math. Statist. 31 (1960) 1015-1027.

[2] L.E. Baum and M. Katz, Convergence Rates in the Law of Large Numbers, Trans. Amer. Math. Soc. 120 (1965) 108-123.

[3] L.E. Baum, M. Katz, and R.P. Read, Exponential Convergence Rates for the Law of Large Numbers, Trans. Amer. Math. Soc. 102 (1962) 187-199.

[4] David Blackwell and J.L. Hodges, Jr., The Probability in the Extreme Tail of a Convolution, Ann. Math. Statist. 30 (1959) 1113-1120.

[5] J.R. Blum, D.L. Hanson, and L.H. Koopmans, On the Strong Law of Large Numbers for a Class of Stochastic Processes, Z. Wahrscheinlichkeitstheorie 2 (1963) 1-11.

[6] H. Chernoff, A Measure of Asymptotic Efficiency for Tests of a Hypothesis Based on the Sum of Observations. Ann. Math. Statist. 23 (1952) 493-507.

[7] Y.S. Chow, Some Convergence Theorems for Independent Random Variables, Ann. Math. Statist. 37 (1966) 1482-1493.

[8] H. Cramer, Sur un Nouveau Théorème-Limite de la Theorie des Probabilites, Actualités Sci. Ind., No. 736, Paris (1938).

[9] P. Erdös, On a Theorem of Hsu and Robbins, Ann. Math. Statist. 20 (1949) 286-291.

[10] W.E. Franck and D.L. Hanson, Some Results Giving Rates of Convergence in the Law of Large Numbers for Weighted Sums of Independent Random Variables, Trans. Amer. Math. Soc. 124 (1966) 347-359.

[11] D.L. Hanson, Some Results Relating Moment Generating Functions and Convergence Rates in the Law of Large Numbers, Ann. Math. Statist. 38 (1967) 742-750.

[12] D.L. Hanson and Melvin Katz, On the Oscillation of Sums of Random Variables, Proc. Amer. Math. Soc. 17 (1966) 864-865.

[13] D.L. Hanson and L.H. Koopmans, On the Convergence Rate of the Law of Large Numbers for Linear Combinations of Independent Random Variables, Ann. Math. Statist. 36 (1965) 559-564.

[14] D.L. Hanson and L.H. Koopmans, Convergence Rates for the Law of Large Numbers for Linear Combinations of Exchangeable and *-Mixing Stochastic Processes, Ann. Math. Statist. 36 (1965) 1840-1852.

[15] D.L. Hanson and L.H. Koopmans, A Probability Bound for Integrals With Respect to Stochastic Processes With Independent Increments, Proc. Amer. Math. Soc. 16 (1965) 1173-1177.

[16] D.L. Hanson and F.T. Wright, Some More Results on Rates of Convergence in the Law of Large Numbers for Weighted Sums of Independent Random Variables, Tran. Amer. Math. Soc. 141 (1969) 443-464.

[17] D.L. Hanson and F.T. Wright, Some Convergence Results for Weighted Sums of Independent Random Variables, Unpublished.

[18] C.C. Heyde and V.K. Rohatgi, A Pair of Complementary Theorems On Convergence Rates in the Law of Large Numbers, Proc. Camb. Phil. Soc. 63 (1967) 73-82.

[19] J.J. Higgins, Communication.

[20] P.L. Hsu and H. Robbins, Complete Convergence and the Law of Large Numbers, Proc. Nat. Acad. Sci. U.S.A. 33 (1947) 25-31.

[21] B. Jamison, S. Orey, and W. Pruitt, Convergence of Weighted Averages of Independent Random Variables, Z. Wahrscheinlichkeitstheorie 4 (1965) 40-44.

[22] Melvin L. Katz, The Probability in the Tail of a Distribution, Ann. Math. Statist. 34 (1963) 312-318.

[23] Melvin L. Katz, Communication.

[24] W.E. Pruitt, Summability of Independent Random Variables, J. Math. Mech. 15 (1966) 769-776.

[25] V.K. Rohatgi, On Convergence Rates in the Law of Large Numbers for Weighted Sums of Independent Random Variables, Proc. Amer. Math. Soc. 20 (1969) 570-574.

[26] W.F. Stout, Some Results on the Complete and Almost Sure Convergence of Linear Combinations of Independent Random Variables and Martingale Differences, Ann. Math. Statist. 39 (1968) 1549-1562.

[27] F.T. Wright, Communication.

A note on σ-finite invariant measures

by

S. Horowitz

1. Definitions and notations

A Markov process is defined to be a quadruple (X,Σ,m,P) where (X,Σ,m) is a measure space with finite positive measure $m,(m(X) = 1)$ and where P is an operator on $L_1(m)$ satisfying:

(i) P is a contraction: $\|P\| \leq 1$.

(ii) P is positive: if $0 \leq f \in L_1(m)$ then $fP \geq 0$.

The operator adjoint to P is defined in $L_\infty(m)$. It will also be denoted by P but will be written to the left of the variable. Thus $\langle fP,g\rangle = \langle f,Pg\rangle$ for $f \in L_1(m)$, $g \in L_\infty(m)$.

The operator P on $L_1(m)$ acts on the finite measures $\lambda \prec m$ as follows:

(1.1) $$\lambda P(A) = \int P1_A(x)\lambda(dx) .$$

Equation (1.1) will occasionally be used for σ-finite positive measures. We shall also define the operator I_A for $A \in \Sigma$ by

(1.2) $$I_A f(x) = 1_A(x) \cdot f(x)$$

(1.3) $$\lambda I_A(B) = \lambda(B\cap A)$$

For every $A \in \Sigma$ we shall define the set

(1.4) $$\tilde{A} = \{x \mid \sum_{n=0}^{\infty} P^n 1_A(x) > 0\}$$

$\tilde{A}$ is the smallest set in the field of the invariant sets Σ_i (see [1] chapter III). The process is said to be <u>conservative</u> if

(1.5) $$\sum_{n=0}^{\infty} P^n 1_A(x) = \infty \quad \text{for almost all} \quad x \in \tilde{A} \quad (m(A) > 0)\ .$$

Throughout this paper, (X,Σ,m,P) is assumed to be a conservative Markov process.

Let us define the operator:

(1.6) $$P_A = I_A \sum_{n=0}^{\infty} (PI_{A^c})^n PI_A$$

It is well known that (A,Σ_A,m,P_A) is a Markov process (see [1] chapter VI). A positive σ-finite invariant μ is called <u>invariant</u> (under P) if:

(1.7) $$\mu = \mu P$$

2. <u>On existence of a σ-finite invariant measure</u>

<u>Theorem</u> 1. The condition (2.1) is necessary and sufficient for the existence of a σ-finite invariant measure μ, supported on $A_1 \subset \tilde{A}$ where $A_1 \in \Sigma_i$, and finite on A for some set $A \in \Sigma$

(2.1) If $B \subset A \cap A_1$ and $m(B) > 0$ then

$$\limsup_{N \to \infty} \frac{\sum_{n=1}^{N} P^n 1_B(x)}{\sum_{n=1}^{N} P^n 1_A(x)} \not\equiv 0 \quad \text{on } \tilde{A}\ .$$

Proof. By the Chacon-Ornstein Theorem (theorem D chapter III of [1], see also chapter VII), if such a measure exists then

$$\lim_{N\to\infty} \frac{\sum_{n=1}^{N} P^n 1_B(x)}{\sum_{n=1}^{N} P^n 1_A(x)}$$ exists and is positive a.e. on A_1 for each

$B \subset A_1$. Hence condition (2.1) is satisfied. To prove the sufficience of condition (2.1), let us prove the following lemmas.

Lemma 1. The process (X,Σ,m,P) has a finite invariant measure supported on $X_1 \subset X$ if and only if the space $\overline{(I-P)L_\infty(m)}$ contains no positive function the support of which is contained in X_1.

Proof. By the Hahn-Banach Theorem we have

$$\overline{(I-P)L_\infty}^{\perp} = \{\nu \mid \nu P = \nu\} \quad \text{where} \quad \nu \in L_\infty^*(m)$$

If λ is a finite invariant measure supported on X_1, then if f is a positive function with $\{f>0\} \subset X_1$ then $\langle f,\lambda\rangle > 0$, hence $f \notin \overline{(I-P)L_\infty(m)}$. Conversely, if there exists no finite invariant measure supported on X_1, then by theorem C of [1] chapter IV, there exists a set $A \subset X_1$ and a sequence of integers $\{n_i\}$ such that $\sum_{i=1}^{\infty} P^{n_i} 1_A \in L_\infty(m)$. Thus if $\nu \in L_\infty^*(m)$ with $\nu P = \nu$ then $\langle 1_A,\nu\rangle = 0$. Hence $1_A \in \overline{(I-P)L_\infty(m)}$ and the lemma is proved.

Lemma 2. Let λ be a finite measure invariant under P_A, then $\mu = \lambda I_A \sum_{n=0}^{\infty} (PI_{A^c})^n$ is a σ-finite measure on $\tilde{A}$ invariant under P.

Proof. This is Theorem C chapter VI of [1].

Lemma 3. For each integer N , and $f \in L_\infty(m)$

$$(2.2) \qquad \left| \sum_{n=1}^{N} P^n I_A f(x) - \sum_{n=1}^{N} P^n P_A f(x) \right| \leq 2 \, \|f\|_\infty .$$

Proof. In the proof of lemma 2 of [2] we obtain for each N and each K and $f \in L_\infty(m)$:

$$\sum_{n=1}^{N} P^n I_A \sum_{k=0}^{K} (PI_{A^c})^k PI_A f(x) = \sum_{n=1}^{N} P^n I_A f(x) + P^N \sum_{k=0}^{K} (PI_{A^c})^k PI_A f(x) -$$

$$- \sum_{k=0}^{K} (PI_{A^c})^k PI_A f(x) - \sum_{n=1}^{N} P^{n-1} (PI_{A^c})^{K+1} PI_A f(x) .$$

Let $K \to \infty$ and then we get

$$\sum_{n=1}^{N} P^n P_A f(x) = \sum_{n=1}^{N} P^n I_A f(x) + P^N \sum_{k=0}^{\infty} (PI_{A^c})^k PI_A f(x) - \sum_{k=0}^{\infty} (PI_{A^c})^k PI_A f(x)$$

Hence:

$$\left| \sum_{n=1}^{\infty} P^n P_A f(x) - \sum_{n=1}^{N} P^n I_A f(x) \right| \leq \left| P^N \sum_{k=0}^{\infty} (PI_{A^c})^k PI_A f(x) \right| + \left| \sum_{k=0}^{\infty} (PI_{A^c})^k PI_A f(x) \right| \leq$$

$$\leq 2 \|f\|_\infty . \qquad \text{(See [1])}$$

and (2.2) is proved.

Proof of Theorem 1. From lemma 1 and lemma 2 we can conclude that it is sufficient to prove that $\overline{(I_A - P_A) L_\infty (A, \Sigma_A, mI_A)}$ contains no positive function the support of which is contained in $A \cap A_1$.

Let us assume that there exists a function $0 \leq f \in L_\infty(A, \Sigma_A, mI_A)$ with $\{f > 0\} \subset A \cap A_1$ and $f \in \overline{(I_A - P_A) L_\infty (A, \Sigma_A, mI_A)}$.

For each $\epsilon > 0$ there exists $g \in L_\infty(A, \Sigma_A, mI_A)$ such that $|f - g + P_A g| \leq \epsilon 1_A$. Thus:

$$\overline{\lim_{N\to\infty}} \frac{\sum_{n=1}^{N} P^n f(x)}{\sum_{n=1}^{N} P^n 1_A(x)} \leq \overline{\lim_{N\to 0}} \frac{\left|\sum_{n=1}^{N} P^n (I_A g - P_A g)(x)\right|}{\sum_{n=1}^{N} P^n 1_A(x)} +$$

$$+ \overline{\lim} \frac{\left|\sum_{n=1}^{N} P^n (f - g + P_A g)(x)\right|}{\sum_{n=1}^{N} P^n 1_A(x)} \leq$$

$$\leq \overline{\lim_{N\to\infty}} \frac{2\|g\|_\infty}{\sum_{n=1}^{N} P^n 1_A(x)} + \epsilon = 0$$

by lemma 3. But ϵ is arbitrary. Hence $\lim_{N\to\infty} \frac{\sum_{n=1}^{N} P^n f(x)}{\sum_{n=1}^{N} P^n 1_A(x)} = 0$ which contradicts condition (2.1). So, theorem 1 is proved.

<u>Theorem 2</u>. The space X can be decomposed into $X = X_1 \cup X_2$ where $X_1, X_2 \in \Sigma_i$ and

1) There exists a σ-finite invariant measure μ equivalent to mI_{X_1}.

2) Every σ-finite invariant measure vanishes on X_2.

3) For every $A \subset X_2$ and for every $\epsilon > 0$ there exists $B \subset \tilde{A}$ with $m(\tilde{A} - B) < \epsilon$ and

$$\lim_{N\to\infty} \frac{\sum_{n=1}^{N} P^n 1_B(x)}{\sum_{n=1}^{N} P^n 1_A(x)} = 0 \quad \text{a.e. on } \tilde{A} .$$

Proof. Let $\quad = \{\tilde{A} \in \Sigma_i \mid A$ satisfy (2.1) for every $B \subset A$, $m(B) > 0\}$. ($\tilde{A}$ is defined in (1.4)). Consider $\sup\{m(\tilde{A}) \mid \tilde{A} \in \quad\} = \alpha$.

There exists a sequence $\{\tilde{A}_n\} \subset \quad$ such that $n(\tilde{A}_n) \quad \alpha$. Let $X_1 = \cup_n \tilde{A}_n$ and hence $X_1 \in \Sigma_i$. By theorem 2.1 there exists a σ-finite invariant measure supported on X_1. Define $X_2 = X - X_1$. Suppose that there exists a σ-finite invariant measure μ which is supported on $E \subset X_2$. Take a set $A \subset E$ with $\mu(A) < \infty$. By theorem 2.1 A satisfy (2.1) for every $B \subset A$, $m(B) > 0$, hence $X_2 \supset \tilde{A} \in \Sigma_i$. $\tilde{A} \cap A_n = \emptyset$ for each n. Denote $A'_n = A_n \cup \tilde{A}$, and then $A'_n \in \quad$ and $m(A'_n) = m(A_n) + m(\tilde{A})$. Hence $m(A'_n) \quad \alpha + m(\tilde{A}) > \alpha$, a contradiction. So, parts 1) and 2) of the theorem are proved.

Let $A \subset X_2$, by Theorem 2.1 there exists a set $B \subset A$ with $m(B) > 0$ and

$$\lim_{N\to\infty} \frac{\sum_{n=1}^{N} P^n 1_B(x)}{\sum_{n=1}^{N} P^n 1_A(x)} = 0 \quad \text{a.e. on } \tilde{A}.$$

Define $B_{ki} = \{x \mid P^k 1_B(x) \geq \frac{1}{i}\}$. It is clear that $\cup_{k,i} B_{ki} = \tilde{B}$ and $i \cdot P^k 1_B \geq 1_{B_{ki}}$, hence:

$$\lim_{N\to\infty} \frac{\sum_{n=1}^{N} P^n 1_{B_{ki}}(x)}{\sum_{n=1}^{N} P^n 1_A(x)} \leq \lim_{N\to\infty} \frac{i \cdot \sum_{n=1}^{N} P^{n+k} 1_B(x)}{\sum_{n=1}^{N} P^n 1_A(x)} = 0 \quad \text{a.e. on } \tilde{A}.$$

Define:

$$(2.3) \qquad \mathcal{K} = \{E \subset \tilde{A} \mid \lim_{N\to\infty} \frac{\sum_{n=1}^{N} P^n 1_E(x)}{\sum_{n=1}^{N} P^n 1_A(x)} = 0 \quad \text{a.e. on } \tilde{A}\}$$

Hence:

$$(2.4) \qquad \sup\{m(E) \mid E \in \mathcal{K},\ E \subset B\} = m(B).$$

Consider: $\alpha = \sup\{m(E) \mid E \in \mathcal{K}\}$. There exists $\{E_n\} \subset \mathcal{K}$ such that $m(E_n)\ \alpha$. It can be supposed that $E_n \subset E_{n+1}$, n (if not, replace E_n by $E'_n = \bigcup_{k=1}^{n} E_k$) and hence $\tilde{E}_n \subset \tilde{E}_{n+1}$. By (2.4) for each $\epsilon > 0$ and for each n, we can find sets $F_n \subset \tilde{E}_n$ such that $m(\tilde{E}_n - F_n) < \epsilon/2^n$, $F_n \in \mathcal{K}$ and $F_n \subset F_{n+1}$. Thus $\lim_{n\to\infty} m(\tilde{E}_n) \leq \lim_{n\to\infty} m(F_n) + \epsilon \leq \alpha + \epsilon$. But ϵ is arbitrary and on the other hand we have $\lim_{n\to\infty} m(\tilde{E}_n) > \alpha$ hence $\lim_{n\to\infty} m(\tilde{E}_n) = \alpha$.

Denote $F = \bigcup_{n=1}^{\infty} E_n$. $F \in \Sigma_i$ and $m(F) = \alpha$. Assume $\alpha < m(\tilde{A})$. By (2.1) there exists a set $B \subset \tilde{A} - F$ and $B \in \mathcal{K}$. Denote $E'_n = E_n \cup B$ and then $E'_n \in \mathcal{K}$ and $m(E'_n) = m(E_n) + m(B)$. Hence $m(E'_n)\ \alpha + m(B) > \alpha$, a contradiction. Thus $\alpha = m(\tilde{A})$ and part 3) of the theorem is proved.

The author wishes to thank Professor A. Brunel for valuable conversations.

References:

[1] S. R. Foguel, "The ergodic theory of Markov processes," Van Nostrand, New York, 1969.

[2] S. Horowitz, "On σ-finite invariant measures for Markov processes," Israel J. Math., vol. 6, 1968, p. 338-345.

Super-mean-valued functions and semipolar sets

by

A. Ionescu Tulcea(1)

Let $X = (\Omega, \mathcal{M}, \mathcal{M}_t, X_t, \theta_t, P^x)$ be a fixed standard process with state space E. The notation and terminology used throughout this paper are those of [1]. The transition semigroup is denoted by (P_t) and the tribes (σ-algebras) of Borel sets, nearly Borel sets and universally measurable sets of E are denoted by $\mathcal{E}$, $\mathcal{E}^n$ and $\mathcal{E}^*$, respectively. For the sake of simplicity we assume that $\mathcal{M} = \mathcal{F}$ and $\mathcal{M}_t = \mathcal{F}_t$ for all $t \geq 0$.

We recall now that a function(2) $f \in \mathcal{E}_+^*$ is called α-excessive if: a) $P_t^\alpha f \leq f$ for all $t \geq 0$, and b) $\lim_{t \to 0} P_t^\alpha f = f$ (pointwise). If f satisfies only condition a) above, f is called α-super-mean-valued. It is well known (and easy to prove directly) that if f is α-super-mean-valued, then $\bar{f} = \lim_{t \to 0} P_t^\alpha f$ exists (pointwise), $\bar{f} \leq f$, $\bar{f}$ is α-excessive and in fact $\bar{f}$ is the largest α-excessive function dominated by f. The function $\bar{f}$ is called the α-excessive regularization of f. Clearly $P_t^\alpha f \leq \bar{f}$ for all $t > 0$. Furthermore, for each $\beta \geq 0$, $U^\beta f = U^\beta \bar{f}$ (see [1], p. 81). This shows that if $\bar{f}$ is finite then $\{f < \bar{f}\}$ is of potential zero. In many problems ("balayage" theory) it is desirable to know that the set $\{f < \bar{f}\}$ is not only of potential zero, but actually semipolar. More specifically we are concerned with the following question: Under what conditions on f is it true that $A_\varepsilon = \{f - \bar{f} \geq \varepsilon\}$ is thin for each $\varepsilon > 0$? This problem has been the object of many interesting and important papers. The previous question also has a supermartingale formulation. It is well known (and easy to see) that if f is α-super-mean-valued, then $\{e^{-\alpha t} f(X_t), \mathcal{F}_t, P^x\}_{t \geq 0}$ is a supermartingale, for each x. Properly reformulated, the above problem amounts to asking under what conditions on f is it true that this supermartingale has right hand limits almost surely.

The problem first arose in classical potential theory. Cartan's well known theorem asserts that if f is the lower envelope of a family of positive (more generally, locally bounded below) superharmonic functions, then f differs from its superharmonic regularization only on a polar set. Cartan's theorem was extended by

Doob to probabilistic potential theory. Doob's theorem (in the context of standard processes) states that if f is the lower envelope of a sequence of excessive functions, then f differs from its excessive regularization $\bar{f}$ on a semipolar set. In the presence of a "reference measure" for X, Doob's theorem remains valid for the lower envelope of an arbitrary family of excessive functions (see [1], p. 196-198). Since classical potential theory and Brownian motion are in a certain sense equivalent, and since Brownian motion is only one example of a standard process, it is clear that Doob's theorem is a generalization of Cartan's theorem. Quite recently Doob's theorem was generalized still further by Getoor and Murali Rao ([3]). Getoor and Murali Rao introduced a new class of α-super-mean-valued functions, the so-called <u>strongly</u> α-<u>super-mean-valued</u> <u>functions</u>. They proved that if f is strongly α-super-mean-valued then $\{f < \bar{f}\}$ is semipolar. The criterion that we shall give below (based on the interplay between the fine topology and the hitting operators) is easily proved and easily applicable; it yields as an immediate corollary the result of Getoor and Murali Rao.

To facilitate the presentation we introduce the following terminology: we say that a stopping time[(3)] S is a "<u>delayed</u> <u>hitting</u> <u>time</u>" if there are $B \in \mathcal{E}^n$ and $t > 0$ such that

$$S = t + T_B \circ \theta_t.$$

We need the following more or less known criterion (but not as well known as it should be!) for upper semi-continuity in the fine topology (see [2], p. 120-121); the added twist in the formulation below is that of using delayed hitting times.

<u>Proposition</u>. <u>Let</u> $f \in b\mathcal{E}^n$. <u>Let</u> $\alpha \geq 0$. <u>Then the following assertions are equivalent</u>:

i) f <u>is upper semi-continuous in the fine topology</u>.

ii) <u>Given any</u> $x \in E$ <u>and sequence</u> (T_n) <u>of delayed hitting times with</u> $T_n \to 0$ a.s. P^x, <u>we have</u>

$$\limsup_n P^\alpha_{T_n} f(x) \leq f(x).$$

We can now state our theorem:

<u>Theorem</u>. <u>Let</u> $f \in b\mathcal{E}^n_+$ <u>be</u> α-<u>super-mean-valued</u>. <u>Let</u> $\bar{f}$ <u>be its</u> α-<u>excessive regularization and for each</u> $\varepsilon > 0$ <u>let</u> $A_\varepsilon = \{f - \bar{f} \geq \varepsilon\}$. <u>Then the following</u>

assertions are equivalent:

i) A_ε is thin for each $\varepsilon > 0$.

ii) Almost surely $t \to f(X_t)$ has right hand limits and the right continuous regularization of $t \to f(X_t)$ is $t \to \bar{f}(X_t)$.

iii) Given any $x \in E$ and sequence (T_n) of delayed hitting times with $T_n \to 0$ a.s. P^x, we have

$$\lim_n P^\alpha_{T_n} f(x) = \bar{f}(x).$$

iv) Given any $x \in E$ and sequence (T_n) of delayed hitting times with $T_n \to 0$ a.s. P^x, we have

$$\limsup_n P^\alpha_{T_n} f(x) \leq \bar{f}(x).$$

Several comments are in order in connection with the above theorem. The implication i) => ii) is immediate, at least as far as the existence of right hand limits at 0 is concerned (the existence of right hand limits for arbitrary $t \geq 0$ is obtained by a standard transfinite induction argument). The implications ii) => iii) and iii) => iv) are obvious. The interesting implication is of course iv) => i). For the proof of this implication we argue as follows: we remark first (on the basis of the previous Proposition and the fact that $\bar{f} \leq f$) that f is finely upper semi-continuous. Thus A_ε is finely closed, that is $A^r_\varepsilon \subset A_\varepsilon$. Now we reason by contradiction. Assuming that A_ε is not thin, let $x \in A^r_\varepsilon$. Then $T = T_{A_\varepsilon} = 0$ a.s. P^x. Define $T_n = t_n + T \circ \theta_{t_n}$ where $t_n > 0$ and $\lim_n t_n = 0$. Then $f(X_{T_n}) - \bar{f}(X_{T_n}) \geq \varepsilon$ a.s. P^x on $\{T_n < \infty\}$. Integrating and applying the inequality in condition iv) to the sequence (T_n) yields $\bar{f}(x) \geq \bar{f}(x) + \varepsilon$, the desired contradiction.

From our point of view the relevant equivalence is i) <=> iv). The criterion given in condition iv) is easily verified in practice. To illustrate this we consider the class of strongly α-super-mean-valued functions introduced by Getoor and Murali Rao. A function f is called strongly α-super-mean-valued if:

a) $f \in \mathcal{E}^n_+$

b) $P^\alpha_T f \leq f$ for every stopping time T.

Let now f be bounded, strongly α-super-mean-valued. Let S be a delayed hitting time. Then $S = t + T_B \circ \theta_t$ for some $B \in \mathcal{E}^n$ and $t > 0$, and hence (Markov property), $P_S^\alpha = P_t^\alpha P_{T_B}^\alpha$. It follows that

$$P_S^\alpha f = P_t^\alpha (P_{T_B}^\alpha f) \le P_t^\alpha f \le \bar{f}$$

and thus condition iv) in the above theorem is trivially satisfied.

Thus for f bounded, strongly α-super-mean-valued, the set $\{\bar{f} < f\}$ is semi-polar. The same conclusion holds for arbitrary (not necessarily bounded) α-super-mean-valued functions (the usual reduction argument; see [1], p. 81).

For further details and proofs see [4].

References

[1] R. M. Blumenthal and R. K. Getoor, Markov Processes and Potential Theory, Academic Press, New York and London (1968).

[2] E. B. Dynkin, Markov Processes, volume I, Die Grundlehren der Math. Wiss., Band 121, Springer-Verlag (1965).

[3] R. K. Getoor and Murali Rao, Another look at Doob's theorem, to appear.

[4] A. Ionescu Tulcea, On super-mean-valued functions and semi-polar sets, to appear.

---

(1) This research was partially sponsored by the U.S. Army Research Office (Durham) under contract DA-31-124-ARO(D)-288.

(2) We recall that if $(G, \mathcal{G})$ is a measurable space we write $f \in \mathcal{G}$ if $f: G \to \bar{R}$ is measurable with respect to $\mathcal{G}$. We also recall that $\mathcal{G}_+ = \{f \in \mathcal{G} \mid f \ge 0\}$ and $b\mathcal{G} = \{f \in \mathcal{G} \mid f \text{ bounded}\}$.

(3) All stopping times considered below are taken with respect to $\{\mathcal{F}_t\}$, of course.

LIFTINGS AND DERIVATION BASES*

by

C. Ionescu Tulcea

We shall discuss in what follows certain relations between derivation bases and liftings. We introduce first several definitions concerning derivation bases and then we recall the definition of a lifting. Afterwards we give several results, the main (new) ones being Theorems 2, 4, 5, 6 and 7.

PART I.

1. - Derivation bases.

Let Z be a set, N an upper integral and $\mathcal{R}$ an algebra of elementary functions (we shall use the notations and terminology introduced in [9]). We assume that $(Z,N,\mathcal{R})$ is <u>strictly</u> <u>localizable</u> (whence $N = \overline{N}$) and that $N \neq 0$.

Define $\mu^{\bullet}$ on $\mathcal{P}(Z)$ to $\overline{R}_+$ by $\mu^{\bullet}(A) = N(\varphi_A)$ for all $A \in \mathcal{P}(Z)$. A set $A \subset Z$ is N-negligible (or $\mu^{\bullet}$-negligible) if $N(\varphi_A) = \mu^{\bullet}(A) = 0$. Denote by $\mathcal{B}$ the tribe of all measurable parts of Z and by $\mathcal{B}_0$ the clan of all $A \in \mathcal{B}$ such that $\mu^{\bullet}(A) < +\infty$. For every set $X \subset Z$ we denote by X' a <u>measurable</u> <u>cover</u> of X. If $\mathcal{U} \subset \mathcal{B}_0$ we denote by $\mathcal{U}^*$ the set of all $A \in \mathcal{U}$ such that $\mu^{\bullet}(A) > 0$.

Let now $E \subset Z$ and $\epsilon > 0$. An ϵ-<u>covering</u> of E is a <u>countable</u> set $\mathcal{E} \subset \mathcal{P}(Z)$ satisfying

$$\mu^{\bullet}(E - \cup\mathcal{E}) = 0 \text{ and } \mu^{\bullet}(\cup\mathcal{E} - E') \leq \epsilon.$$

---

*Research supported by the U. S. Army Research Office (Durham) under contract DAHCOH 68 C 0005. For more details, proofs and more complete references see On liftings and derivation bases, forthcoming in the Journal of Mathematical Analysis and Applications.

A <u>strong covering</u> of E, where $0 < \mu^{\cdot}(E) < +\infty$, is a set $\mathcal{C} \subset \mathcal{B}_o^*$ such that for every $\epsilon > 0$ there is an ϵ-covering of E consisting of disjoint sets belonging to $\mathcal{C}$.

A <u>derivation basis</u> on Z is a family $\mathcal{F} = (\mathcal{F}(z))_{z \in Z}$, where for every $z \in Z$, $\mathcal{F}(z)$ is a filter basis on $\mathcal{B}_o^*$. If $\mathcal{F}$ is a derivation basis on Z we denote by $\mathcal{C}(\mathcal{F})$ the set of all parts of Z which belong to some set belonging to some filter basis $\mathcal{F}(z)$, with $z \in Z$.

<u>Let now</u> $\mathcal{F} = (\mathcal{F}(z))_{z \in Z}$ <u>be a derivation basis on</u> Z.

An $\mathcal{F}$-<u>covering</u> of E, where $0 < \mu^{\cdot}(E) < +\infty$, is a set $\mathcal{C} \subset \mathcal{B}_o^*$ such that $\mathcal{C} \cap \mathcal{A} \neq \emptyset$, for every $z \in E$ and $\mathcal{A} \in \mathcal{F}(z)$.

We say that $\mathcal{F}$ is a <u>strong derivation basis on</u> Z if for every $E \subset Z$, where $0 < \mu^{\cdot}(E) < +\infty$, every $\mathcal{F}$-covering of E is a strong covering of E.

Let now $\mathcal{U}$ be a set of parts of Z containing $\mathcal{C}(\mathcal{F})$ and let ψ be a mapping of $\mathcal{U}$ into R. Let ψ/μ be the mapping $A \mapsto \psi(A)/\mu^{\cdot}(A)$ of $\mathcal{C}(\mathcal{F})$ into R.

Define

$$\underline{D}_{\mathcal{F}}\psi(z) = \liminf_{\mathcal{F}(z)} \psi/\mu$$

and

$$\overline{D}_{\mathcal{F}}\psi(z) = \limsup_{\mathcal{F}(z)} \psi/\mu$$

for every $z \in Z$. Then $\underline{D}_{\mathcal{F}}\psi$ and $\overline{D}_{\mathcal{F}}\psi$ are mappings of Z into $\overline{R}$ ($= [-\infty, +\infty]$). If $z \in Z$ and $\underline{D}_{\mathcal{F}}\psi(z) = \overline{D}_{\mathcal{F}}\psi(z)$ we write

$$D_{\mathcal{F}}\psi(z) = \underline{D}_{\mathcal{F}}\psi(z) = \overline{D}_{\mathcal{F}}\psi(z),$$

and call $D_{\mathcal{F}}\psi(z)$ the <u>derivative</u> of ψ at z (with respect to $\mathcal{F}$).

If $f: Z \to R$ is measurable and if $N(\varphi_A f) < +\infty$ for $A \in \mathcal{B}_o$ we define $\psi_f: \mathcal{B}_o \to R$ by

(1) $$\psi_f(A) = \int \psi_A f d\mu$$

for $A \in \mathcal{B}_o$ (here $\mu = \mu_{(N, \mathcal{R})}$ is the integral associated with $(N, \mathcal{R})$ (see [9], p. 6)). Then (see [11], [12], [3], [4] and [5]):

<u>Theorem</u> 1. - <u>If</u> $\mathcal{F}$ <u>is a strong derivation basis on</u> Z

$$D_{\mathcal{F}}\psi_f(z) = f(z),$$

N-<u>almost everywhere</u>.

Let M^∞ be the algebra of all bounded real-valued measurable functions defined on Z. Notice that if $f \in M^\infty$ then we have $N(\varphi_A f) < +\infty$ for all $A \in \mathcal{B}_o$. A <u>weak derivation basis</u> on Z is a derivation basis $\mathcal{F}$ on Z such that for every $f \in M^\infty$,

$$D_{\mathcal{F}}\psi_f(z) = f(z),$$

N-almost everywhere. Every strong derivation basis on Z is a weak derivation basis.

2. - <u>Liftings and derivation bases</u>.

For any two functions f and g defined on Z we write $f \equiv g$ whenever $f(z) = g(z)$, N-almost everywhere. A <u>lifting of</u> M^∞ is a mapping $\rho: M^\infty \to M^\infty$ having the following properties:

(I) $\rho(f) \equiv f$;

(II) $f \equiv g$ implies $\rho(f) = \rho(g)$;

(III) $\rho(1) = 1$;

(IV) $f \geq 0$ implies $\rho(f) \geq 0$;

(V) $\rho(\alpha f + \beta g) = \alpha\rho(f) + \beta\rho(g)$;

(VI) $\rho(fg) = \rho(f)\rho(g)$.

Given $(Z, N, \mathcal{R})$ strictly localizable, there exists a lifting of the corresponding algebra M^∞ (see [9], Chapters III and IV).

For any sets A and B in $\mathcal{B}$ we write $A \equiv B$ if and only if $\varphi_A \equiv \varphi_B$, that is if and only if,

$$A \Delta B = (A - B) \cup (B - A)$$

is N-negligible. A <u>lifting of</u> $\mathcal{B}$ is a mapping $\theta: \mathcal{B} \to \mathcal{B}$ having the following properties:

(I') $\theta(A) \equiv A$;

(II') $A \equiv B$ implies $\theta(A) = \theta(B)$;

(III') $\theta(Z) = Z$ and $\theta(\emptyset) = \emptyset$;

(IV') $\theta(A \cap B) = \theta(A) \cap \theta(B)$;

(V') $\theta(A \cup B) = \theta(A) \cup \theta(B)$.

If ρ is a lifting of M^∞ then there exists a <u>unique</u> lifting θ of $\mathcal{B}$ such that

(2) $$\rho(\varphi_A) = \varphi_{\theta(A)},$$

for all $A \in \mathcal{B}$. Conversely if θ is a lifting of $\mathcal{B}$ then there exists a <u>unique</u> lifting ρ of M^∞ satisfying the equations (2) for all $A \in \mathcal{B}$.

A <u>lower density</u> of $\mathcal{B}$ is a mapping $\theta: \mathcal{B} \to \mathcal{B}$ satisfying (I') - (IV').

For any <u>lower density</u> θ of $\mathcal{B}$ we define

$$Z(\theta) = \bigcup_{A \in \mathcal{B}_o} \theta(A)$$

(notice that $Z - Z(\theta)$ is N-negligible) and

$$\mathcal{B}_o(\theta) = \{\theta(A) | A \in \mathcal{B}_o\}.$$

Let now $\mathcal{F} = (\mathcal{F}(z))_{z \in Z}$ be a derivation basis on Z and θ a lower density of $\mathcal{B}$. We say that $\mathcal{F}$ <u>is associated with</u> θ when:

(α) if $A \in \mathcal{L}(F)$ then $A \subset \theta(A)$;

(β) if $D \in \mathcal{B}_o(\theta)$ and $z \in D$ then there is $\mathcal{A} \in \mathcal{F}(z)$ contained in $\mathcal{P}(D)$.

If for each $z \in Z(\theta)$ we denote by $\mathcal{F}_\theta(z)$ the filter basis consisting of the sections of the set

$$\{\mathbb{B} | B \ni z,\ B \in \mathcal{B}_o(\theta)\},$$

and if for each $z \notin Z(\theta)$ we denote by $\mathcal{F}_\theta(z)$ an arbitrary filter basis on $\mathcal{B}_o(\theta)^*$, then

$$\mathcal{F}_\theta = (\mathcal{F}_\theta(z))_{z \in Z}$$

is a derivation basis on Z *associated with* θ.

We may now state the:

Theorem 2. - *If* θ *is a lower density of* $\mathcal{B}$ *and* $\mathcal{F}$ *a derivation basis on* Z *associated with* θ *then* $\mathcal{F}$ *is strong*.

This theorem is essentially due to D. Kölzow, who proved that $\mathcal{F}_\theta$ is a strong derivation basis if θ is a lifting (see [10], Theorem 19, p. 56).

We notice here that it was shown by J. Dieudonné in [1], that the existence of a derivation basis, with convenient properties implies the existence of a lifting. At the time of the publication of [1] it was not known however, whether or not liftings always exist. As we have indicated above, we know now that in the case of strictly localizable spaces liftings do exist. Theorem 1 shows that, in the case of strictly localizable spaces strong derivation bases also exist (and this is proved using the existence of a lower density, which is equivalent with the existence of a lifting).

In the rest of this section we assume that $f: Z \to R$ is measurable and that $N(\varphi_A f) < +\infty$ for all $A \in \mathcal{B}_o$. The mapping $\psi_f: \mathcal{B}_o \to R$ is defined by the equations (1).

If θ is a *lower density* of $\mathcal{B}$ and $\mathcal{F}$ is a derivation basis on Z associated with θ, then by Theorem 2, $\mathcal{F}$ is strong. By Theorem 1 we have

$$D_{\mathcal{F}} \psi_f(z) = f(z),$$

N-almost everywhere.

For derivation bases on Z associated with θ, this result can be obtained by a different method. In fact consider the topology

$$\mathcal{T}_\theta = \{A \mid A \in \mathcal{B},\ A \subset \theta(A)\}$$

on Z (for the definition of the topologies $\mathcal{T}_\theta$ and T_θ (see below) and their properties, see [6] and [9], Chap. V). The topology $\mathcal{T}_\theta$ has, among others the following property:

(3) A mapping $f:Z \to \overline{R}$ is measurable if and only if there exists an N-negligible set $C_f \supset Z - Z(\theta)$, such that f is continuous at each $z \in Z - C_f$.

On the basis of this result we obtain immediately that if $\mathfrak{F}$ is a derivation basis on Z associated with θ, then

$$D_{\mathfrak{F}} \psi_f(z) = f(z)$$

for every $z \notin C_f$.

If θ is a lifting of $\mathfrak{B}$ we also define the topology T_θ spanned by $\{\theta(A) | A \in \mathfrak{B}\}$. The topology T_θ has, among others, the following property:

(4) If $f:Z \to R$ is measurable there exist a unique $f^* \in C_{\overline{R}}(Z)$ such that $f^* \equiv f$.

On the basis of this result we obtain immediately that if $\mathfrak{F}$ is a derivation basis on Z associated with (the lifting) θ then ("clearly $\psi_f = \psi_{f^*}$")

$$D_{\mathfrak{F}} \psi_f(z) = f^*(z)$$

for every $z \in Z(\theta)$.

Remark. - Notice that these considerations, using the topologies $\mathcal{T}_\theta$ and T_θ, do not show that a derivation basis associated with a lower density (or with a lifting) is strong.

PART II.

1. - Derivation bases on locally compact spaces.

In this and next section we assume that Z is a locally compact space, we denote by μ a positive (Radon) measure on Z and by $\mu^{\bullet}$ the essential upper integral corresponding to the measure μ. Then $\mu^{\bullet}$ is an upper integral in the sense defined in [9], p. 1 and $(Z,\mu^{\bullet},\mathcal{K}(Z))$ is strictly localizable.

Let now $\mathcal{U} \subset \mathcal{B}_o$. A derivation basis $\mathcal{F}$ on Z, is said to be of type $\mathcal{U}$ if $\mathcal{C}(\mathcal{F}) \subset \mathcal{U}$.

Let $\mathcal{K}_\sigma$ be the set of all elements of $\mathcal{B}_o$ which are countable unions of compact sets. It follows from the results in Section 2, PART I that for every lower density θ of $\mathcal{B}$ there exists a derivation basis on Z of type $\mathcal{K}_\sigma$, associated with θ.

Let $\mathcal{F} = (\mathcal{F}(z))_{z \in Z}$ be a derivation basis on Z. We shall discuss below the following condition:

(C) For every open set $U \subset Z$ and $z \in U$ there is $\mathcal{a} \in \mathcal{F}(z)$ contained in $\mathcal{P}(U)$.

Denote by $\mathcal{K}_c$ the set of all relatively compact parts of Z belonging to $\mathcal{K}_\sigma$.

The following result is used in the proof of Theorem 7 below (see for instance [3]; stronger results are valid but they will not be given here):

Theorem 3. - Let $\mathcal{F}$ be a strong derivation basis on Z of type $\mathcal{K}_c$ satisfying (C). Let ν be a measure on Z and let $\nu = f\cdot\mu + \sigma$, where f is locally μ-integrable and σ is singular with respect to μ. Then

$$D_{\mathcal{F}}\nu(z) = f(z),$$

N-almost everywhere.

A strong lifting of M^∞ (see [7] or [9], Chap VIII) is a lifting ρ of M^∞ satisfying:

(VII) $\rho(f) = f$ for every $f \in C^b(Z)$.

A couple (Z,μ) has the strong lifting property if there exists a strong lifting of M^∞. The problem as to whether or not every couple (Z,μ), with Supp $\mu = Z$, has the strong lifting property is open.

A strong lower density of $\mathcal{B}$ is a lower density θ of $\mathcal{B}$ satisfying:

(VII') $\theta(U) \supset U$ for every open set $U \subset Z$.

Notice that a lifting of M^∞ is strong if and only if the corresponding lifting of $\mathcal{B}$ (defined by the equations (2)) is strong. If there exists a strong lower density of $\mathcal{B}$ we deduce that (Z,μ) has the strong lifting property.

Theorem 4. - *Let θ be a strong lower density of $\mathcal{B}$. Then:* 4.1) *Every derivation basis on Z associated with θ is strong and satisfies* (C). 4.2) *There is a derivation basis on Z of type $\mathcal{K}_c$ associated with θ.*

The following theorem gives a property equivalent with the strong lifting property:

Theorem 5. - *Let Z be a locally compact space and μ a positive measure on Z. The following assertions are equivalent:*

5.1) *The couple (Z,μ) has the strong lifting property.*

5.2) *There is a strong derivation basis on Z of type $\mathcal{K}_c$ satisfying* (C).

We take this opportunity to state the following *open* problem: Let $\mathcal{E}$ be the algebra of all real-valued bounded Borel functions on Z. Decide whether or not there is a lifting (or even a linear lifting) ρ of M^∞ such that $\rho(M^\infty) \subset \mathcal{E}$.

2. - *Approximate identities.*

Let Z be a locally compact group and μ a Haar measure on Z. Let $f:Z \to R$. For every $s \in Z$ we denote $\gamma(s)f$ the mapping $z \mapsto f(s^{-1}z)$ of Z into R.

A lifting ρ of M^∞ *commutes with* Z if

(VIII) $\rho(\gamma(s)f) = \gamma(s)\rho(f)$

for all $f \in M^\infty$ and $s \in Z$. There is always a lifting of M^∞ which commutes with Z (see [8]).

A lifting θ of $\mathcal{B}$ *commutes with* Z if

(VIII') $\theta(sA) = s\theta(A)$

for all $A \in \mathcal{B}$ and $s \in Z$. We notice that a lifting of M^∞ commutes with Z if and only if the corresponding lifting of $\mathcal{B}$ (defined by the equations (2)) commutes with Z.

A derivation basis $\mathcal{F} = (\mathcal{F}(z))_{z \in Z}$ on Z commutes with Z if for all $s \in Z$ and $z \in Z$ the filter basis $\mathcal{F}(sz)$ is the image of $\mathcal{F}(z)$ by the (extension to $\mathcal{P}(Z)$ of the) mapping $x \mapsto sx$ of Z onto Z.

Theorem 6. - Let θ be a lifting of $\mathcal{B}$ commuting with Z. There exists then a derivation basis on Z of type $\mathcal{K}_c$ associated with θ and commuting with Z.

Denote by B_c^∞ the algebra of all mappings of Z into R which have compact support, are bounded and Borel measurable. An approximate identity of Z (of type B_c^∞) is a filter basis $\mathcal{F}$ on B_c^∞ having the following properties:

i) $\mathcal{A} \in \mathcal{F}$ and $h \in \mathcal{A}$ implies $h \geq 0$ and $\int_Z h d\mu = 1$;

ii) for every $V \in \mathcal{V}(e)$ there is $\mathcal{A} \in \mathcal{F}$ such that $h \in \mathcal{A}$ implies $\mathrm{Supp}\, h \subset V$.

Let Δ be the modular function of the group Z. Let λ be a measure on Z. We define

$$\lambda * f(z) = \int f(s^{-1}z)d\lambda(s) \text{ and } f*\lambda(z) = \int f(zs^{-1})\Delta(s^{-1})d\lambda(s)$$

for $f \in B_c^\infty$ and $z \in Z$. We denote for $z \in Z$, by $(\lambda,\gamma)(z)$ and $(\lambda,\delta)(z)$, respectively, the mappings $g \mapsto \lambda * g(z)$ and $g \mapsto g*\lambda(z)$ of B_c^∞ into R.

Theorem 7. - There exist approximate identities $\mathcal{J}$ and $\mathcal{D}$ of Z (of type B_c^∞) such that if $\lambda = f\cdot\mu + \sigma$, where f is locally μ-integrable and σ is singular with respect to μ, then

$$\lim_{\mathcal{J}} (\lambda,\gamma)(z) = f(z) \text{ and } \lim_{\mathcal{D}} (\lambda,\delta)(z) = f(z),$$

N-almost everywhere.

The proof of Theorem 7 is based on Theorems 3 and 6. Results of this type can be used to obtain pointwise inversion formulas for Fourier transforms on locally compact groups (see also [2]).

REFERENCES

1. J. Dieudonné, Sur le théorème de Lebesgue-Nikodym (IV), J. Indian Math.Soc.15, 77-86 (1951).

2. R. E. Edwards and E. Hewitt, Pointwise limits for sequences of convolution operators, Acta. Math., 113, 181-218 (1965).

3. O. Haupt, G. Aumann and Chr. Pauc, Differential und Integralrechnung, Vol, III, Berlin, 1955.

4. C. A. Hayes and C. Pauc, Full individual and class differentiation theorems and their relations to halo and Vitali properties, Canadian J. Math., 7, 221-274 (1955).

5. C. A. Hayes and C. Pauc, Derivation and Martingales, Ergebnisse der Mathematik und ihrer Grenzgebiete, Band 49, Springer-Verlag (1970).

6. A. Ionescu Tulcea, Liftings compatible with topologies, Bull. Soc. Math. de Grèce 8, 116-126 (1967).

7. A. Ionescu Tulcea and C. Ionescu Tulcea, On the lifting property, IV, Disintegration of measures. Ann. Inst. Fourier (Grenoble) 14, 445-472 (1964).

8. A. Ionescu Tulcea and C. Ionescu Tulcea, On the existence of a lifting commuting with the left translations of an arbitrary locally compact group, Proceedings, Fifth Berkeley Symposium on Math. Stat. and Probability, p. 63-97. Univ. of California Press (1967).

9. A. Ionescu Tulcea and C. Ionescu Tulcea, Topics in the theory of lifting, Ergebnisse der Mathematik und ihrer Grenzgebiete, Band

48, Springer-Verlag, 1969.

10. D. Kölzow, Differentiation von Massen, Lecture Notes in Mathematics. Band 65, Springer-Verlag, 1968.

11. R. de Possel, Sur la dérivation abstraite des fonctions d'ensemble, J. de Math. pures et appl. 15, 391-409 (1936).

12. R. de Possel, Sur la généralisation de la notion de système dérivant, C. R. Acad. Sci. Paris 224, 1137-1139 (1947).

Northwestern University

LIPSCHITZ FUNCTIONS AND THE PREVALENCE OF STRICT ERGODICITY FOR CONTINUOUS-TIME FLOWS

by Konrad Jacobs*

Mathematisches Institut der Universität
Erlangen-Nürnberg

Summary: In a recent paper, R. Jewett has shown that every weakly mixing transformation in a separable probability space can be considered, up to a measure algebra isomorphism, as a strictly ergodic homeomorphism in some compact metric set. The present paper provides the analogous result for continuous-time flows: neglecting some measure algebra isomorphism, weakly mixing flows in separable probability spaces can be considered as shift flows on strictly ergodic subsets of a compact metric space made out of certain Lipschitz functions. As a preparatory tool, we use the Ambrose-Kakutani theorem in order to obtain flows built under functions. A combination of Jewett's devices and new ideas is then applied in order to obtain the desired embedding.

*Research done during a visit at The Ohio State University, Columbus, Ohio, U.S.A., 1969/70 .

Let Ω be a compact metric space and $T:\Omega \to \Omega$ a homeomorphism. A minimal strictly T-invariant compact subset $\Omega_o \neq \emptyset$ of Ω is said to be <u>strictly</u> <u>ergodic</u> if there is exactly one normalized T-invariant measure m living on Ω_o. General compactness techniques show that a minimal invariant compact $\emptyset = \Omega_o \subseteq \Omega$ always carries at least one normalized T-invariant measure. Its unicity (implying its ergodicity) and hence the strict ergodicity of Ω_o is equivalent to the existence, uniformly for all $\omega \in \Omega_o$, of a constant $\lim_n \frac{1}{n} \sum_{k=o}^{n-1} f(T^k\omega)$ for every $f \in C(\Omega)$. The limit is then $m(f) = \int f dm$. Of course, it is sufficient to have this for a set of functions $f \in C(\Omega)$ whose linear span is uniformly dense in $C(\Omega)$. The measure m as well as the resulting dynamical system $(\Omega, \mathcal{B}, m, T)$ (as well as the dynamical system $(\Omega_o, \mathcal{B}_o, m, T)$ arising by restriction to Ω_o) are then also called strictly ergodic.

In his important paper [5], Jewett proved that for every weakly mixing abstract dynamical system $(\Omega, \mathcal{B}, m, T)$ (with an abstract normalized measure space $(\Omega, \mathcal{B}, m)$ and a measurable invertible m-preserving T) we may always, neglecting an isomorphism of measure algebras, assume that Ω is compact metric, T a homeomorphism, and m strictly ergodic, provided $\mathcal{B}$ is countably generated mod m. This implies the long questioned result, that every measure-theoretical property of abstract dynamical systems which is compatible with weak mixing, is also compatible with strict ergodicity, separability provided. Especially, every Bernoulli scheme can be considered as lying in some strictly ergodic set (of course not in the Bernoulli space where components are independent). If the measure space $(\Omega, \mathcal{B}, m)$ is sufficiently regular, the measure algebra isomorphism can be given by a measurable point mapping. With a slight modification, Jewett's result may be restated in more detail as follows: Every real function $0 \leq f \leq 1$ an the basic space Ω of an abstract dynamical system gives rise to a mapping

$$\psi : \omega \rightarrow (\cdots, f(T^{-1}\omega), f(\omega), f(T\omega), \cdots)$$

of Ω into the cartesian product

$$\Omega' = \cdots \times \langle 0,1 \rangle \times \langle 0,1 \rangle \times \langle 0,1 \rangle \times \cdots .$$

The shift $T' : (\cdots, x_{-1}, x_0, x_1, \cdots) \rightarrow (\cdots, x_0, x_1, x_2, \cdots)$ is a homeomorphism of the compact metric space Ω' and we have $T' \circ \psi = \psi \circ T$. If f is measurable, then ψ is measurable, and if $\mathcal{B}$ is the smallest Borel field in which f is measurable, then ψ gives an isomorphism of measure algebras for every measure m in Ω and its ψ-image m' in Ω'. This m' is strictly ergodic iff for every continuous function $M(\omega')$ on Ω' we have the existence of a constant average

$$\lim_{n \to \infty} \frac{1}{n} \sum_{k=0}^{n-1} M(\psi(T^k_\omega))$$

uniformly on Ω minus a strictly invariant m-nullset not depending on M. By the Weierstrass-Stone theorem, it is possible to restrict oneself to a sequence $M_1, M_2, \cdots$ of continuous functions on Ω', each of which depends only on a finite number of components, e.g., polynomials with rational coefficients. Jewett [5] constructs a f with all the above properties as an almost-everywhere limit of functions $f^1, f^2, \cdots$ where each f^n generates $\mathcal{B}$ and is obtained from f^{n-1} by a skillful modification on a set of a measure tending quickly to 0 with n, such that f^n takes over all good averaging properties with respect to $M_1, \cdots, M_{n-1}$ acquired in the earlier steps, and acquires in addition good averaging properties with respect to M_n. One of the basic ideas behind this modification is that a real function on the integers which consists of pieces of bounded length, each of them with good averaging properties, inherits these averaging properties, even uniformly in time. Throughout the construction, compactness of Ω' or finite products $\langle 0,1\rangle \times \cdots \times \langle 0,1\rangle$, and equicontinuity of functions on these spaces play an important role.

In the present paper, Jewett's result is carried over to continuous-time flows. Our proofs rest heavily on Jewett's ideas. The main novelty is the proper choice of a continuous-time analogon to the discrete-time product space $\Omega' = \cdots \times \langle 0,1\rangle \times \langle 0,1\rangle \times \langle 0,1\rangle \times \cdots$. We propose the space L^A (with some $A > 0$) of all functions φ on the real line R which fulfil $0 \leq \varphi \leq 1$ and the Lipschitz condition $|\varphi(s) - \varphi(t)| \leq A|s - t|$. Some apriori arguments for this choice are the following:

1) In the same way as Ω' can serve as a model space for discrete-time instrumental records (such as daily morning temperatures), L^A can serve as a model space for continuous-time records made by instruments which have an inertia (such as temperature curves recorded in a weather station).

2) L^A has already shown some analogies to Ω' concerning ϵ-entropy (see Kolmogorov-Tikhomirov [6]).

The definite argument for our present choice is, of course, nothing but the successful employment of spaces L^A in our construction. To be precise, we are unable so far to find every weakly mixing flow isomorphically reproduced in a strictly ergodic subset of some L^A, but only in some infinite product space $L^A \times L^A \times \cdots$. Another difficulty arises from the fact that in a continuous-time flow there may be nullsets which cover the whole basic space in a small time interval.

Basic facts about continuous-time flows are listed in §1. §2 contains a theory of L^A and related spaces, as far as they are needed in §3 which contains the construction whose consequences are stated in §4.

§1. Basic facts about continuous-time flows.

Definition 1.1. Let $(\Omega, \mathcal{B}, m)$ be a measure space and $(T_t)_{t \in R}$ a one-parameter group of measurable m-preserving mappings of Ω onto itself. Then $(\Omega, \mathcal{B}, m, (T_t)_{t \in R})$ is called a (m-preserving continuous-time) flow.

1) The flow $(\Omega, \mathcal{B}, m, (T_t)_{t \in R})$ is called measurable if the mapping $(\omega,t) \to T_t\omega$ of the product measurability space $\Omega \times R$ onto the measurability space Ω is measurable.

2) The flow $(\Omega, \mathcal{B}, m, (T_t)_{t \in R})$ is called

a) ergodic, if $\Omega = \Omega' + \Omega''$, $\Omega',\Omega'' \in \mathcal{B}$, $T_t\Omega' = \Omega' \bmod m$, $T_t\Omega'' = \Omega'' \bmod m$ $(t \in R)$ implies $m(\Omega') = 0$ or $m(\Omega'') = 0$.

b) weakly mixing, if $\Omega \in \mathcal{B}$, $m(\Omega) = 1$ and

$$\lim_{t\to\infty} \frac{1}{t}\int_0^t |m(E \cap T_{-u}F) - m(E)m(F)|du = 0 \quad . \qquad (E,F \in \mathcal{B})$$

This implies that for any finite system $\Omega_1, \cdots, \Omega_b \in \mathcal{B}$ with $m(\Omega_1), \cdots, m(\Omega_b) > 0$ and any $t_o > 0$ there is a $C \geq t_o$ such that

$$m(\Omega_\beta \cap T_{-C}\Omega_\gamma) > 0 \qquad (\beta,\gamma = 1,\cdots,b).$$

3) The set $\Omega_o \subseteq \Omega$ is called strictly $(T_t)_{t \in R}$-invariant if $T_t\Omega_o = \Omega_o$ $(t \in R)$.

Definition 1.2. Let Ω be a compact metric space and $(T_t)_{t \in R}$ a one-parameter group of homeomorphisms of Ω such that the mapping $(\omega,t) \to T_t\omega$ of $\Omega \times R \to \Omega$ is continuous; $(T_t)_{t \in R}$ is then called continuous. A closed subset Ω_o of Ω is called

1) minimal invariant, if $\Omega_o \neq \emptyset$, $T_t\Omega_o = \Omega_o$ $(t \in R)$ and if

$\emptyset \neq \Omega' \subseteq \Omega_o$, $T_t\Omega' = \Omega'$ $(t \in R)$, Ω' closed implies $\Omega' = \Omega_o$.

2) strictly ergodic, if it is minimal invariant and there is only one measure m in Ω which fulfills the following conditions:

a) $m(\Omega_o) = m(\Omega) = 1$, i.e., m is normalized and lives on Ω_o.

b) $T_t m = m$ $(t \in R)$, i.e. m is $(T_t)_{t \in R}$-invariant.

Some well-known facts are collected in the following:

Theorem 1.3. Let Ω, $(T_t)_{t \in R}$ be as in Definition 1.2.

1) The closed $(T_t)_{t \in R}$-invariant subset $\Omega_o \neq \emptyset$ of Ω is minimal invariant iff for every $\omega \in \Omega_o$ and every neighborhood U of ω there is a $L > 0$ such that

$$\{t \mid T_t\omega \in U\} \cap \langle s, s + L\rangle \neq \emptyset \quad (s \in R).$$

2) Every closed $(T_t)_{t \in R}$-invariant subset of Ω contains a minimal-invariant subset.

3) If $\emptyset \neq \Omega_o \subseteq \Omega$ is closed and $(T_t)_{t \in R}$-invariant, then there is at least one normalized invariant measure m living on Ω_o.

4) The closed minimal invariant set $\emptyset \neq \Omega_o \subseteq \Omega$ is strictly ergodic iff for every $f \in C(\Omega)$ and every $\omega \in \Omega_o$, the averages

$$\frac{1}{t}\int_o^t f(T_{u+s}\omega)du$$

tend to some constant, uniformly for $s \in R$. This constant is then independent of $\omega \in \Omega_o$, and is $m(f) = \int f dm$, where m is the unique normalized invariant measure living on Ω_o.

5) Every closed invariant set $\emptyset \neq \Omega_o \subseteq \Omega$ fulfilling the condition

of 4) for all $f \in C(\Omega)$ contains exactly one strictly ergodic subset.

6) The unique normalized invariant measure attached to a strictly ergodic set is always ergodic.

The proof is an easy continuous-time analogon of proofs well-known in the discrete-time case (see e.g. Oxtoby [7], Jacobs [3], [4]).

The conditions to be achieved by our later constructions are summed up in the following:

Theorem 1.4. Let $(\Omega, \mathcal{B}, m, (T_t)_{t \in R})$ be a measurable flow such that $m(\Omega) = 1$. Let Ω' be a compact metric space and $(T'_t)_{t \in R}$ a continuous one-parameter group of homeomorphisms of Ω'. Let $\psi: \Omega \to \Omega'$ be a measurable mapping such that $\psi(T_t) = T'_t(\psi)$ $(t \in R)$ and put $m' = \psi m$, which implies that $(\Omega', \mathcal{B}', m', (T'_t)_{t \in R})$ (with $\mathcal{B}'$ = the natural Borel field in Ω') is a measurable flow. Then m' lives on a strictly ergodic subset of Ω' iff for every $f' \in C(\Omega')$ there is a constant and a m-nullset N such that for every $\omega \in \Omega \setminus N$,

$$\frac{1}{t} \int_0^t f'(T'_{u+s}(\psi\omega))du$$

tends to this constant uniformly for $s \in R$. The mapping ψ induces an isomorphism of the measure algebras $\mathcal{B}$ mod m and $\mathcal{B}'$ mod m' iff $\mathcal{B}$ is mod m the smallest Borel field on Ω for which ψ is measurable.

§ 2. The spaces $L^{A,n}$ and ${}_aL_b^{A,n}$

In this section we investigate spaces of Lipschitz functions such as to provide some tools for the constructions to be made in § 3.

We adopt the following general notation: If φ is a function defined on a subset J of the real line R (with values in an arbitrary set), and if the closed interval $\langle a, b\rangle$ is contained in J, then ${}_a\varphi_b$ denotes the restriction of φ to $\langle a, b\rangle$. We define ${}^s\varphi$ on $J-s$ by ${}^s\varphi(t) = \varphi(t + s)$ $(t + s \in J)$. Thus in case $J = R$ the symbol ${}_0({}^t\varphi)_c$ means ${}_t\varphi_{t+c}$ shifted to $\langle 0, c\rangle$.

Definition 2.1. Let $0 < A < \infty$.

1) We denote by L^A this system of all real functions φ defined on the real line R which fulfil

a) $0 \leq \varphi(t) \leq 1$ $\quad (t \in R)$

b) $|\varphi(s) - \varphi(t)| \leq A\,|s - t|$ $\quad (s, t \in R)$

i.e. φ admits the Lipschitz constant A.

2) Let $0 < n \leq \infty$. We put

$$L^{A,n} = \prod_{\nu=1}^{n} L^A$$

i.e. $L^{A,n}$ is the system of all R^n-valued functions $\varphi = (\varphi^1, \varphi^2, \ldots)$ such that each component function φ^ν belongs to L^A. Especially, $L^{A,1} = L^A$.

3) Let $-\infty < a < b < \infty$, $0 < n \leq \infty$. We put

$${}_aL_b^{A,n} = \{{}_a\varphi_b \mid \varphi \in L^{A,n}\}.$$

This is the system of all n-tuples of real functions φ on $\langle a, b\rangle$ which fulfil 1)a), b) there. Again we write ${}_aL_b^A$ instead of ${}_aL_b^{A,1}$.

4) a) Let $-\infty < a < b < \infty$. For $\varphi, \psi \in {}_aL_b^A$ write

$$\| \varphi - \psi \| = \sup_{a \le t \le b} | \varphi(t) - \psi(t) | \qquad \text{("uniform norm')}$$

Let $0 < n \le \infty$ and $\varphi = (\varphi^1, \varphi^2, \dots),\ \psi = (\psi^1, \psi^2, \dots) \in {}_aL_b^{A,n}$.

Then we define

$$\| \varphi - \psi \| = \sum_{\nu=1}^{n} \frac{1}{2^\nu} \| \varphi^\nu - \psi^\nu \|$$

b) Let $0 < n \le \infty$. For $\varphi = (\varphi^1, \varphi^2, \dots),\ \psi = (\psi^1, \psi^2, \dots) \in L^{A,n}$ we define

$$\| \varphi - \psi \| = \sum_{n=1}^{\infty} \frac{1}{2^n} \| {}_{-n}\varphi_n - {}_{-n}\psi_n \|$$

Observe that always $\| \varphi - \psi \| \le 2$

Theorem 2.2. 1) Each of the spaces L^A, $L^{A,n}$, $L^{A,\infty}$, ${}_aL_b^A$, ${}_aL_b^{A,n}$, ${}_aL_b^{A,\infty}$ is a compact metric space with the metric given in definition 2.1 .

2) In each of the spaces L^A, $L^{A,n}$, $L^{A,\infty}$ the shifts T_s defined for arbitrary real s by

$$(T_s \varphi)(t) = {}^s\varphi(t) = \varphi(t + s) \qquad (t \in R)$$

form a continuous one-parameter group of homomorphisms, i.e. the mapping

$$(t, \varphi) \to T_t \varphi$$

is continuous. We call $(T_t)_{t \in R}$ the shift flow in the corresponding space.

3) If $0 < A \le A'$, then $L^A \subseteq L^{A'}$, $L^{A,n} \subseteq L^{A',n}$, ${}_aL_b^A \subseteq {}_aL_b^{A'}$, ${}_aL_b^{A,n} \subseteq {}_aL_b^{A',n}$ $(0 < n \le \infty,\ -\infty < a < b < \infty)$.

The proof is an easy exercise. Since we are dealing with compact metric spaces, every continuous real function on e.g. ${}_aL_b^A$ extends to some continuous function on ${}_aL_b^{A'}$ if $A \le A'$. Observe that in $L^{A,\infty}$ metric convergence $\varphi^k = (\varphi^{k1}, \varphi^{k2}, \dots) \to \varphi = (\varphi^1, \varphi^2, \dots)$ $(k \to \infty)$ means that for more and more ν the functions $\varphi^{k\nu}$ are uniformly close to the corresponding φ^ν on larger and larger intervals, i.e. for every $\epsilon > 0$ and $n > 0$ there is a $k_0 > 0$ such that $k \ge k_0$ implies

$$| \varphi^{k\nu}(t) - \varphi^{\nu}(t) | < \epsilon \qquad (|t| \leq n,\ \nu = 1, \ldots, n).$$

The Lipschitz property of the real functions involved here shows that

$$\lim_k \varphi^{k\nu}(t) = \varphi^{\nu}(t) \qquad (\nu = 1,2, \ldots.)$$

for all t from a dense subset of R implies metric convergence $\varphi^k \to \varphi$. Later on we will have to deal with continuous functions on ${}_aL_b^{A,n}$ and $L^{A,n}$. The evaluation functions $\pi_{t\nu}(\varphi) = \varphi^{\nu}(t)$ are among the continuous functions on $L^{A,n}$ and separate the points of that space, hence their polynomials are uniformly dense in $C(L^{A,n})$; this holds even if we restrict t to a dense subset of R. Similar observations apply to ${}_aL_b^{A,n}$. If M is a continuous function on the latter space, then $M'(\varphi) = M({}_a\varphi_b)$ defines a continuous function M' on $L^{A,n}$. We indulge ourselves a slight sloppiness of language in speaking of functions on $L^{A,n}$ which can be considered as functions on ${}_aL_b^{A,n}$. Of course, these functions are uniformly dense in $C(L^{A,n})$ if we let a,b vary. Finally, every continuous function on $L^{A,n}$ can be considered as the restriction of some continuous function on $L^{A',n}$ if $A \leq A'$.

For the remaining part of this section, the Lipschitz constant A is kept fixed.

Theorem 2.3. Let $0 < n \leq \infty$ and

1) $0 < c < \infty$ and $M \in C({}_oL_c^{A,n})$. Then for every $\epsilon > 0$ there is a $\delta > 0$ such that $\varphi, \psi \in L^{A,n}$, $J \subseteq R$ and

$$\| {}_t\varphi_{c+t} - {}_t\psi_{c+t} \| < \delta \qquad (t \in J)$$

implies

$$| M({}_o({}^t\varphi)_c) - M({}_o({}^t\psi)_c) | < \epsilon \qquad (t \in J)$$

2) $M \in C(L^{A,n})$. Then for every $\epsilon > 0$ there is a $\delta > 0$ such that $\varphi, \psi \in L^{A,n}$ and

$$\| {}_t\varphi_{t+c} - {}_t\psi_{t+c} \| < \delta \qquad (t \in R)$$

implies

$$|M({}^t\varphi) - M({}^t\psi)| < \epsilon \qquad (t \in R)$$

The proof is an easy exercise.

Definition 2.4 . I) Let $0 < n \leq \infty$, $-\infty < a < a+c < b < \infty$, $0 < \delta$, $A < \infty$ and let M be a continuous real-valued function on ${}_oL^A_c$.

1) A function $\varphi \in {}_aL^{A,n}_{b+c}$ is said to be δ-good for M and the real number α if

$$\left| \frac{1}{b-a} \int_a^b M({}_o({}^s\varphi)_c)\, ds - \alpha \right| \leq \delta$$

2) A function $\varphi \in {}_aL^{A,n}_{b+c}$ is said to be δ-good for M and α by $D > 0$ if $a + D < b$ and

${}_s\varphi_{s+D+c}$ is δ-good for M and α, for every $a \leq s \leq b - D$.

3) A function $\varphi \in {}_aL^{A,n}_{b+c}$ is said to be δ-good for M and α after $C > 0$ if $a + C < b$ and if φ is δ-good for M and α by every D with $C \leq D < b - a$.

II) Let $0 < n \leq \infty$. $0 < \delta < \infty$ and let M be a continuous real-valued function on $L^{A,n}$. A function $\varphi \in L^{A,n}$ is said to be

a) δ-good for M and the real α <u>by D</u> if

$$(1) \qquad \left| \frac{1}{t} \int_0^t M\,({}^{s+u}\varphi)\, du - \alpha \right| \leq \delta \qquad (s \in R)$$

holds for $t = D$

b) δ-good for M and the real α <u>after D</u> if

(1) holds for $t \geq D$.

c) good for M and the real α , if for every $\delta > 0$ there is a D such that φ is δ-good for M and α after D .

d) good for M if it is good for M and some real α (which is, of course, uniquely determined) .

If, for II) , M can be considered as a function on ${}_oL_c^{A,n}$, $\varphi \in L^{A,n}$ is e.g. δ-good for M and α by D iff ${}_s\varphi_{s+D+c}$ is δ-good for M (as a function on ${}_oL_c^{A,n}$) and α , for every real s.

<u>Theorem 2.5.</u> Let $0 < n \leq \infty$, $0 < c < \infty$, $0 < C_o < -\infty$, $0 < \delta < \infty$, $s , \alpha \in R$, and let M be a continuous real function on ${}_oL_c^{A,n}$. Then the following sets are closed (and hence compact) subsets of $L^{A,n}$.

1) The set $G_s(\delta, M, \alpha, C_o)$ of all $\varphi \in L^{A,n}$ for which ${}_s\varphi_{s+C_o+c}$ is δ-good for M and α .

2) The set $G(\delta, M, \alpha, C_o)$ of all $\varphi \in L^{A,n}$ which are δ-good for M and α <u>by</u> C_o .

3) The set $G^*(\delta, M, \alpha, C_o)$ of all $\varphi \in L^{A,n}$ which are δ-good for M and α <u>after</u> C_o .

Theorem 2.6. There is a sequence $c_n \nearrow \infty$ and a sequence of continuous real functions $M_n : {}_oL^{2A,n}_{c_n} \to \langle 0, 1\rangle$ such that the following holds :

Let φ , $\varphi^k \in L^{2A,\infty}$, $\delta_k \searrow 0$, $D_k \nearrow \infty$, $\alpha_k \in R$ $(k = 1, 2, \dots)$ be such that

1) φ^k is δ_k-good for M_j and α_j by D_j $(j = 1, \dots, k)$

2) $\varphi^k (t) \to \varphi (t)$ $\qquad (t \in R)$

Then φ is good for every continuous real function M on $L^{2A,\infty}$.

Proof: Since every $\varphi \in L^{2A,\infty}$ is a sequence $(\varphi^1 , \varphi^2, \dots)$ of functions $\varphi \in L^{2A}$, and since the continuous real "evaluation functions" $\pi_{t\nu}$ defined on $L^{2A,\infty}$ by

$$\pi_{t\nu} (\varphi) = \varphi^\nu(t)$$

separate the points of $L^{2A,\infty}$ even if we restrict t to rational values, we deduce from the Weierstrass - Stone theorem that there is a sequence $M_1, M_2, \dots$ of continuous $\langle o, 1\rangle$ - valued functions on $L^{2A,\infty}$ such that M_n can be considered as a function on ${}_oL^{2A,n}_{c_n}$ for some $c_n > 0$ and the linear span of the functions $M_n' (\varphi) = M_n({}_o({}^{-\frac{c_n}{2}} \varphi)_{c_n})$ is uniformly dense in $C (L^{2A,\infty})$; we might e.g. take some polynomials in the $\pi_{t\nu}$ with rational t , and determine the $c_n > 0$ accordingly. We may even assume that for each n there is an infinity of j such that $M_j = M_n$ up to some obvious identification, and that $c_n \nearrow \infty$. Observing that pointwise convergence implies metric convergence in $L^{2A,n}$; we reduce the rest of the proof to the following argument: Let k_o be fixed and $j > k_o$ such that $M_j = M_{k_o}$ and $\delta_j < \delta$, where $\delta > 0$ was fixed in advance. We know that every φ^k with $k \geq j$ is δ_j-good for $M_j = M_{k_o}$ and α_j by D_j. Enlarging k if necessary and approximating φ, also using Theorem 2.3, we see: every ${}_s\varphi_{s+D_j+c_j}$ is 2δ-good for M_{k_o} and α_j $(s \in R)$. The rest is now an easy exercise for which we give the following hint only. Cut φ into pieces of length D_j and form $\frac{1}{t}\int_o^t M_{k_o}\left({}_o({}^{s+u}\varphi)_{c_{k_o}}\right) du$ for t large against D_j. We still remark that we may enlarge the c_n without essentially changing the M_n if we identify functions which differ only by a restriction map among some spaces ${}_oL_c^{2A,\infty}$.

<u>Theorem 2.7.</u> Let $0 < n, A, c, \delta, \varepsilon < \infty$ be given with $\varepsilon \leq A$. Then there exist $0 < C, D, \eta < \infty$ with $\frac{\eta}{\varepsilon} < \frac{C}{2}$, $\eta < \varepsilon$ such that the following holds: Given

1) a continuous function $M : {}_oL_c^{2A,n} \to \langle 0, 1\rangle$ and a real α

2) a sequence $a_k \in R$ (k integer) such that

$$a_k < a_k + C \leq a_{k+1} \leq a_k + 3C \qquad \text{(k integer)}$$

3) a sequence $\sigma_u \in \{-1, 0, 1\}$ (k integer)

4) a sequence $\varphi^k \in {}_{a_k}L^{A,n}_{a_{k+1}+c}$ (k integer)

such that

5) φ^k is δ-good for M and α.

6) $\| {}_{a_k}\varphi^{k-1}_{a_k+c} - {}_{a_k}\varphi^k_{a_k+c} \| < \eta$ (k integer)

7) $\sigma_k = 0$ only if

$${}_{a_k}\varphi^{k-1}_{a_k+c} = {}_{a_k}\varphi^k_{a_k+c} ,$$

put

$$b_k = a_k + \sigma_k \frac{\eta}{\epsilon} \qquad \text{(k integer)}$$

and define ρ^k for every integer k with $\sigma_k \neq 0$ as the linear R^n-valued function

a) on $\langle a_k, b_k \rangle$, with $\rho^k(a_k) = \varphi^{k-1}(a_k)$, $\rho^k(b_k) = \varphi^k(b_k)$ if $\sigma_k = 1$

b) on $\langle b_k, a_k \rangle$, with $\rho^k(b_k) = \varphi^{k-1}(b_k)$, $\rho^k(a_k) = \varphi^k(a_k)$ if $\sigma_k = -1$

and define, for every integer k with $\sigma_k \neq 0$

$$\varphi(t) = \varphi^k(t) \quad \begin{cases} \text{for } a_k \leq t \leq b_k \text{ if } \sigma_k = 1 \\ \text{for } b_k \leq t \leq a_k \text{ if } \sigma_k = -1 \end{cases}$$

and then for every integer k and all $a_k \leq t \leq a_{k+1}$ for which $\varphi(t)$ was yet undefined:

$$\varphi(t) = \varphi^k(t) .$$

Then the R^n-valued function $\varphi = (\varphi^1, \ldots, \varphi^n)$, thus defined on R has the following properties.

8) $\varphi \in L^{A+\epsilon,n}$ $\qquad (\subseteq L^{2A,n})$

9) the subset $\{{}_o({}^t\varphi)_c \mid t \in R\}$ of ${}_oL_c^{A+\epsilon,n}$ is contained in the ϵ-neighborhood of the set

$$\bigcup_{k \text{ integer}} \{{}_o({}^t\varphi^k)_c \mid a_k \leq t \leq a_{k+1}\}$$

10) φ is $(\delta+\epsilon)$-good for M and α after D .

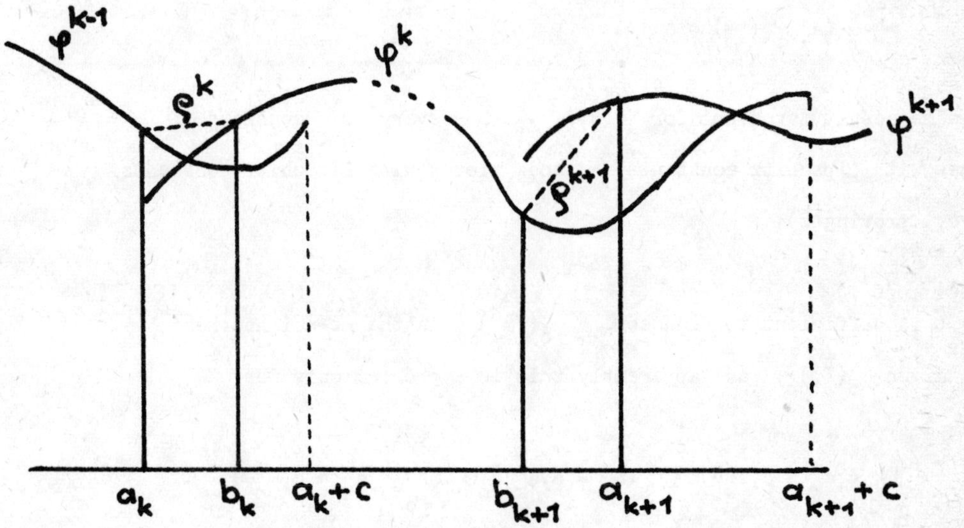

(case $n=1$, $\sigma_k=1$, $\sigma_{k+1}=-1$)

Proof. 8) In case $\sigma_k = 1$, $\rho^{k\nu}$ has the Lipschitz constant

$$\frac{\epsilon}{\eta} \mid \rho^{k\nu} (b_k) - \rho^{k\nu} (a_k) \mid$$

$$= \frac{\epsilon}{\eta} \mid \varphi^{k\nu} (b_k) - \varphi^{k-1,\nu} (a_k) \mid$$

$$< \frac{\epsilon}{\eta} (\mid \varphi^{k\nu} (b_k) - \varphi^{k\nu} (a_k) \mid + \eta)$$

$$= \frac{\epsilon}{\eta} (A \cdot \frac{\eta}{\epsilon} + \eta) = A + \epsilon$$

The same result turns out for $\sigma = -1$. Thus every φ^ν consists of pieces with Lipschitz constants A and pieces with Lipschitz constants $A + \epsilon$, proving 8).

9) It is sufficient to find some ${}_o({}^t\varphi^k)_c$ in the ϵ-neighborhood of a given ${}_o({}^t\varphi)_c$, and apparently this is a problem only for

$$t \in \bigcup_{\sigma_k=1} \langle a_k - c, b_k \rangle \cup \bigcup_{\sigma_k=-1} \langle b_k - c, a_k \rangle \cup \bigcup_{\sigma_k=0} \langle a_k - c, {}_k \rangle \quad .$$

We content ourselves to settle the case

$\sigma_k = -1$, $b_k - c \leq t \leq a_k$. Here

$$\varphi^\nu(s) = \begin{cases} \varphi^{k-1,\nu}(s) & \text{for } t \leq s \leq b_k \\ \rho^{k\nu}(s) & \text{for } b_k \leq s \leq a_k \\ \varphi^{k\nu}(s) & \text{for } a_k \leq s \leq t+c \end{cases}$$

Now

$$|\rho^{k\nu}(s) - \varphi^{k-1,\nu}(s)| \leq |\rho^{k\nu}(s) - \sigma^{k\nu}(b_k)| + |\varphi^{k-1,\nu}(b_k) - \varphi^{k-1,\nu}(s)|$$

$$\leq (A+\epsilon) \frac{\eta}{\epsilon} + A \frac{\eta}{\epsilon} < \epsilon \qquad (b_k \leq s \leq a_k)$$

if η is small enough, and

$$|\varphi^{k\nu}(s) - \varphi^{k-1,\nu}(s)| < \eta < \epsilon \qquad (a_k \le s \le t+c) .$$

This shows that

$$\| {}_o({}^t\varphi)_c - {}_o({}^t\varphi^{k-1})_c \| < \epsilon$$

in this case.

10) For each integer k, $M({}_o({}^s\varphi)_c)$ coincides with $M({}_o({}^s\varphi^k)_c)$ on an interval which is obtained from $\langle a_k, a_{k+1} \rangle$ by breaking off at most a left "tail" of length $\frac{\eta}{\epsilon}$ and a right "tail" of length $\frac{\eta}{\epsilon} + c$. If C is large enough and η is small enough, these "tails" make an arbitrarily small percentage in length of $\langle a_k, a_k+1 \rangle$ (which has a length $\ge C$). Thus we can achieve, by choice of C and η, that φ is made up of pieces which are $(\delta + \frac{\epsilon}{2})$- good for M and α and of bounded length, plus some percentwise rare pieces. It is now an easy exercise to determine D such that 10) holds.

Remark. In this construction it is always possible to shrink η and enlarge C, and then enlarge D, without jeopardizing the approximations formulated in 8), 9), 10).

We conclude this section with some remarks about first entrance times.

Theorem 2.8. Let Ω be a measurable space and $(T_t)_{t \in R}$ a one-parameter group of invertible mappings of Ω. For every subset E of Ω and every real function σ on Ω we define (utilizing $\inf \emptyset = \infty$)

$$t_{\sigma,E}(\omega) = \inf \{t | t > \sigma(\omega),\ T_t\omega \in E\}$$

and call this the first entrance time of ω into E after $\sigma(\omega)$. Assume now that Ω is a compact metric space and $(T_t)_{t\in R}$ is a continuous group of homeomorphisms of Ω (definition 1.2). Then for every open or closed $E \subseteq \Omega$ and every measurable σ, the function $t_{\sigma,E}$ is measurable.

Proof. If E is open, we have for every real β

$$\{\omega | t_{\sigma,E}(\omega) < \beta\} = \bigcup_{\substack{\xi < t < \beta \\ \xi,t \text{ rational}}} [\{\omega|\sigma(\omega)<\xi\} \cap \{T_t\omega\in E\}]$$

Here $\supseteq$ is obvious, and $\supseteq$ follows from the continuity of $(T_t)_{t\in R}$. This proves the measurability of $T_{\sigma,E}$ for open E. Now, if E is closed, find open $E_1 \supseteq E_2 \supseteq \ldots \supseteq E$ with intersection E, such that E_k is contained in the **1/k**-- neighborhood of E. Then

$\tau_{\sigma,E_k} \nearrow \tau_{\sigma,E}$ as is easily shown e.g. with compactness arguments. This proves the measurability of $t_{\sigma,E}$.

Especially, we obtain the measurability of first entrance times for the compact subsets of $L^{A,k}$ given in Theorem 2.5.

§3. Modification of time - L^A functions.

Throughout this section, we keep a weakly mixing measurable flow $(\Omega, \mathcal{B}, m, (T_t)_{t \in R})$ fixed.

We employ the following notation: If f is a function defined on Ω with values in some set S, then for every $\omega \in \Omega$

$$f^{\omega}(t) = f(T_t\, \omega) \qquad (t \in R)$$

defines a S-valued function f^{ω} on the real line R. Clearly, if $f = (f^1, \ldots, f^n)$ is a R^n-valued function, there $f^{\omega} = (f^{1\omega}, \ldots, f^{n\omega})$, and an analogous formula holds for R^{∞}-valued functions.

Definition 3.1. Let $0 < A < \infty$.

1) By time-L^A we denote the system of all real-valued measurable functions on Ω such that $f^{\omega} \in L^A$ for every $\omega \in \Omega \setminus N_f$ where N_f is a strictly invariant null set.

2) Let $0 < n \leq \infty$. By time-$L^{A,n}$ we denote the system of all R^n-valued measurable functions f on Ω such that $f^{\omega} \in L^{A,n}$ for every $\omega \in \Omega \setminus N_f$ where N_f is a strictly invariant null set. Especially, time-$L^{A,1}$ = time-L^A.

For the rest of this section Lipschitz constant A is kept fixed.

Theorem 3.2. Let $0 < n \leq \infty$. Then for every $f \in$ time-$L^{A,n}$, the mapping

$$\Psi : \omega \to f^{\omega}$$

and the strictly invariant null set N_f (definition 3.1) define a measurable mapping of $\Omega \setminus N_f$ into the compact matric space $L^{A,n}$ which commutes with $(T_t)_{t \in R}$ (acting in $\Omega \setminus N$ resp. in $L^{A,n}$ (being the shift flow in the latter space)).

Proof. Since a direct product of measurable mappings is measurable, it is sufficient to settle the case $n = 1$. Now the evaluation functions

$\pi_t : \varphi \to \varphi(t)$ are continuous functions separating the points of L^A hence they generate the natural Borel field in L^A. Thus it suffices to prove that $\omega \to \pi_t(f^{\omega})$ is measurable for every fixed t. But this is obvious because of $\pi_t(f^{\omega}) = f(T_t\,\omega)$. Furthermore

$$T_t f^{\omega}(s) = f(T_{t+s}\omega) = [(T_t f)^{\omega}](s).$$

The next theorem shows that time-L^A functions are abundant.

Theorem 3.3. $\bigcup_{A>0}$ time-L^A is norm-total in L^1_m (i.e. its linear span is L^1_m-norm dense in L^1_m).

Proof: It is sufficient to approximate an arbitrary measurable function g on Ω fulfilling $0 \leq g \leq 1$ by time-L^A functions. For almost every $\omega \in \Omega$ the function f^{ω} on R is measurable. By Wiener's local ergodic theorem, there is, for every $\epsilon > 0$ a $B > 0$ such that the measurable function

$$f(\omega) = \frac{1}{B}\int_0^B g(T_u\,\omega)du$$

fulfils $\|f - g\|_1 < \epsilon$. Now, for reals $s < t$ and $\omega \in \Omega$

$$|f^{\omega}(s) - f^{\omega}(t)| \leq \frac{1}{B}\left|\int_0^B g(T_{s+u}\omega)du - \int_0^B g(T_{t+u}\omega)du\right|$$

$$\leq \begin{cases} \frac{1}{B}\left(\left|\int_s^t g(T_u\omega)du\right| + \left|\int_{s+B}^{t+B} g(T_u\omega)du\right|\right) < \frac{2}{B}\,|s-t| & \text{for } s \leq t \leq s+B \\ \frac{2}{B}\cdot B & \text{otherwise.} \end{cases}$$

This shows $f^{\omega} \in L^A$ for $A = \frac{2}{B}$, i.e. f is in time-L^A.

Theorem 3.4. Let $0 < A < \infty$ and let $\mathcal{B}$ be countably generated mod m. Then there is a sequence $f^1, f^2, \ldots, \in$ time-L^A such that for every n, $\mathcal{B}$ coincides mod m with the smallest Borel field on which $f^n, f^{n+1}, \ldots,$ are measurable.

Proof: Let the sets $E_1, E_2, \ldots,$ generate $\mathcal{B}$ mod m and assume that for every k there is an infinity of indices j such that $E_k = E_j$.

Define $B = \min [1, A]$ and

$$f^k(\omega) = \frac{B}{2} \int_0^{\frac{1}{k}} 1_{E_k}(T_n\omega)d\omega = \frac{B}{2k} \cdot \frac{1}{\frac{1}{k}} \int_0^{\frac{1}{k}} 1_{E_k}(T_n\omega)dn$$

clearly f^k is a time-L^A function. Moreover for every n and k there is a subsequence f^{i_ν} of $f^n, f^{n+1}, \ldots,$ such that $\|\frac{2j_\nu}{B} f^{j_\nu} - 1_{E_k}\|_1 \longrightarrow 0$ proving the desired statement concerning generation of $\mathcal{B}$.

For later use we prove the following

Theorem 3.5. Let $f^1, f^2, \ldots, \in$ time-L^A be such that every "tail" $f^n, f^{n+1}, \ldots,$ generates $\mathcal{B}$ mod m. Let $h^1, h^2, \ldots \in$ time-L^A and $N_1, N_2, \ldots \in \mathcal{B}$ be such that $m(N_k) \to 0$ and $N_1 \supseteq N_2 \supseteq N_3 \ldots$ and

$$h^j(\omega) = f^j(\omega) \qquad (j \geq k, \ \omega \notin N_k).$$

Then every "tail" $h^n, h^{n+1}, \ldots$ generates $\mathcal{B}$ mod m.

Proof: Let $E \in \mathcal{B}$ be arbitrary. For every n there is a measurable function H_n defined on R^∞ such that $0 \leq H_n \leq 1$ and $H_n(f^n, f^{n+1}, \ldots) = 1_E$ m - a.e. Now

$$\{\omega | H_n(h^n(\omega), h^{n+1}(\omega), \ldots) \neq H(f^n(\omega), f^{n+1}(\omega), \ldots)\} \subseteq N_n$$

hence

$$\|H_n(h^n, h^{n+1}, \ldots) - 1_E\| \leq m(N_n)$$

Define

$$H_{nj}(x_0, x_1, \ldots) = H_{n+j}(x_j, x_{j+1}, \ldots).$$

Then

$$H_{nj}(h^n, h^{n+1}, \ldots) = H_{n+j}(h^{n+j}, h^{n+j+1}, \ldots)$$

which proves

$\|H_{nj}(h^n,h^{n+1},\dots) - 1_E\| \leq m(N_{n+j}) \to 0 \ (j \to \infty)$. This shows that $h^n, h^n, \dots$ generate $\mathcal{B}$ mod m .

We turn now to flows built under functions.

Let $(X,\mathcal{B},p,T)$ be a dynamical system (i.e. $T:X \to X$ invertibly measurable and p-preserving with $p(X) < \infty$. Let r be a strictly positive measurable function on X, bounded away from 0 by some $c > 0$. From the new space

$$\Omega = \{\omega = (x,s) \mid x \in X,\ 0 \leq s < r(x)\} \subseteq X \times \mathbb{R}$$

define the Borel field $\mathcal{B}$ in Ω as the restriction of the product Borel field in $X \times R$ to Ω, define m to be the restriction to Ω of the product measure of p and Lebesgue measure in $X \times R$, and finally define

$$T_t(x,s) = \begin{cases} (x,s+t) & \text{for} \quad 0 \leq s+t < r(x) \\ (Tx, s+t - r(x)) & \text{for} \quad r(x) \leq s+t < r(x)+r(Tx) \\ \\ \text{etc.} \end{cases}$$

Then $(\Omega,\mathcal{B},m,(T_t)_{t \in R})$ is a measurable m-preserving flow with $m(\Omega) = \int r(x)p(dx)$. It is called the flow built under the ("roof") function r , based on (the "floor") $(X,\mathcal{B},p,T)$. Every such flow is proper, i.e. for every $E \in \mathcal{B}$ with $p(E) > 0$ there is a $F \subseteq E$ in $\mathcal{B}$ with $m(F \triangle T_{-t}F) > 0$ for some $t > 0$.

A well-known theorem of Ambrose-Kakutani [1], [2] says that every proper measure preserving measurable flow with finite measure is measure-algebraically isomorphic to a flow built under a function. Hence we are, for our purposes, always allowed to assume that our measurable flow is built under some function r and based on some $(X,\mathcal{B},p,T)$, if we --as we now do--restrict ourselves to proper flows.

A representation as a flow built under a function is not at all unique. As a matter of fact, there are two methods which allow to modify the floor" and the "roof" and which involve at most the elimination of some strictly invariant null set. This implies that we may apply them countably often in our entire constructions.

1) Shrinking the base X -

Let $X_0 \in \mathcal{B}$ and T_0 the transformation induced on X_0 by T, i.e. put

$$X_0^r = \{x \mid x \in X_0, T^k x \notin X_0 \ (1 \leq k < r), T^r x \in X_0\}$$

and

$$T_0 x = T^r x \text{ for } x \in X_0^r .$$

this defines a mapping $T_0 : X_0 \to X_0$ m - a.e. on X_0 and, denoting by $\mathcal{B}_0, p_0$ the restrictions of $\mathcal{B}$, p to X_0, we have $T_0 p_0 = p_0$. We construct a new "roof" function r_0 p_0- a.e. on X_0 by

$$(1) \quad r_0(x) = \sum_{k=0}^{r-1} r(T^k x) \quad (x \in X_0^r)$$

and it is clear that the flow built under r_0 on $(\mathcal{B}_0, p_0, T_0)$ is identical to the original one, up to a one-to-one invertibly measure preserving mapping, after the elimination of some strictly invariant subset from Ω. As (1) shows, r majorizes the restriction of r to X_0, and may be unbounded even if r is bounded. As a matter of fact, we may always achieve an arbitrarily prescribed lower bound for r_0 by suitable choice of X_0: First of all, Kac's theorem (see e.g. Jacobs [4]) implies $\Sigma\, r p(X_0^r) = p(X)$ so that for $p(X_0)$ sufficiently small, we have $p(X_0^r) > 0$ for some r greater than a prescribed lower bound. Passing from X_0 to such a X_0^r we the lower bound $c \cdot r$ for the new "roof" function.

2) Shifting the base X. -

Assume, $r(x) > c > 0 \quad (x \in X)$. Define

$$Y = X$$

$$s(x) = r(x) \qquad (x \in Y)$$

$$S = T \qquad (\text{on } Y) \quad ,$$

Let $(S_t)_{t\in R}$ be the flow built under the "roof" function s, based on $(Y,\mathcal{B},p,S)$. The mapping φ, defined for $0 \leq d \leq c$ by

$$\varphi(x,s) = \begin{cases} (x,s-d) & \text{for } s \geq d \\ (S^{-1}x,\ s-d+r(S^{-1}x) & \text{for } s < d \end{cases}$$

is an isomorphism of $(T_t)_{t\in R}$ with $(S_t)_{t\in R}$. It moves a set of the form $\{(x,s): x \in A,\ s = d\}$ into the "floor" of the new space. This can be used in order to achieve the following: let $G \subseteq \Omega$ have positive measure. Then there is at least one $d \geq 0$ such that

$$p(\{x \mid (x,d) \in G\}) > 0 .$$

Shrinking the base and then applying the above shifting operation we may assume that $X \times \{0\} \subseteq G$.

The crucial part of iterative construction to be established subsequently is contained in

Theorem 3.6. Let $(\Omega,\mathcal{B},m,(T_t)_{t\in R})$ be a weakly mixing flow built under a function. Let $0 < n < \infty$ and $f = (f^1,\ldots,f^n) \in$ time-$L^{A,n}$, $0 < c < \infty$ $M : {}_0L_c^{2A,n} \to \langle 0,1\rangle$ be continuous. Then for every $0 < \varepsilon, a < \infty$ there is a $D > 0$, a $h = (h^1,\ldots,h^n) \in$ time-$L^{A+\varepsilon,n}$ and a strictly invariant null-set N' containing $N_f \cup N_h$ (definition 3.1) such that the following statements hold:

1) There is a set $N \in \mathcal{B}$ such that $m(N) < \epsilon$

and

$$T_s\{f \neq h\} \subseteq N \qquad (|s| \leq a)$$

2) The subset

$$\{ {}_0({}^t h^\omega)_c \mid t \in R, \xi \in \Omega \setminus N'\}$$

of ${}_0L_c^{A+\epsilon,n}$ is contained in the ϵ-neighborhood of the set

$$\{ {}_0({}^t f^\xi)_c \mid t \in R, \xi \in \Omega \setminus N'\}$$

$$\subseteq {}_0L_c^{A,n} \subseteq {}_0L_c^{A+\epsilon,n} \quad .$$

3) For every $\omega \in \Omega \setminus N'$ the R^n - valued function $h^\omega = (h^{1\omega},\ldots,h^{n\omega})$ $\in L^{A+\epsilon,n}$ is ϵ-good for M and

$$\alpha = \int M({}_0(f^\omega)_c)m(d\omega)$$

after D .

Remark. Remember that e.g. ${}^t f^\omega(s) = f(T_{t+s}\omega)$.

Proof. I) Send m into ${}_0L_c^{A,n}$ by the measurable mapping

$$\chi : \omega \to {}_0f_c^\omega$$

and call $\chi(m) = m'$. Give for the moment some $\eta > 0$ of which we will dispose later on. Since ${}_0L_c^{A,n}$ is compact metric, we may find a disjoint decomposition

$$ {}_0L_c^{A,n} = L^1 + \ldots + L^b$$

where $L^1,\ldots, L^b$ are m'-almost clopen sets (i.e. sets whose boundaries are m'-nullsets) of diameter $< \eta$. After a renumeration we may assume

$$m(L^1),\ldots, m(L^q) > 0 = m(L^{q+1}) = \ldots = m(L^b) \quad .$$

Let $L = L^1 + \ldots + L^q$ and $\bar{L}$ the closure of L, hence $L' = {}_0L_c^{A,n} \setminus \bar{L}$ is open and $m'(L') = 0$. Since $f \in$ time-$L^{A,n}$, we find that for the set $\Omega' = \chi^{-1}(L')$ and every $x \in X$ the section

(2) $\{t \mid 0 \leq t < r(x),\ (x,t) \in \Omega'\}$

is a relatively open subset of
the interval $\langle 0\ ,\ r(x))$, hence it is either empty or of strictly positive Lebesgue measure. From $m(\Omega') = m'(L') = 0$ and Fubini's theorem we deduce now the existence of a p-nullset $N' \subseteq X$ such that for $x \notin N'$ the set (2) is empty. The set $N = \bigcup_{t \in R} T_t(N' \times \{0\})$ is a strictly $(T_t)_{t \in R}$- invariant m-nullset, and χ sends every $\omega \in \Omega \setminus N$ into $\overline{L} = \overline{(L^1 + \ldots + L^q)} = \overline{L^1} \cup \ldots \cup \overline{L^q}$. If we therefore put $\Omega^\beta = \chi^{-1}\ (\overline{L^\beta} \setminus (\overline{L^1} \cup \ldots \cup \overline{L^{\beta-1}})) \setminus N$ $(\beta = 1, \ldots, q)$ forgetting about N and replacing q by b again, we can say : Ω decomposes, after the elimination of a strictly invariant m-nullset, disjointly into measurable sets $\Omega^1, \ldots, \Omega^b$ such that $m(\Omega^1), \ldots, m(\Omega^b) > 0$ and $R^\beta = \chi(\Omega^\beta)$ has diameter $<_\eta$ $(\beta = 1, \ldots, b)$. (Observe that $m(\Omega^\beta) = m'(\overline{L^\beta}) = m'(L^\beta)$ as the L^β are m'-almost clopen) .

II) We want to apply theorem 2.7 with $\frac{\epsilon}{2}$ and $\frac{\epsilon}{2}$ in the places of δ and ϵ there. Choose therefore C, D, η according to theorem 2.7 (with these replacements) and remember that we are always allowed to enlarge C, and subsequently D, keeping η fixed, without jeopardizing the resulting approximations. Define in $L^{A,n}$ the subset $G_C = G_C(\frac{\epsilon}{2}) = \{\varphi \mid \varphi \in L^{A,n}$,

$$|\frac{1}{t}\int_0^t M\left({}_0({}^u\varphi)_c\right)du - \alpha| \le \frac{\epsilon}{2}, |\frac{1}{t}\int_{-t}^0 M\left({}_0({}^u\varphi)_c\right)du - \alpha| \le \frac{\epsilon}{2} \quad (t \ge C)\};$$

clearly, this is a closed set, and since the mapping

$$\varphi : \omega \to f^{\omega}$$

of $\Omega \to L^{A,n}$ is measurable, the sets

$$\Omega_C = \Omega_C(\tfrac{\epsilon}{2}) = \varphi^{-1} G_C \quad N_C = N_C(\tfrac{\epsilon}{2}) = \Omega \setminus \Omega_C$$

are measurable. By the individual ergodic theorem, we can find a C such that

$$m(N_C) < \epsilon$$

We will later on still enlarge C several times.

Enlarging C if necessary, we can enforce

$$m(\Omega_C \cap \Omega^{\beta}) > 0 \quad (\beta = 1,\dots,b);$$

enlarging C once more and using the property of weak mixture, we can enforce

$$m(\Omega_C \cap \Omega^{\beta} \cap T_{-C}\,\Omega^{\gamma}) > 0 \quad (\beta,\gamma = 1,\dots,b).$$

This implies : for every β,γ there is an $\omega_{\beta\gamma}$ such that

a) ${}_0f_c^{\omega_{\beta\gamma}} \in \Omega^{\beta}$, ${}_Cf_{C+c}^{\omega_{\beta\gamma}} \in \Omega^{\gamma}$

b) ${}_0f_{C+c}^{\omega_{\beta\gamma}}$ is $\frac{\epsilon}{2}$-good for M and α.

III) Applying the modifications of flows built under a function which were previously discussed, we may cast out some strictly invariant null set and then assume

$$r(x) \ge 6\,(C + c)$$

$$X \times \{0\} \subseteq \Omega_C .$$

This implies : for every $x \in X$ and $C \leq d \leq 2C$,

a) ${}_0f^{(x,0)}_{d+c}$ is $\frac{\varepsilon}{2}$ -good for M and α

b) ${}_{r(x)-d}\,f^{(x,0)}_{r(x)+c}$ is $\frac{\varepsilon}{2}$ -good for M and α

We might say metaphorically : $\frac{\varepsilon}{2}$ -good f^{ω} - pieces of lengths disponiable between C+c and 2C+c are "standing on the floor" X and "hanging from the roof".

VI) Choose some $x \in X$ and define $t_0 = 0 < t_1 < \dots < t_{k-1} < t_k = r(x)$ (all these reals will depend on x, including $k = k(x)$) successively in the following way: Check whether there is some $C < t \leq 2C$ with $T_t(x,0) = (x,t) \in \Omega_C$. If yes, put $\tau_1 = \inf\{t \mid C < t \leq 2C ,$

$(x,t) \in \Omega_C\}$ observe that $(x,\tau_1) \in \Omega_C$ and check next whether there is some $\tau_1 + C < \tau < \tau_1 + 2C$ with $(x,\tau) \in \Omega_C$. If yes, define τ_2 as the infimum over all such t and observe $(x,\tau_2) \in \Omega_C$. We work up our way in steps of lengths between C and 2C until we either obtain some $r(x) - 3C \leq \tau_j \leq r(x) - C$; in this case we put $k = j + 1$ and end our search for a further τ_{j+2} .
Or we arrive at same τ_j with $j \geq 0$ such that $\tau_j < r(x) - 3C$ and $(x,t) \in N_C$ for $\tau_j + C < t \leq \tau_j + 2C$. In this case we define $\tau_{j+1} = \tau_j + C$.
If $\tau_{j+1} \geq r(x) - 3C$ (hence $\leq r(x) - 2C$), we end with $k = j+2$. If τ $\tau_{j+1} < r(x) - 3C$ we check whether there is some $\tau_{j+1} + C < t \leq \tau_{j+1} + 2C$ with $(x,t) \in \Omega_C$ etc. We see that in any case we obtain

$$\tau_j + C \leq \tau_{j+1} \leq \tau_j + 2C \quad (0 \leq j < k-1)$$

$$\tau_{k-1} + C \leq \tau_k \leq \tau_{k-1} + 3C$$

and for each $0 < j < k-1$ either $(x,\tau_j) \in \Omega_C$ or $(x,\tau) \in N_C$ for $\tau_j < \tau \leq \tau_j + C$. Next we assign $\sigma_j = 1$ if $1 < j < k$ and $(x,\tau_{j-1}) \in \Omega_C$, $(x,\tau) \in N_C$ $(\tau_j < \tau \leq \tau_j + C)$ and $\sigma_j = -1$ if $(x,\tau) \in N_C$ $(\tau_j < \tau \leq \tau_j + C)$ and $(x,\tau_{j+1}) \in \Omega_C$. Furthermore we assign $\sigma_0 = \sigma_k = 0$ and $\sigma_j = 0$ if $1 < j < k$ and (x,τ_{j-1}), $(x,\tau_j) \in \Omega_C$. In all other cases we assign $\sigma_j = \pm 1$ arbitrarily. Finally, we define for $0 \leq j < k$, $1 \leq \nu \leq n$ $\varphi^j = {}_{\tau_j}f^{(x,0)}_{\tau_{j+1}+C}$ if $j = 0, k-1$ or $(x,\tau_j) \in \Omega_C$. In all other cases we have $0 < j < k-1$ and $(x,\tau) \in N_C$ for $\tau_j < \tau \leq \tau_{j+1}$. Determine β, γ such that $(x,\tau_j) \in \Omega^\beta$, $(x,\tau_{j+1}) \in \Omega^\gamma$ and define $\varphi^k = {}_{\tau_j}F^{\omega}_{\beta\gamma\,\tau_j+C}$

Assume that we have finished this construction for all $x \in X$. Then we choose any x and follow the orbit $(T_t(x,0))_{t \in R}$ forward and backward. Going forward, we encounter successively the results of our construction over x, Tx, $T^2x, \ldots$ Backwards we encounter it over $T^{-1}x, T^{-2}x, \ldots$ Apparently we obtain the situation of theorem 2.7, over the real line except for the method of numeration. Define now $h(T_t(x,0)) = \varphi(t)$, where φ is given according to theorem 2.7. This defines uniquely a $h \in$ time-$L^{A+\epsilon,n}$ on Ω, and it is immediate that

$$\{\omega | h(\omega) \neq f(\omega)\} \subseteq N_C .$$

We turn now to the question of measurability. Investigating the dependence of $k = k(x)$, $\tau_1 = \tau_1(x), \ldots, \tau_k = \tau_{k(x)}(x)$ on x, we see that every $\tau_j(x)$ defines a function $\tau_j(\omega) = \tau_j(x)$ $(\omega = (x,0) \in X \times \{0\}$ on a subset of $X \times \{0\}$ which is the restriction to the intersection of its domain with $X \times \{0\}$ of a measurable function defined on a measurable subset of Ω, namely, a function obtained by finitely many vectors lottice operations from functions of the form

$$t_{\sigma,G_C}(f^{\omega})$$

This proves (by theorem 2.8) that every $\tau_j(x)$ is a measurable function on a measurable subset of X, and this in turn implies the measurability of h. It is essential here that we have restricted ourselves to the Borel field which is the restriction to Ω of the product Borel field in $X \times R$.-Statements 4) and 5) of our theorem follow now from theorem 2.7. if we e.g. set $h^\nu(\omega) = 0$ on the strictly invariant nullset cast out during the construction.

VII) In order to obtain 3), we use the trivial estimate $T_s N_C(\frac{\epsilon}{2}) \subseteq N_C(\frac{\epsilon}{2} + \frac{2a}{C})$

$(|s| \leq a)$ and $T_s N_C(\frac{\epsilon}{2} + \frac{2a}{C}) \subseteq N_C(\epsilon)$ $(C \geq \frac{4a}{\epsilon})$

Enlarging C, we enforce $m(N_C(\epsilon)) < \epsilon$. Thus 1) holds with $N = N_C(\epsilon)$.

Iterating the result of theorem 3.6 we obtain

Theorem 3.7. Let $(\Omega, \mathcal{B}, m, (T_t)_{t \in R})$ be as in theorem 3.6 and let $f^1, f^2, \ldots \in$ time-L^A such that for every $n > 0$, $f^n, f^{n+1}, \ldots$ generate $\mathcal{B}$ mod m (see theorem 3.4). Then for every $0 < \epsilon < A$ there is a sequence $h^1, h^2, \ldots \in$ time-L^{2A}, i.e. $h = (h^1, h^2, \ldots) \in$ time-$L^{2A,\infty}$ a strictly invariant null set N' and sets $N_1, N_2, \ldots \in \mathcal{B}$ such that the following holds :

1) $m(N_1) + m(N_2) + \ldots < \epsilon$

2) $\{f^\nu \neq h^\nu\} \subseteq N_\nu \quad (\nu = 1,2,\ldots)$

3) For every $n > 0$, $h^n, h^{n+1}, \ldots$ generate $\mathcal{B}$ mod m .

4) For every $M \in C(L^{2A,\infty})$, $\alpha = \int M(h^\omega)m(d\omega)$ and for every $\omega \in \Omega \setminus N'$ the function $h^\omega = (h^{1\omega}, h^{2\omega}, \ldots) \in L^{2A,\infty}$ is good for M and α .

Proof. Observe that 3) follows from 1) and 2) by theorem 3.5 .

Choose continuous mappings $M_n : {}_0L^{2A,\infty}_{c_n} \to \langle 0,1 \rangle$ n=1,2,...) according to theorem 2.6. Remember that we may and will assume that for every n there are infinitely many $j > n$ such that $M_j = M_n$ up to a trivial identification .

Choose now $0 < \epsilon_1, \epsilon_2, \ldots < \infty$ such that the following holds:

1) $2\epsilon_1 + 2\epsilon_2 + \ldots < \epsilon$

2) $|M_k(\varphi) - M_k(\psi)| < \frac{\epsilon k}{2^{n-k}}$

if $1 \leq k \leq n$, $\varphi, \psi \in {}_0L^{2A,k}_{c_k}$, $\|\varphi - \psi\| < \epsilon_{n+1}$

Observe that we are allowed to enlarge c_n, provided we then shrink $\epsilon_{n+1}, \epsilon_{n+2}, \ldots$ suitably.

1) Apply theorem 3.6 with $n = 1$ in order to obtain $h^1=(h^{11}) \in \text{time-}L^{A+\epsilon_1}$, $D_1 > 0$, a strictly invariant null set N_1' and a set $N_1 \in \mathcal{B}$ such that

   a) $m(N_1) < \epsilon_1$

   b) $T_t\{h^{11} \neq f^1\} \subseteq N_1 \qquad (|t| \leq 1)$

   c) For every $\omega \in \Omega \setminus N_1'$, the function $h^{\omega} \in L^{A+\epsilon_1}$ is ϵ_1- good for α_1 after D_1, where

$$\alpha_1 = \int M_1(f^{1\omega})m(d\omega)$$

2) We may enlarge c_2 such that $c_2 \geq D_1 + c_1$ (implying a shrinking of $\epsilon_3, \epsilon_4, \ldots$ which come to action only later on). Apply theorem 3.6 with $n = 2$ in order to obtain $h^2 = (h^{21}, h^{22}) \in \text{time-}L^{A+\epsilon_1+\epsilon_2,2}$, $D_2 > D_1$, a strictly invariant null set N_2' and a set $N_2 \in \mathcal{B}$ such that

   a) $m(N_2) < \epsilon_2$

   b) $T_t\{h^{21} \neq h^{11}\} \cup T_t\{h^{22} \neq f^2\} \subseteq N_2 \qquad (|t| \equiv 2)$

   c) For every $\omega \in \Omega \setminus N_2'$, the function $h^{2\omega} \in L^{A+\epsilon_1+\epsilon_2,2}$ is ϵ_2-good for α_2 after D_2, where

$$\alpha_2 = \int M_2(h^{11\omega}, f^{2\omega})m(d\omega)$$

   d) $\left\{ {}_0({}^t h^{2\omega})_{c_2} \,\middle|\, t \in R, \omega \in S \setminus N_2' \right\}$ is contained in the ϵ_2-neighborhood of $\left\{ {}_0({}^t h^{11\xi}, f^{2\xi})_{c_2} \,\middle|\, t \in R, \xi \in \Omega \setminus N_2' \right\}$. This implies: for every $\omega \in \Omega \setminus N_2'$ there is a $\xi \in \Omega \setminus N_2'$ such that

$$|M_1({}_0({}^t h^{1\omega})_{c_1}) - M_1({}_0({}^t h^{21\xi})_{c_1})| < \frac{\epsilon_1}{2} \qquad (0 \leq t \leq D_1)$$

   and consequently $h^{21\omega} \in L^{A+\epsilon_1+\epsilon_2}$ is still $\epsilon_1 + \frac{\epsilon_1}{2}$ - good for α_1 by D_1

   e) Assume we have constructed

h^{11}

h^{21}, h^{22}

. . . .

$h^{n-1,1}, \ldots, h^{n-1,n-1}$

N_{n-1}, D_{n-1}. Then we enlarge C_n such that $C_n \geq D_{n-1} + C_{n-1}$ and apply theorem 3.6 in order to obtain $h^n = (h^{n1},\dots, h^{nn}) \in$ time-$L^{A+\epsilon_1+\dots+\epsilon_n, n}$, $D_n \supset D_{n-1}$ a strictly invariant null set N'_n and a set $N_n \in \mathcal{B}$ such that

a) $m(N_n) < \epsilon_n$

b) $\bigcup_{\nu=1}^{n-1} T_t \{h^{n\nu} \neq h^{n-1,\nu}\} \cup T_t \{h^{nn} \neq f^n\} \subseteq N_n \qquad (|t| \leq n)$

c) For every $\omega \in \Omega \setminus N'_n$ the function $h^{n\omega} \in L^{A+\epsilon_1+\dots+\epsilon_n, n}$ is ϵ_n- good for α_n after D_n, where

$$\alpha_n = M_n(h^{n-1,1,\omega},\dots, h^{n-1,n-1,\omega}, f^{n\omega})m(d\omega)$$

d) $\{ {}_0({}^t h^{n\omega})_{C_n} \mid t \in R,\ \omega \in \Omega\setminus N'_n\}$ is contained in the ϵ_n-neighborhood of $\{ {}_0({}^t h^{n-1,1,\xi},\dots, {}^t h^{n-1,n-1,\xi}, {}^t f^{n\xi})_{C_n} \mid t \in R,\ \xi \in \Omega\setminus N'_n\}$. This implies : for every $\omega \in \Omega\setminus N'_n$ there is a $\xi \in \Omega\setminus N'_n$ such that

$$|M_j({}_0({}^t(h^{n1},\dots,h^{nj})^{\omega})_{C_j}) - M_j({}_0({}^t(h^{n-1,1},\dots,h^{n-1,j})^{\xi})_{C_j})| < \frac{\epsilon_j}{2^{n-j}}$$

$(j = 1,\dots,n-1),\ 0 \leq t \leq D_j)$

Working on in this way we obtain

$$h^{nj} \in \text{time-}L^{A+\epsilon_1+\dots+\epsilon_n} \quad (\eta = 1,2,\dots\ j = 1,\dots,n)$$

such that the following statements hold .

a) $T_t \{h^{nj} \neq h^{n-1,j}\} \subseteq N_n \qquad (n = j+1,j+2,\dots, |t| \leq n)$

where $m(N_n) < \epsilon_n \quad (n = 1,2,\dots)$. From

$$\sum_{n > j} m(N_n) < \epsilon_{j+1} + \epsilon_{j+2} + \dots$$

we see that the strictly invariant measurable

$$N = \bigcap_n \bigcup_{k \geq n} \bigcup_{|t| \leq k; j \leq k} T_t\{h^{kj} \neq h^{k-1,j}\}$$

is a m-nullset. For $\omega \in N$ we have

$$\lim h^{nj}(\omega) = h^j(\omega)$$

where h^j is measurable.

From theorem 2.6 we infer now that for every $\omega \notin N \cup N_1' \cup N_2' \cup \ldots$, $h^\omega = (h^{1\omega}, h^{2\omega}, \ldots)$ is good for every continuous real function M on $L^{2A,\infty}$. An easy application of the individual ergodic theorem gives us one more strictly invariant null set such that for every ω all strictly invariant nullsets obtained, h^ω in good for every $M \in C(L^{2A,\infty})$ and $\alpha = \int M(h^\omega)m(d\omega)$ (use the fact that $C(L^{2A,\infty})$ is separable; we could have obtained this result also by following the α - values occurring throughout our construction steps).

§ 4. An Isomorphy Theorem

We sum up our results in the following

Theorem 4.1. Let $(\Omega, \mathcal{B}, m, (T_t)_{t\in R})$ be a weakly mixing measurable flow. Then there is a measure-algebraically isomorphic flow $(\Omega', \mathcal{B}', m', (T'_t)_{t\in R})$ such that

1.) $\Omega' = L^{2A,\infty}$ for some $0 < A < \infty$.

2.) $(T'_t)_{t\in R}$ is the shift flow in Ω'.

3.) m' lives on a strictly ergodic subset of Ω',

provided $\mathcal{B}$ is countably generated mod m.

Proof. The theorem of Ambrose-Kakutani [1] [2] allows us to assume that $(\Omega, \mathcal{B}, m, (T_t)_{t\in R})$ is a flow built under a function. Theorems 3.4 and 3.7 yield, for an arbitrary $0 < A < \infty$ a $h = (h^1, h^2, \ldots) \in$ time - $L^{2A,\infty}$ generating $\mathcal{B}$, such that for every ω avoiding a certain strictly invariant null set, h^ω is good for every $M \in C(L^{2A,\infty})$ and $\int M(h^\omega)\, m(d\omega)$. Our result follows now from Theorem 1.4.

BIBLIOGRAPHY

[1] Ambrose, W. Representation of ergodic flows, Ann. of Math. (2), 42, 723-739 (1941).

[2] Ambrose, W., and S. Kakutani, Structure and continuity of measurable flows, Duke Math. J. 9, 25-42 (1942)

[3] Jacobs, K. Neuere Methoden und Er gebnisse der Ergodentheoric Berlin-Gottingen-Heidelberg. Springer Verlag, 1960.

[4] Jacobs, K. Lecture notes on ergodic theory, 2 vol.s., Aarhus, 1963.

[5] Jewett, R., The prevalence of uniquely ergodic systems, J. Math. Mech., to appear 1970.

[6] Kolmogorov, T. A., and V. M. Tikhomirov, ε-entropy and ε-capacity of sets in functional spaces, Uspehi Mat. Nauk (N.S.) 14 (1959) No. 2 (86), 3-86, engl-Transl. in Transl. A. M. S. (second series) vol. 17 (1961), 277-373.

[7] Oxtoby, J. C., Ergodic Sets, Bull. A. M. S. 58, 116-136 (1952).

WEAK RATIO CONVERGENCE OF MEASURES IN INFINITE MEASURE SPACES

by

Eugene M. Klimko

Purdue University

We present a ratio analogue of the notion of weak convergence and give several equivalent forms of this notion. We also give a uniformity theorem which contains a ratio version of the Glivenko-Cantelli theorem.

The basic measurable space is $(X,\mathcal{B})$. In addition, we assume that $d(x,y)$ is a metric on X such that the topology $\mathcal{T}$ determined by d is separable. We shall deal with finite measures λ, φ, λ_n, φ_n all defined on $\mathcal{B}$. $\mathcal{B}$ is assumed to be the class of Borel sets, i.e. $\mathcal{B}$ is generated by $\mathcal{T}$. Let C_1 be the class of all bounded continuous real-valued functions on X and let C_2 be the class of all non-negative bounded continuous functions g with $\int g d\varphi > 0$.

<u>Definition</u>. We say that (λ_n, φ_n) weak ratio converges to (λ, φ) if and only if

$$\lim_{n\to\infty} \frac{\int f d\lambda_n}{\int g d\varphi_n} = \frac{\int f d\lambda}{\int g d\varphi} \tag{1}$$

for all $f \in C_1$, $g \in C_2$.

In particular, if λ_n and φ_n converge weakly to λ and φ respectively (weak convergence in the usual sense, see e.g. [1]) then the sequence (λ_n, φ_n) weak ratio converges to (λ, φ). The ratio version of the Glivenko-Cantelli theorem serves as an example where weak convergence of λ_n or φ_n may fail but weak ratio convergence holds.

We shall use the notation A^- to denote the topological closure of the set A and A° will be the interior of A. A continuity set for a measure λ is one whose boundary has λ measure zero. We now present the following theorem analogous to the Portmanteau theorem for the usual weak convergence; it gives several equivalent forms of the notion of weak ratio convergence.

Theorem 1. The following are equivalent.

(i) $$\lim_{n\to\infty} \frac{\int f d\lambda n}{\int g d\varphi_n} = \frac{\int f d\lambda}{\int g d\varphi} \quad \text{for } f \in C_1,\ g \in C_2$$

(ii) $$\limsup \frac{\lambda_n(F)}{\varphi_n(G)} \leq \frac{\lambda(F)}{\varphi(G)} \quad \text{for } F \text{ closed, } G \text{ open}$$

(iii) $$\liminf \frac{\lambda_n(G)}{\varphi_n(F)} \geq \frac{\lambda(G)}{\varphi(F)} \quad \text{for } F \text{ closed, } G \text{ open}$$

(iv) $$\lim_{n\to\infty} \frac{\lambda_n(A)}{\varphi_n(B)} = \frac{\lambda(A)}{\varphi(B)}$$

for all continuity sets A of λ and B of φ.

Proof. We show that (i) implies (ii). Let F be closed and G open. Let $\epsilon > 0$. Then for k sufficiently large, $\lambda(F') < \lambda(F) + \epsilon$ and $\varphi(G') > \varphi(G) - \epsilon$ where $F' = \{x : d(x, F) \leq \frac{1}{k}\}$ and $G' = \{x : d(x, G^c) \leq \frac{1}{k}\}^c$. Let

$$\begin{aligned} \gamma(t) &= 1 \quad \text{for} \quad t \leq 0 \\ &= 1-t \quad \text{for} \quad 0 < t < 1 \\ & \ 0 \quad \text{for} \quad t \geq 1 \\ \gamma_k(t) &= \gamma(t,k). \end{aligned} \tag{2}$$

We set $f(x) = \gamma_k(d(x,F))$ and $g(x) = 1 - \gamma_k(d(x,G^c))$ where k is as above. Then f and g are uniformly continuous and since $1_G(x) \geq g(x)$, $1_F(x) \leq f(x)$ for all $x \in X$, the following holds

$$\frac{\lambda_n(F)}{\varphi_n(G)} \leq \frac{\int f d\lambda_n}{\int g d\varphi_n} \overset{n}{\to} \frac{\int f d\lambda}{\int g d\varphi} .$$

Since $F' = \{F > 0\}$, $f \leq 1$ and $g = 1$ on G', it follows that

$$\int f d\lambda = \int_{F'} f d\lambda \leq \lambda(F') \leq \lambda(F) + \epsilon .$$

Similarly $\int g\,d\varphi \geq \varphi(G) - \epsilon$. Therefore

$$\limsup \frac{\lambda_n(F)}{\varphi_n(G)} \leq \frac{\int f\,d\lambda}{\int g\,d\varphi} \leq \frac{\lambda(F)+\epsilon}{\varphi(G)-\epsilon} .$$

Since ϵ is arbitrary, (ii) follows. A dual argument proves (iii). We next show that (ii) implies (i). Let f, g be bounded continuous functions with $g \geq 0$ and $\int g\,d\varphi > 0$. We shall show that

$$\limsup_n \frac{\int f\,d\lambda_n}{\int g\,d\varphi_n} \leq \frac{\int f\,d\lambda}{\int g\,d\varphi} \tag{3}$$

from which (i) follows by replacing f with -f in (3). Since f and g are bounded, we may and do assume that $0 \leq f \leq 1$, $0 \leq g \leq 1$. Let k be fixed and $F_i = \{x : \frac{i}{k} \leq f(x)\}$ $i = 0,1,\ldots, k$. By the arguments given in [1] p. 13, we have

$$\limsup_n \frac{\int f\,d\lambda_n}{\int d\varphi_n} \leq \frac{1}{k} \sum_{i=1}^{k-1} \limsup_n \frac{\lambda_n(F_i)}{\varphi_n(X)} + \frac{1}{k} \limsup \frac{\lambda_n(X)}{\varphi_n(X)} \leq$$

$$\frac{\int f\,d\lambda}{\int d\varphi} + \frac{1}{k}\frac{\lambda(X)}{\varphi(X)} .$$

Since k is arbitrary, (3) follows with $g \equiv 1$. Using the preceding calculations with the role of λ and φ interchanged and g replacing f, we have

$$\lim_n \frac{\int f\,d\lambda_n}{\int d\varphi_n} \cdot \frac{\int d\lambda_n}{\int g\,d\varphi_n} = \frac{\int f\,d\lambda}{\varphi(X)} \frac{\lambda(X)}{\int g\,d\varphi}$$

since $\lim_n \lambda_n(X)/\varphi_n(X)$ exists, the conclusion (i) follows. Similar arguments show that (iii) implies (i). We now show that (ii) implies (iv). Let A and B be continuity sets for λ and φ. Then

$$\frac{\lambda(A^-)}{\varphi(B^\circ)} \geq \limsup \frac{\lambda_n(A^-)}{\varphi_n(B^\circ)} \geq \liminf \frac{\lambda_n(A)}{\varphi_n(B)} \geq \frac{\lambda(A^\circ)}{\varphi(B^-)} .$$

Since A and B are continuity sets $\lambda(A^\circ) = \lambda(A^-) = \lambda(A)$, $\varphi(B^\circ) = \varphi(B^-) = \varphi(B)$, and (iv) follows. To prove that (ii) follows from (iv) we note that the sets $A_\delta = \{x : d(x, F) = \delta\}$ are boundaries of the sets $F_\delta = \{x : d(x, F) < \delta\}$ and the sets $B_\delta = \{x : d(x, G^c) = \delta\}$ are boundaries of the sets $G_\delta = \{x : d(x, G^c) \leq \delta\}^c$. There are at most countably many sets A_δ and B_δ of positive measure, hence there is a sequence $\delta_k \downarrow 0$ for which F_{δ_k}, G_{δ_k} are continuity sets of λ, φ. By (iv) we have

$$\limsup \frac{\lambda_n(F)}{\varphi_n(G)} \leq \limsup_n \frac{\lambda_n(F_{\delta_k})}{\varphi_n(G_{\delta_k})} = \frac{\lambda(F_{\delta_k})}{\varphi(G_{\delta_k})} .$$

Letting $\delta_k \downarrow 0$ we obtain (ii). A similar argument proves (iii). Theorem 1 is proved.

Remark. Theorem 1 holds if the assumption that $(X,\mathcal{T})$ is a metric space is relaxed to the assumption that $(X,\mathcal{T})$ is completely regular.

We now consider sequences of measurable functions $\xi_n \to \xi$ and $\eta_n \to \eta$ converging almost everywhere. Let D be the set of points x for which there is a sequence $x_n \to x$ and such that $\xi_n x_n \not\to \xi x$. Similarly E is the set of points for which $\eta_n y_n \not\to \eta y$. We now present a ratio version of a theorem due to H. Rubin.

Theorem 2. Let ξ_n, η_n, ξ, η, D, E be as described above. Let $D, E \in \mathcal{B}$, $\lambda(D) = 0$, $\varphi(E) = 0$ and let (λ_n, φ_n) weak ratio converge to (λ, φ). Then $(\lambda_n \circ \xi_n^{-1}, \varphi_n \circ \eta_n^{-1})$ weak ratio converges to $(\lambda \circ \xi^{-1}, \varphi \circ \eta^{-1})$.

Proof. Let G be open and F be closed. Let x be such that $x \in D^c$ and $\xi(x) \in G$. Then there is a k and a δ such that if $d(x,y) < \delta$ and $i \geq k$ then $\xi_i(y) \in G$. Therefore, x is interior to $A_k = \cap_{i \geq k} \xi_i^{-1} G$ and $\xi^{-1} G \subset D \cup U_k A_k^\circ$. Since $\lambda(D) = 0$ and $A_k^\circ \uparrow$, we have $\lambda(\xi^{-1} G) = \lambda(U_k A_k^\circ) < \lambda(A_k^\circ) + \epsilon$ for k sufficiently large. Similar arguments yield $\varphi(\eta^{-1} F^c) < \varphi(B_j^\circ) + \epsilon$ or $\varphi(\eta^{-1} F) > \varphi(B_j^{\circ c}) - \epsilon$. Since (λ_n, φ_n) weak ratio converges to (λ, φ) it follows that

$$\frac{\lambda(A_k^\circ)}{\varphi(B_j^{\circ c})} \leq \liminf \frac{\lambda_n(A_k^\circ)}{\varphi_n(B_j^{\circ c})} .$$

Since $A_k^\circ \subset \xi_n^{-1}(G)$ for large n and $B_j^{\circ c} \supset \eta_n^{-1}(F)$ for large n, we have

$$\frac{\lambda(\xi^{-1}G) + \epsilon}{\varphi(\eta^{-1}F) - \epsilon} \leq \frac{\lambda(\overset{\circ}{A_k})}{\varphi(\overset{\circ}{B_j}{}^{c})} \leq \liminf \frac{\lambda_n(\xi^{-1}G)}{\varphi_n(\eta^{-1}F)}$$

Since ϵ is arbitrary, the proof is complete.

Our next theorem gives a uniformity condition. We assume that $(X,\mathcal{J})$ is a separable metric space. We need only the following Lemma (see [3] for a proof).

Lemma 1. Let μ be a measure on X and let $\mathcal{G}$ be an equicontinuous family of functions on X. Then for each $\epsilon > 0$, there exists a sequence of sets A_j, $j = 1,2,\ldots$ such that

(1) $\bigcup_{j=1}^{\infty} A_j = X$

(2) $A_i \cap A_j = \emptyset \quad i \neq j$

(3) A_j is a continuity set for μ.

(4) $|f(x) - f(y)| < \epsilon$ for $x,y \in A_j$, $f \in \mathcal{G}$.

In the following theorem, we deal with equicontinuous families of functions $\mathcal{G}$, i.e., for each $\epsilon > 0$, there is a δ such that $\sup_{f\in\mathcal{G}}|f(x) - f(y)| < \epsilon$ if $d(x,y) < \delta$.

Theorem 3. Let $\mathcal{G}$, $\mathcal{G}'$ be classes of continuous functions on X possessing the properties

(i) $\mathcal{G}$ is uniformly bounded above.

(ii) $\mathcal{G}'$ is uniformly bounded away from zero on a fixed set B^* and $\mathcal{G}^1 \subset C_2$.

(iii) $\mathcal{G}$ and $\mathcal{G}'$ are equicontinuous.

If (λ_n, φ_n) weak ratio converges to (λ, φ), then

$$\sup_{f\in\mathcal{G}, g\in\mathcal{G}'} \left| \frac{\int f \, d\lambda_n}{\int g \, d\varphi_n} - \frac{\int f \, d\lambda}{\int g \, d\varphi} \right| \xrightarrow{n} 0 .$$

Proof. Let A_n and B_n be the sets in Lemma 1. Let $x_i \in A_i$, $y_j \in B_j$ and

λ^*, φ^* be the discrete measures such that all of the mass of A_i is at x_i and that of B_i is at y_i. Then

$$\left|\frac{\int f d\lambda}{\int g d\varphi} - \frac{\int f d\lambda^*}{\int g d\varphi^*}\right| \leq \frac{\sum_i \sum_j \left|\int_{B_j} g d\varphi^* \int_{A_i} f d\lambda - \int_{A_i} f d\lambda^* \int_{B_j} g d\varphi\right|}{\int g d\varphi \int g d\varphi^*} \leq \tag{4}$$

$$\frac{\epsilon\lambda(X)}{\int g d\varphi} + \frac{\epsilon\varphi(X)}{\int g d\varphi} \frac{\int |f| d\lambda^*}{\int g d\varphi^*} .$$

Since

$$\left|\int_{A_i} |f| d\lambda^* - \int_{A_i} |f| d\lambda\right| \leq \int_{A_i} \big||f(x_i)| - |f|\big| d\lambda \leq \epsilon\lambda(A_i),$$

we have as a bound on the last inequality in (4)

$$\frac{\epsilon\lambda(X)}{\int g d\varphi} + \frac{\epsilon\varphi(X)}{\int g d\varphi} \cdot \frac{\int |f| d\lambda + \epsilon\lambda(X)}{\int g d\varphi - \epsilon\varphi(X)} < \epsilon'$$

for some ϵ'. We next consider

$$\left|\frac{\int f d\lambda_n^*}{\int g d\varphi_n^*} - \frac{\int f d\lambda^*}{\int g d\varphi^*}\right| = \left|\frac{\sum_i f(x_i)\lambda_n^*(A_i)}{\sum_y g(y_j)\varphi_n^*(B_j)} - \frac{\sum_i f(x_i)\lambda^*(A_i)}{\sum_j g(y_j)\varphi^*(B_j)}\right| \leq \tag{5}$$

$$\frac{M}{m}\left|\frac{\sum_i \lambda_n^*(A_i)}{\sum_j \varphi_n^*(B_j \cap B^*)} - \frac{\sum_i \lambda^*(A_i)}{\sum_j \varphi^*(B_j \cap B^*)}\right| \leq \frac{M}{m}\left|\frac{\lambda_n(X)}{\varphi_n(B^*)} - \frac{\lambda(X)}{\varphi(B^*)}\right| ,$$

where M and m are the corresponding bounds on $\mathcal{G}$ and $\mathcal{G}'$. Since (λ_n, φ_n) weak ratio converges to (λ, φ) the theorem is valid with $\lambda_n = \lambda_n^*$, $\varphi_n = \varphi_n^*$, $\lambda = \lambda^*$, $\varphi = \varphi^*$. The arguments leading to (5) are valid with subscripts and these approximations complete the proof of the theorem.

We now illustrate the previous concepts with an example. Let ξ, η be random variables on X, τ a transformation on X which preserves some σ-finite measure μ. The measures

$$\lambda_n[s,x] = \sum_{j=0}^{n-1} 1_{[s,x]}(\xi \circ \tau^j)$$

$$\varphi_n[t,y] = \sum_{j=0}^{n-1} 1_{[t,y]}(\eta \circ \tau^j)$$

$$\lambda[s,x] = \int 1_{[s,x]}(\xi)d\mu$$

$$\varphi[t,y] = \int 1_{[t,y]}(\eta)d\mu$$

are defined on the sets $\tilde{X} = [s,x_o]$, $\tilde{Y} = [t,y_o]$ with $\lambda(\tilde{X}) < \infty$, $0 < \varphi(\tilde{Y}) < \infty$. It follows from the Chacon-Ornstein ratio ergodic theorem that $\lambda_n[s,x]/\varphi_n[t,y] \to \lambda[s,x]/\varphi[t,y]$ for every x,y and also with open intervals rather than closed intervals (see [2]). It follows from Theorem 1 that (λ_n, φ_n) weak ratio converges to (λ, φ). By means of functions f of the type described by (2), we may approximate $1_{[s,x]}$ in such a way that $1_{[s,x]} = f$ except on a set A whose λ measure can be made arbitrarily small. Similarly we can approximate $1_{[t,y]}$ $y \geq y_1$ by functions g with $g = 1$ on $[t,y_1]$ where $y_1 \geq t$ and $\varphi[t,y_1] > 0$. These arguments yield the following

$$\lim_{n\to\infty} \sup_{\substack{s\leq x\leq x_o \\ y_1\leq y\leq y_o}} \left| \frac{\sum_{i=0}^{n} 1_{[s,x]}(\xi\circ\tau^i)}{\sum_{i=0}^{n} 1_{[t,y]}(\eta\circ\tau^i)} - \frac{\int 1_{[s,x]}(\xi)d\mu}{\int 1_{[t,y]}(\eta)d\mu} \right| = 0 \text{ a.e.}$$

which is the ratio version of the Glivenko-Cantelli theorem proved in (2).

REFERENCES

1. Billingsley, P., Convergence of Probability Measures. Wiley, New York, 1968.

2. Klimko, E.M., On the Glivenko-Cantelli theorem for infinite invariant measures. Ann. Math. Statist. 38, 1273-1277 (1967).

3. Ranga Rao, R., Relations between weak and uniform convergence of measures with applications. Ann. Math. Statist. 33, 659-680 (1962).

TRANSFORMATIONS WITHOUT FINITE INVARIANT MEASURE HAVE FINITE STRONG GENERATORS

by Ulrich Krengel*
The Ohio State University

Summary: The following theorem is proved: If T is a nonsingular invertible transformation in a separable probability space $(\Omega, \mathfrak{F}, \mu)$ and there exists no T-invariant probability measure $\mu_0 \ll \mu$, then the system of sets A for which $\xi = \{A, A^c\}$ is a strong generator (i.e. for which $A, TA, T^2A, \ldots$ generates $\mathfrak{F}$ mod μ) is dense in every increasing exhaustive subalgebra $\mathfrak{L}$ of $\mathfrak{F}$ (i.e. in every $\mathfrak{L} \subseteq \mathfrak{F}$ with $T^k\mathfrak{L} \uparrow \mathfrak{F}$). In particular for $\mathfrak{L} = \mathfrak{F}$ it follows that nonsingular transformations without finite invariant measure have finite strong generators (of size 2).

The greatest difficulty appears in the case where a finite invariant measure exists on $\mathfrak{L}$ but not on $\mathfrak{F}$. To show that this can happen we construct an ergodic Bernoulli shift (with nonidentical factor measures) for which no invariant probability measure $\mu_0 \ll \mu$ exists and for which the restriction of μ to an exhaustive $\mathfrak{L}$ is invariant.

*Research supported by the National Science Foundation, Grant GP-9354.

1. Introduction: One of the earliest results of ergodic theory is the theorem which asserts that every measure preserving (m.p.) invertible transformation T of a probability space $(\Omega,\mathcal{F},\mu)$ has an isomorphic representation as a shift in an infinite product space. By this theorem the ergodic theory of m.p. transformations in a probability space satisfying minimal regularity conditions is in a certain sense equivalent to the theory of stationary processes.

During the last decade refinements and generalizations of this theorem became of interest. Rokhlin [12] showed for aperiodic transformations that the state space of the process can always be chosen countable, and that the process in this case can be required to be deterministic. Abstractly this is formulated by introducing the concept "generator." A finite or countable sequence $\xi = \{A_1,A_2,\cdots\} = \{A_i,\ i \in I\}$ of disjoint measurable sets A_i with union Ω is called a partition of Ω. We shall employ the usual notation $\mathbb{Z} = \{0,\pm1,\pm2,\cdots\}$, $\mathbb{Z}^+ = \{0,1,2,\cdots\}$, $\mathbb{N} = \{1,2,3,\cdots\}$. If $\{B_j\}$ is a family of sets, $\sigma\{B_j\}$ denotes the smallest σ-algebra containing the sets B_j. We identify sets which differ only by nullsets. ξ is called a generator if $\mathcal{F} = \sigma\{T^kA_i : i \in I,\ k \in \mathbb{Z}\}$; ξ is called a strong generator if $\mathcal{F} = \sigma\{T^kA_i,\ i \in I,\ k \in \mathbb{Z}^+\}$.

If ξ is a generator, T may be viewed as the shift of a process with state space I. By this we mean the following: let $\Omega^* = I^{\mathbb{Z}} = \{\omega^* = (\cdots,i_{-1},i_o,i_1,i_2,\cdots) : i_j \in I,\ j \in \mathbb{Z}\}$ and denote the product-σ-algebra by $\mathcal{F}^*$. The mapping

$$X_j : \omega^* = (\cdots,i_{-1},i_o,i_1,\cdots) \to i_j = X_j(\omega^*)$$

of Ω^* into I is called the j-th coordinate mapping. The shift S in

Ω^* is defined by $X_j(S\omega^*) = X_{j+1}(\omega^*)$. The rule

(1.1) $$X_j(\varphi(\omega)) = i \quad \text{iff } \omega \in T^{-j}A_i \qquad (j \in \mathbb{Z},\ i \in I)$$

defines a measurable mapping $\varphi:\Omega \to \Omega^*$ with $\varphi \circ T = S \circ \varphi$. Let μ^* be the measure $\mu\varphi^{-1}$ in $\mathfrak{F}^*$. Whether or not ξ is a generator φ is a homomorphism [1] of the algebras $\mathfrak{F}$ and $\mathfrak{F}^*$ (modulo nullsets). It is an isomorphism of the algebras $\mathfrak{F}$ and $\mathfrak{F}^*$ if and only if ξ is a generator. If in addition $(\Omega,\mathfrak{F},\mu)$ is a Lebesgue space [10] φ is an isomorphism mod μ of T and S. The existence of generators of size n is therefore necessary and sufficient for an invertible T in a Lebesgue space to have an isomorphic representation as a shift S for a process (X_j) with a state space of size n. Under the isomorphism φ the partition $T^k\xi$ corresponds to the σ-algebra $\mathfrak{F}^*(-k)$ generated by X_{-k}, (i.e. by the sets $\{X_{-k} = i\}$). ξ is a strong generator if and only if the σ-algebra $\mathfrak{F}^*(-\infty,0)$ generated by $X_0,X_{-1},X_{-2},\cdots$ is the full σ-algebra $\mathfrak{F}^*$. This means that the coordinate-mappings X_j for $j \geq 1$ are functions of $\{X_0,X_{-1},X_{-2},\cdots\}$, i.e. that the process (X_j) is deterministic.

If T has a finite or countable generator, $\mathfrak{F}$ must be countably generated, i.e. there must exist a sequence $F_1,F_2,\cdots \in \mathfrak{F}$ with $\mathfrak{F} = \sigma\{F_j\}$. This assumption will be made throughout.

All these considerations remain valid if T is merely a nonsingular transformation; i.e. if $T:\Omega \to \Omega$ is 1-1, onto, T and T^{-1} measurable and if $\mu(A) = 0$ implies $\mu(T^{-1}A) = \mu(TA) = 0$. (X_j) is stationary if and only if T is measure-preserving. If the entropy h(T) of a m.p. transformation T is infinite, T cannot have a finite generator.

Therefore transformations having a nonvanishing finite invariant measure $\mu_o \ll \mu$ need not have finite generators. Rokhlin's question whether ergodic m.p. transformations with finite entropy have finite generators was open for several years. Rokhlin [11] had proved the existence of countable generators with finite entropy. Krieger [7] gave a positive answer to Rokhlin's question by using Rokhlin's result, some preliminary coding and an adaptation of an unpublished coding technique of Blum and Hanson, see e.g. Jacobs [2, p. 287]. Moreover, using different coding techniques, Krieger showed that the minimal size n of a generator lies between $e^{h(T)}$ and $e^{h(T)} + 1$.

Parry [9] proved the existence of countable strong generators for nonsingular aperiodic transformations. In fact, if $\mathcal{B}$ is an increasing exhaustive sub-σ-algebra of $\mathfrak{F}$, i.e. if $\mathcal{B} \subseteq \mathfrak{F}$ satisfies $T^{-1}\mathcal{B} \subseteq \mathcal{B}$ and $\cup_{k\geq 0} T^k\mathcal{B}$ generates $\mathfrak{F}$, the generator can be found in $\mathcal{B}$. This requires almost no change in Parry's proof but in our result it is crucial.

<u>Theorem</u>: If T is a nonsingular invertible transformation in a countably generated probability space $(\Omega,\mathfrak{F},\mu)$ and there exists no T-invariant probability measure $\mu_o \ll \mu$, then the system of sets A for which $\xi = \{A,A^c\}$ is a strong generator is dense in every increasing exhaustive sub-σ-algebra $\mathcal{B}$ of $\mathfrak{F}$.

Sets A for which $\{A,A^c\}$ is a strong generator will be called strongly generating sets.

The fact that ξ can be found in $\mathcal{B}$ has some interesting consequences. Assume that T is the shift in a product space Ω belonging to a process $(Y_k, k \in \mathbb{Z})$. In general the "isomorphic" process (X_k) does not reflect the probabilistic properties of (Y_k) because the ergodic theoretic isomorphism completely distorts the time structure. It is for example possible that (Y_k) is completely nondeterministic and (X_k) is deterministic. (Definitions: Let $\mathfrak{F}(i,k)$ denote the σ-algebra $\sigma(Y_j,\ i \leq j \leq k)$ generated by $Y_j (i \leq j \leq k)$, $\mathfrak{F}(-\infty)$ the "remote past" $\bigcap_{k \geq 0} \mathfrak{F}(-\infty,-k)$ and $\mathfrak{F}(+\infty)$ the "remote future" $\bigcap_{k \geq 0} \mathfrak{F}(k,\infty)$. (Y_k) is called (forward) completely nondeterministic if $\mathfrak{F}(-\infty) = \{\emptyset,\Omega\}$, (forward) deterministic if $\mathfrak{F}(-\infty) = \mathfrak{F}$, backward completely nondeterministic if $\mathfrak{F}(+\infty) = \{\emptyset,\Omega\}$, backward deterministic if $\mathfrak{F}(+\infty) = \mathfrak{F}$.) In general X_o depends on all Y_k, $k \in \mathbb{Z}$; if ξ belongs to the increasing exhaustive σ-algebra $\mathcal{B} = \mathfrak{F}(0,\infty)$ then X_o depends only on $Y_o, Y_1, \cdots$. This does not preserve much of the time structure, however it seems to be the best one can get ergodic theoretically. In particular $\varphi^{-1}\mathfrak{F}^*(k,\infty) \subseteq \mathfrak{F}(k,\infty)$. Therefore $\mathfrak{F}(+\infty) = \{\emptyset,\Omega\}$ implies $\mathfrak{F}^*(+\infty) = \{\emptyset,\Omega^*\}$.

For stationary processes (Y_k) with finitely many states $\mathfrak{F}(-\infty)$ is just the Pinsker sub-σ-algebra of $\mathfrak{F}$, so that $\mathfrak{F}(-\infty) = \mathfrak{F}(+\infty)$, see e.g. [8,p. 73-74]. Therefore stationary processes with finitely many states are forward deterministic if and only if they are backward deterministic. Our result implies that this is not necessarily the case if the shift is nonsingular. We may even require that the shift is ergodic and has an infinite invariant measure, so that entropy theory applies. To obtain examples it is sufficient to apply our theorem to Markov shifts for null-recurrent aperiodic Markov chains, see [6], or to any other conservative K-automorphisms in infinite measure spaces. We therefore have the following:

<u>Corollary</u>: There exists a process (X_k) with two states which is

forward deterministic and backward completely nondeterministic and for which the associated shift is nonsingular and ergodic and has an infinite invariant measure.

The existence of strongly generating sets A trivially remains valid in our theorem if μ is σ-finite. It was shown in [5] that for infinite μ $\mathfrak{F}$-measurable strongly generating sets of finite measure exist if T is also assumed conservative and measure preserving. Various implications for entropy theory were given in [5]. Our present construction of a strongly generating set is different from that in [5]. When applied to the situation in [5] it does not result in a strongly generating set of finite measure.

2. Proof of the theorem: Let $\mathcal{B}$ be an increasing, exhaustive sub-σ-algebra of $\mathfrak{F}$ and let $\beta_o > 0$ and $F_o \in \mathcal{B}$ be given. We have to find a strongly generating set $A \in \mathcal{B}$ with $\mu(A \Delta F_o) < \beta_o$.

A measure ν defined on an invariant sub-σ-algebra $\mathfrak{F}_1$ of $\mathfrak{F}$ (i.e. $T^{-1}\mathfrak{F}_1 \subseteq \mathfrak{F}_1$) or on a larger subalgebra of $\mathfrak{F}$ will be called T-invariant on $\mathfrak{F}_1$ if $\nu(T^{-1}F) = \nu(F)$ holds for all $F \in \mathfrak{F}_1$. The restriction of ν to $\mathfrak{F}_1$ is denoted by $\nu|\mathfrak{F}_1$. ν is called absolutely continuous to μ on $\mathfrak{F}_1$, if $(\nu|\mathfrak{F}_1) \ll (\mu|\mathfrak{F}_1)$, i.e. if $\mu(F) = 0$, $F \in \mathfrak{F}_1$ imply $\nu(F) = 0$. We then write $\nu \ll \mu(\mathfrak{F}_1)$. ν is called equivalent to μ on $\mathfrak{F}_1$ ($\nu \sim \mu(\mathfrak{F}_1)$) if $\nu \ll \mu(\mathfrak{F}_1)$ and $\mu \ll \nu(\mathfrak{F}_1)$. For $\nu \ll \mu(\mathfrak{F}_1)$ $\mathrm{supp}_{\mathfrak{F}_1}(\nu)$ denotes the $\mathfrak{F}_1$-measurable support $\{\omega : d(\nu|\mathfrak{F}_1)/d(\mu|\mathfrak{F}_1) > 0\}$ of ν. We have assumed that no T-invariant probability measure $\nu \ll \mu$ exists on $\mathfrak{F}$, but there may exist T-invariant probability measures $\nu \ll \mu$ $(\mathcal{B})$ on $\mathcal{B}$. Let $I(\mathcal{B})$ be the class of all such measures. An example will be given in section 3.

Let P be the maximal support of measures from $I(\mathcal{S})$. To find P let $\alpha = \sup\{\mu(\mathrm{supp}_{\mathcal{S}}(\nu)):\nu \in I(\mathcal{S})\}$. (If $I(\mathcal{S}) = \emptyset$ let $\alpha = 0$ and $P = \emptyset$.) If $\alpha > 0$ pick $\nu_n \in I(\mathcal{S})$ with $\mu(\mathrm{supp}_{\mathcal{S}}(\nu_n)) \to \alpha$. Then $\lambda = \Sigma_{n=1}^{\infty} 2^{-n}\nu_n$ belongs to $I(\mathcal{S})$ and $\mathrm{supp}_{\mathcal{S}}(\lambda) = P$ contains $\mathrm{supp}_{\mathcal{S}}(\nu)$ for all $\nu \in I(\mathcal{S})$. The "pure" cases $P = \Omega$ and $P = \emptyset$ require quite different constructions of the strongly generating set A. In the "mixed" case, when both P and $N = \Omega \setminus P$ have positive measure the first of these constructions is applied on P and the second on N and the constructions must be made compatible. It will be clear from our proof in the mixed case how A can be constructed in the simpler pure cases. Let us therefore assume that $\mu(P)$ and $\mu(N)$ are positive. As the statement of the theorem is unchanged if μ is replaced by a finite equivalent measure we may assume $\mu(P) = \mu(N) = 1$. Since λ is an invariant probability measure on $\mathcal{S}$ it follows that $T^{-1}P = P$. The restrictions of T to P and N will again be denoted by T. The restrictions of $\mathcal{F}$, $\mathcal{S}$ and μ to P and N will be denoted by $\mathcal{F}_P$, $\mathcal{S}_P$, μ_P and $\mathcal{F}_N$, $\mathcal{S}_N$, μ_N respectively. Let $\mathcal{S}^k = T^k\mathcal{S}$, $\mathcal{S}_P^k = T^k\mathcal{S}_P$, $\mathcal{S}_N^k = T^k\mathcal{S}_N$ $(k \in \mathbb{Z})$, $\mathcal{S}^{\infty} = \bigcup_{k\geq 0}\mathcal{S}^k$, $\mathcal{S}_P^{\infty} = \bigcup_{k\geq 0}\mathcal{S}_P^k$ and $\mathcal{S}_N^{\infty} = \bigcup_{k\geq 0}\mathcal{S}_N^k$. The measure λ can be extended to $\mathcal{S}^{\infty}$ by $\lambda(T^kF) = \lambda(F)$, $(T^kF \in \mathcal{S}^k)$. The extended "measure" λ on the algebra $\mathcal{S}^{\infty}$ is again carried by P and we may consider it as a measure on $\mathcal{S}_P^{\infty}$. The first lemma is trivial, if λ can be extended to the σ-algebra $\mathcal{F}_P$ generated by $\mathcal{S}_P^{\infty}$. (However, this is not necessarily possible unless $(\Omega,\mathcal{F},\mu)$ is a Lebesgue space. Even in the case of Lebesgue spaces the extension is not quite trivial. It requires a generalization of the Daniell-Kolmogorov theorem for arbitrary increasing subalgebras--not necessarily in a product space.)

<u>Lemma 1</u>: Under the above assumptions there exists for every ϵ with $0 < \epsilon < 1/4$ a $k > 0$ and a set $U \in \mathcal{S}_P^k$ such that

(2.1) $$\mu_P(U) < \varepsilon \quad \text{and} \quad \lambda(U) > 1 - \varepsilon.$$

<u>Proof</u>: Define an outer measure λ^* and an inner measure λ_* on $\mathfrak{F}_P$ by

(2.2) $$\lambda^*(F) = \inf_{\substack{G \in \mathscr{G}^\infty \\ G \supseteq F}} \lambda(G); \quad \lambda_*(F) = \sup_{\substack{G \in \mathscr{G}^\infty \\ G \subseteq F}} \lambda(G) .$$

Let $\theta_1 = \sup_{F \in \mathfrak{F}_P}(\lambda^*(F) - \lambda_*(F))$. If $\theta_1 = 0$ let $k_1 = 1$ and $D_1 = \emptyset$. If $\theta_1 > 0$ find $E_1 \in \mathfrak{F}_P$ such that $\lambda^*(E_1) - \lambda_*(E_1) > 2^{-1}\theta_1$. Find $k_1 > 0$ and $A_1, B_1 \in \mathscr{G}_P^{k_1}$ such that $A_1 \supseteq E_1 \supseteq B_1$ and $\mu(A_1 \setminus B_1) < 2^{-2}\theta_1\varepsilon$. In this case let $D_1 = A_1 \setminus B_1$. In both cases $\mu(D_1) \leq 2^{-1}\varepsilon\lambda(D_1)$. We put $D^1 = D_1$ and define further sets D_j and $D^j = D_1 \cup \cdots \cup D_j$ inductively.

If $i \geq 1$ is odd and $k_1 < k_2 < \cdots < k_i$, and $D_j \in \mathscr{G}_P^{k_j}$ $(j = 1, \cdots, i)$ have just been determined let

(2.3) $$\theta_{i+1} = \sup\{\lambda(E) : E \in \mathscr{G}_P^\infty,\ E \subseteq P \setminus D^i,\ \mu(E) \leq 2^{-1}\varepsilon\lambda(E)\}.$$

Find $k_{i+1} > k_i$ and $D_{i+1} \in \mathscr{G}_P^{k_{i+1}}$ such that $D_{i+1} \subseteq P \setminus D^i$ and

(2.4) $$\lambda(D_{i+1}) \geq 2^{-1}\theta_{i+1} \quad \text{and} \quad \mu(D_{i+1}) \leq 2^{-1}\varepsilon\lambda(D_{i+1}).$$

If $i \geq 1$ is even let

(2.5) $$\theta_{i+1} = \sup\{(\lambda^*(F) - \lambda_*(F)) : F \in \mathfrak{F},\ F \subseteq P \setminus D^i\}.$$

If $\theta_{i+1} = 0$ let $k_{i+1} = k_i + 1$ and $D_{i+1} = \emptyset$. If $\theta_{i+1} > 0$ find $E_{i+1} \in \mathfrak{F}$ with $E_{i+1} \subseteq P \setminus D^i$ such that $\lambda^*(E_{i+1}) - \lambda_*(E_{i+1}) > 2^{-1}\theta_{i+1}$. Then there exist a $k_{i+1} > k_i$ and sets $A_{i+1}, B_{i+1} \in \mathscr{G}_P^{k_{i+1}}$ such that $P \setminus D^i \supseteq A_{i+1} \supseteq E_{i+1} \supseteq B_{i+1}$ and $\mu(A_{i+1} \setminus B_{i+1}) < 2^{-2}\theta_{i+1}\varepsilon$. In this case let $D_{i+1} = A_{i+1} \setminus B_{i+1}$. Clearly $\lambda(D_{i+1}) > 2^{-1}\theta_{i+1}$. In both cases

(2.6) $$\mu(D_{i+1}) \leq 2^{-1}\varepsilon\lambda(D_{i+1}).$$

This completes the inductive definition of $k_1 < k_2 < \cdots$ and of the disjoint sets $D_1, D_2, \cdots$. Let $D = \bigcup_{i=1}^{\infty} D_i$.

Since λ_* is an interior measure we have $\lambda_*(D) \geq \Sigma_{i=1}^{\infty} \lambda_*(D_i)$. We claim that equality holds. Otherwise there is a $\theta > 0$ and a set $E \in \mathscr{L}_P^{\infty}$ with $E \subseteq D$ such that $\lambda(E) > \Sigma_{i=1}^{\infty} \lambda_*(D_i) + \theta = \Sigma_{i=1}^{\infty} \lambda(D_i) + \theta$. For sufficiently large odd i we have $\lambda(D_{i+1}) < \theta/4$ and $\mu(E \setminus D^i) < 2^{-1}\epsilon\theta$. Since $\lambda(E \setminus D^i) > \theta$ the set D_{i+1} cannot have been chosen in accordance with (2.4).

Assume $\lambda^*(D) > \lambda_*(D)$. For every i we have $\lambda^*(D) = \lambda^*(D \setminus D^i) + \lambda(D^i)$, $\lambda_*(D) = \lambda_*(D \setminus D^i) + \lambda(D^i)$, and therefore

(2.7) $$\lambda^*(D \setminus D^i) - \lambda_*(D \setminus D^i) = \lambda^*(D) - \lambda_*(D) > 0.$$

Thus $\theta_{i+1} \geq \lambda^*(D) - \lambda_*(D)$ for all even $i \geq 1$, so that $\Sigma_{i=1}^{\infty} \lambda(D_i) = \infty$, which is a contradiction. Hence $\lambda^*(D) = \lambda_*(D)$.

It follows by the same argument that for all $\mathfrak{F}$-measurable $V \subseteq P \setminus D = P_o$ $\lambda^*(V) = \lambda_*(V)$. Therefore λ^* restricted to P_o is a measure on $\mathfrak{F} \cap P_o$. Let $P_k = \bigcup_{|i| \leq k} T^i P_o$ and for $F \in \mathfrak{F}$ let $\tilde{\lambda}(F) = \lim_{k \to \infty} \lambda^*(F \cap P_k)$. $\tilde{\lambda}$ is a finite T-invariant measure on the invariant set $\bigcup_{k \geq 1} P_k = P_{\infty}$. If $\tilde{\lambda}(F) > 0$ then there is a $k \geq 0$ such that $\lambda^*(F \cap P_k) > 0$. Then there is an i with $|i| \leq k$ such that $\lambda^*(T^i F \cap P_o) > 0$. But in P_o $\lambda^* = \lambda_*$ and on $\mathscr{L}_P^{\infty}$ λ and μ are equivalent. Thus $\mu(T^i F \cap P_o) > 0$. By the nonsingularity of T with respect to μ we have $\mu(F) > 0$. We have proved $\tilde{\lambda} \ll \mu$. Since $\tilde{\lambda}$ is finite and T-invariant it must have total measure zero. It follows that $\lambda^*(D) = 1$.

Now for large enough i $U = D^i$ clearly satisfies $\lambda(U) > 1 - \epsilon$ and in view of (2.4) and (2.6) also $\mu(U) < \epsilon$. ┘

Next we shall derive some preliminary results about the restriction of T to $(N, \mathcal{B}_N, \mu_N)$. A set W is called weakly wandering if there exists an increasing sequence $k_1 < k_2 < \cdots$ of integers such that the sets W, $T^{-k_1}W$, $T^{-k_2}W$, $\cdots$ are disjoint.

Lemma 2: For every $\epsilon > 0$ there exists a weakly wandering set $W \in \mathcal{B}_N$ with $\mu_N(W) > 1 - \epsilon$.

(Lemma 2 is well-known to ergodic theorists but may not have been explicitly stated. Here is a short proof: By Theorem 1 of [4] N is a countable disjoint union of $\mathcal{B}_N$-measurable sets N_1, N_2, $\cdots$ such that for all i

(2.8) $$\lim_{n\to\infty} \frac{1}{n} \Sigma_{k=o}^{n-1} \mu_N(T^{-k}N_i) = 0.$$

This can also be derived without too much work from a theorem of Sucheston [13, Theorem 8]. Obviously N_i in (2.8) can be replaced by $N^i = \bigcup_{j=1}^{i} N_j$. For large i $\mu_N(N^i) > 1 - \frac{\epsilon}{2}$. Modify this N^i as in [13, p. 333] by a set of μ_N-measure less than $\epsilon/2$ to obtain a weakly wandering set.)

Lemma 3: For any sequence $(\epsilon_n)_{n=o}^{\infty}$ of positive numbers there exists an increasing sequence $0 = n_o < n_1 < n_2 < \cdots$ of integers and a sequence $W_o, W_1, \cdots$ of $\mathcal{B}_N$-measurable weakly wandering sets such that $\mu(W_i) > 1 - \epsilon_i$ $(i = 0,1,\cdots)$ and

(2.9) $$\mu_N(T^{n_i}(\bigcup_{k\neq i} T^{-n_k}W_k)) < \epsilon_i \qquad (i = 0,1,\cdots).$$

Proof: By the previous lemma we can find weakly wandering sets $W_i \in \mathcal{B}_N$ with $\mu(W_i) > 1 - \epsilon_i$. For $A \in \mathfrak{F}_N$ let $\sigma_n(A) = (2n + 1)^{-1} \sum_{k=-n}^{n} \mu_N(T^kA)$. Elementary arguments show that $\sigma_n(W)$ tends to zero if W is weakly wandering. We may assume that the sequence ϵ_n is decreasing. Clearly $\sigma_n(W_o \cup W_1)$ tends to zero. Therefore there exists an $n_1 > n_o = 0$ such that $\mu_N(T^{n_1}(W_o \cup W_1)) < 2^{-1}\epsilon_1$ and $\mu_N(T^{-n_1}(W_o \cup W_1)) < 2^{-1}\epsilon_1$. For $j = 1$ this implies the inequalities

(2.10) $$\mu_N(T^{n_i}(\bigcup_{\substack{k\neq i\\ k\leq j}} T^{-n_k}W_k)) < \epsilon_i(\Sigma_{\ell=1}^{j} 2^{-\ell}), \quad 0 \leq i \leq j.$$

At the end of step $j \geq 1$ integers $n_1 < n_2 < \cdots < n_j$ have been determined in such a way that (2.10) holds. As

$$\sigma_n(\bigcup_{i=o}^{j} T^{n_i}W_{j+1}) + \sigma_n(\bigcup_{k=o}^{j} T^{-n_k}W_k) \to 0$$

there must exist an $n_{j+1} > n_j$ such that

(2.11) $$\mu_N(T^{-n_{j+1}}(\bigcup_{i=o}^{j} T^{n_i}W_{j+1})) < 2^{-(j+1)}\,\epsilon_{j+1} \quad \text{and}$$

(2.12) $$\mu_N(T^{n_{j+1}}(\bigcup_{k=o}^{j} T^{-n_k}W_k)) < 2^{-(j+1)}\,\epsilon_{j+1}\,.$$

It follows from (2.10), (2.11) and (2.12) that (2.10) holds with j replaced by j + 1. Now (2.9) follows since (2.10) holds for all j. ┘

We shall now begin the construction of the desired strongly generating set $A \in \mathcal{B}$. The σ-algebra $\mathcal{B}$ is countably generated mod μ since the dimension of $L_2(\Omega,\mathcal{B},\mu)$ does not exceed the dimension of $L_2(\Omega,\mathfrak{F},\mu)$. Let $F_1, F_2, \cdots$ be a sequence of $\mathcal{B}$-measurable sets generating $\mathcal{B}$. We may assume that F_i is contained in N if $i \geq 1$ is even and that F_i is contained in P if i is odd. We may further assume that each F_i occurs infinitely often in the sequence $\{F_j, j \geq 1\}$. It is then sufficient to show that $\mathcal{S}(A) = \sigma\{T^kA, k \geq 0\}$ contains sets which approximate the sets F_i up to a set of measure 2^{-i}. This implies $\mathcal{S}(A) \supseteq \mathcal{B}$ and in view of the inclusion $T^k\mathcal{S}(A) \subseteq \mathcal{S}(A)$ also $T^k\mathcal{B} \subseteq \mathcal{S}(A)$ $(k \geq 0)$.

Thus $\mathscr{S}(A) = \mathfrak{F}$.

Let $F_o \in \mathscr{B}$ and β_o with $0 < \beta_o < 1/4$ be given. We shall find a strongly generating set $A \in \mathscr{B}$ such that $\mu(F_o \Delta A) < \beta_o$. For $i \geq 1$ let $\beta_i = \min\{\beta_o, 2^{-i}\}$. Apply lemma 3 with $\epsilon_n = 2^{-3}\beta_n$ to obtain a sequence $W_o, W_1, W_2, \cdots$ of weakly wandering $\mathscr{B}_N$-measurable sets with

(2.13) $$\mu_N(W_i) > 1 - 2^{-2}\beta_i \qquad (i \geq 0)$$

and an increasing sequence $(n_i)_{i=o}^{\infty}$ with $n_o = 0$ such that

(2.14) $$\mu_N(T^{n_i}(\bigcup_{k \neq i} T^{-n_k} W_k)) < 2^{-3}\beta_i \qquad (i = 0,1,2,\cdots).$$

If a strictly increasing sequence of natural numbers is given and lemma 1 shall be applied, then the number k in lemma 1 can be required to belong to the given increasing sequence because the σ-algebras $\mathscr{B}_P^j$ are increasing. For the same reason k can be required to be an arbitrarily late element of the increasing sequence.

The measures λ and μ_P are equivalent on $\mathscr{B}_P$. Therefore there exists a $\delta_o > 0$ such that for $X \in \mathscr{B}_P$ $\lambda(X) > 1 - \delta_o$ implies $\mu_P(X) > 1 - 2^{-2}\beta_o$. Apply lemma 1 to obtain a subsequence $0 = k_{o,1} < k_{o,2} < \cdots$ of $(n_i)_{i=o}^{\infty}$ and a sequence $U_{o,1}, U_{o,2}, \cdots$ with $U_{o,i} \in \mathscr{B}_P^{k_{o,i}}$ such that

(2.15) $$\lambda(U_{o,i}) > 1 - 2^{-i}\delta_o \qquad (i \geq 1) \qquad \text{and}$$

(2.16) $$\mu_P(U_{o,i}) \leq 2^{-3}\beta_i \leq 2^{-(i+2)} \qquad (i \geq 2).$$

The set $U_o = \bigcap_{i=o}^{\infty} T^{-k_{o,i}} U_{o,i}$ belongs to $\mathscr{B}_P$. As λ is invariant on $\mathscr{B}_P^{\infty}$ (2.15) implies $\lambda(T^{-k_{o,i}} U_{o,i}) > 1 - 2^{-i}\delta_o$. By the choice of δ_o and by (2.14) we obtain

$$\mu_P(U_o) > 1 - 2^{-2}\beta_o \quad \text{and} \tag{2.17}$$

$$\mu_P(T^{k_{o,i}}U_o) \leq 2^{-3}\beta_i \leq 2^{-(i+2)} \qquad (i \geq 2). \tag{2.18}$$

It is convenient to introduce the notation $Y_{n_k} = T^{-n_k}W_k$ and to leave Y_j undefined for $j \notin \{n_i, i \geq 0\}$. By (2.14) and by the monotonicity of (β_i) we have

$$\mu(T^{k_{o,j}}(\cup_{\{\ell:k_{o,\ell} \neq k_{o,j}\}} Y_{k_{o,\ell}})) < 2^{-2}\beta_o. \tag{2.19}$$

Starting with $\{k_{o,i}; i \geq 0\}$ and U_o we shall inductively define increasing sequences $(k_{r,i}, i \geq 1)$ and sets $U_r \in \mathcal{B}$. For $r \geq 1$ the sequence $(k_{r,i}, i \geq 1)$ will be obtained by forming a subsequence of $(k_{r-1,i})$. The sequences $(k_{o,i}), (k_{1,i}), \cdots, (k_{r,i})$ and the sets $U_o, \cdots, U_r$ are constructed in such a way that the following four sets of inequalities are satisfied:

$$\mu(T^{k_{i,1}}U_i) > 1 - 2^{-2}\beta_i \qquad (i = 0,\cdots,r) \tag{2.20}$$

$$\mu(T^{k_{i,1}}U_j) < 2^{-(j+2)}\beta_i \qquad (0 \leq i,j \leq r,\ i \neq j,\ j \text{ odd}) \tag{2.21}$$

$$\mu(T^{k_{i,j}}(\cup_{\{\ell:k_{o,\ell} \neq k_{i,j}\}} Y_{k_{o,\ell}})) < 2^{-2}\beta_i \qquad (i \leq r, \text{ all } j). \tag{2.22}$$

$$\mu(T^{k_{\ell,i}}U_j) \leq 2^{-(i-1)} \qquad (0 \leq j \leq \ell \leq r,\ i \geq 1). \tag{2.23}$$

(Note that (2.23) is trivial for $i = 1$ since all U_j will be contained in N or in P.)

Assume $(k_{r,i})$ and U_r has been determined and r is even. Find an integer $\nu_{r+1} \geq 2$ such that for $i \geq \nu_{r+1}$

$$\mu(T^{k_{r,i}}(U_o \cup \cdots \cup U_r)) < 2^{-(r+2)}\beta_{r+1}. \tag{2.24}$$

Determine $\delta_{r+1} > 0$ such that for $X \in \mathcal{B}_P$ with $\lambda(X) < \delta_{r+1}$

$$\mu(T^{k_{s,1}}X) < 2^{-(r+2)}\beta_{r+1} \qquad (s = 0,\cdots,r). \tag{2.25}$$

This is possible since the measures $\mu_P \circ T^{k_{s,1}}$ are equivalent to λ on $\mathcal{B}_P$. Now find $k_{r+1,1} \in \{k_{r,i},\ i \geq \nu_{r+1}\}$ and $U_{r+1,1} \in \mathcal{B}_P^{k_{r+1,1}}$ such that $\lambda(U_{r+1,1}) < \delta_{r+1}$ and

$$\mu(U_{r+1,1}) > 1 - 2^{-3}\beta_{r+1}. \tag{2.26}$$

Since $\mu \circ T^{k_{r+1,1}}$ and λ are equivalent on $\mathcal{B}_P$ there exists a $\delta'_{r+1} > 0$ such that for $X \in \mathcal{B}_P$ $\lambda(X) < \delta'_{r+1}$ implies $\mu(T^{k_{r+1,1}}X) < 2^{-3}\beta_{r+1}$. By lemma 1 there exist numbers $k_{r+1,2} < k_{r+1,3} < \cdots$ in $\{k_{r,j} : k_{r,j} > k_{r+1,1}\}$ and sets $U_{r+1,2}, U_{r+1,3}, \cdots$ with $U_{r+1,i} \in \mathcal{B}_P^{k_{r+1,i}}$ such that

$$\mu(U_{r+1,j}) < 2^{-(j-1)} \qquad (j \geq 1) \qquad \text{and} \tag{2.27}$$

$$\lambda(U_{r+1,j}) > 1 - 2^{-j}\delta'_{r+1} \qquad (j \geq 2). \tag{2.28}$$

Let $U_{r+1} = \bigcap_{j=1}^{\infty} T^{-k_{r+1,j}}U_{r+1,j}$. The set $\bigcap_{j=2}^{\infty} T^{-k_{r+1,j}}U_{r+1,j}$ belongs to $\mathcal{B}_P$. By the invariance of λ and by (2.28) its measure is at least $1 - \delta'_{r+1}$. By the choice of δ'_{r+1} we obtain $(\mu \circ T^{k_{r+1,1}})(\bigcap_{j=2}^{\infty} T^{-k_{r+1,j}}U_{r+1,j}) > 1 - 2^{-3}\beta_{r+1}$. Together with (2.26) this proves (2.20) for $i = r+1$. The inequality (2.21) follows for $i = r+1$ and $j < r+1$ from the choice of ν_{r+1}, because $k_{r+1,1}$ is some $k_{r,i}$ to which (2.24) applies. By the invariance of λ we get $\lambda(U_{r+1}) \leq \lambda(U_{r+1,1}) < \delta_{r+1}$. As $U_{r+1} \in \mathcal{B}_P$ the choice of δ_{r+1} and (2.25) imply (2.21) for $j = r+1$ and $i < j$. The inequality (2.22) follows for $i = r+1$ and all j from (2.14) because each $k_{r+1,j}$ is some n_ℓ with $\ell < r+1$ and because the β_i are decreasing. The inequality (2.23) follows for $\ell = r+1$, $j = r+1$ and $i \geq 2$ from (2.27) and the definition of U_{r+1}. For $\ell = r+1$, $i \geq 2$, $j \leq r$ it follows from the validity of (2.23) for $\ell = r$ because $k_{r+1,i}$ is some $k_{r,v}$ with $v \geq i$. This completes the construction of U_{r+1} and $(k_{r+1,i})$ and the verification of (2.20)-(2.23) with r replaced by r+1 if r is even. Now let r be odd. By (2.23) we can find an integer $\nu_{r+1} \geq 2$ such that for $i \geq \nu_{r+1}$

(2.29) $$\mu(T^{k_{r,i}}U_j) < 2^{(j+2)}\beta_{r+1} \qquad (j \leq r).$$

Let $k_{r+1,1} = k_{r,\nu_{r+1}}$ and $U_{r+1} = Y_{k_{r+1,1}}$. (2.29) proves (2.21) for $i = r+1$. For $j = r+1$ (2.21) need not be proved since r+1 is even. (2.20) follows since $T^{k_{r+1,1}}U_{r+1}$ is some W_i with $i \geq r+1$. Similarly (2.22) follows from (2.14) because $k_{r+1,j}$ is some n_i with $i \geq r+1$. By chosing $k_{r+1,2} < k_{r+1,3} < \cdots$ from $\{k_{r,i} : i > \nu_{r+1}\}$ such that the sequence $(k_{r+1,i})$ increases sufficiently fast we get (2.23) for $\ell = r+1$, $j = r+1$ from (2.14). The validity of (2.23) for $\ell = r+1$, $j \leq r$ follows from the validity of (2.23) for $\ell = r$ since $k_{r+1,i}$ is some $k_{r,h}$ with $h \geq i$. The inductive construction is now complete. The strongly generating set A is now defined by

(2.30) $$A = (F_o \cap (U_o \cup W_o)) \cup \bigcup_{i=1}^{\infty} (T^{-k_{i,1}}F_i \cap U_i).$$

Clearly A belongs to $\mathcal{B}$. By (2.17) and (2.13) we get

(2.31) $$\mu(U_o \cup W_o) \geq 2 - 2^{-1}\beta_o.$$

It follows from (2.21) and $k_{o,1} = 0$ that

(2.32) $$\mu(\bigcup_{i=o}^{\infty} U_{2i+1}) < 2^{-2}\beta_o.$$

The set $\bigcup_{i=1}^{\infty} U_{2i}$ is a subset of $\bigcup_{k=1}^{\infty} T^{-n_k} W_k$. Therefore (2.14) implies

(2.33) $$\mu(\bigcup_{i=1}^{\infty} U_{2i}) < 2^{-2}\beta_o.$$

The inequalities (2.31), (2.32) and (2.33) imply the desired inequality $\mu(F_o \Delta A) < \beta_o$. It is therefore now sufficient to prove $\mu(T^{k_{i,1}} A \Delta F_i) < \beta_i$ $(i \geq 1)$.

For $i \geq 1$ $k_{i,1}$ is some $k_{o,h}$ with $h \geq 2$ and $h \geq i$. Thus (2.18) implies

(2.34) $$\mu(T^{k_{i,1}} U_o) < 2^{-3}\beta_i.$$

Since $k_{i,1}$ is some n_j with $j \geq i$ and the β_j are decreasing (2.14) yields

(2.35) $$\mu(T^{k_{i,1}} W_o) < 2^{-3}\beta_i.$$

The inequality

(2.36) $$\mu(F_i \Delta T^{k_{i,1}}(T^{-k_{i,1}} F_i \cap U_i)) < 2^{-2}\beta_i \qquad (i \geq 1)$$

follows from (2.20) because both F_i and U_i are contained in P if i is odd and in N if i is even. The set $M_i = \bigcup_{\{j:i \neq j \geq 1, j \text{ even}\}} U_j$ is contained in $\bigcup_{\{\ell:k_{o,\ell} \neq k_{i,1}\}} Y_{k_{o,\ell}}$. Using (2.22) we get $\mu(T^{k_{i,1}} M_i) < 2^{-2}\beta_i$. On the other hand (2.21) implies $\mu(T^{k_{i,1}} \bigcup_{\{j:i \neq j \geq 1, j \text{ odd}\}} U_j) < 2^{-2}\beta_i$. Combining these inequalities we get

(2.37) $$\mu(T^{k_{i,1}} \bigcup_{\{j:i \neq j \geq 1\}} U_j) < 2^{-1}\beta_i.$$

Now (2.34), (2.35), (2.36) and (2.37) imply $\mu(T^{k_{i,1}} A \Delta F_i) < \beta_i$ $(i \geq 1)$. $\lrcorner$

3. <u>An ergodic Bernoulli shift without finite invariant measure:</u> We now give an example of an ergodic nonsingular invertible transformation T in a probability space $(\Omega,\mathfrak{F},\mu)$ and of an exhaustive increasing sub-σ-algebra $\mathcal{B} \subseteq \mathfrak{F}$ such that μ is invariant on $\mathcal{B}$ and no invariant probability measure $\bar{\mu} \ll \mu$ exists on $\mathfrak{F}$. The example is a Bernoulli shift with non-identical factor measures. It seems likely that T does not even have a σ-finite invariant measure. It would then be the first known example of a K-automorphism without σ-finite invariant measure.

Let $\Omega = \{0,1\}^{\mathbb{Z}}$, T = shift in Ω, $\mathfrak{F}$ = product σ-algebra $\sigma(X_i, i \in \mathbb{Z})$ where X_i is the i-th coordinate mapping. Let $\mathcal{B} = \mathfrak{F}(0,\infty) = \sigma(X_0,X_1,X_2,\cdots)$. For μ we take a product-measure $\mu = \prod_{i=-\infty}^{+\infty}{}^{\times} \mu_i$ with $\mu_i(\{0\}) = \mu_i(\{1\}) = \frac{1}{2}$ $(i \geq 0)$, $\mu_{-i}(\{0\}) = \frac{1}{2} + a_i$, $\mu_{-i}(\{1\}) = \frac{1}{2} - a_i$ $(i \geq 1)$. The numbers a_i will be such that $0 \leq a_i \leq \frac{1}{4}$. They are determined by induction below.

We shall also consider the measure $\nu = \prod_{i=-\infty}^{+\infty}{}^{\times} \nu_i$ with $\nu_i(\{0\}) = \nu_i(\{1\}) = \frac{1}{2}$ $(i \in \mathbb{Z})$, i.e. the measure of the 2-shift. For any measure φ, the measure $T\varphi$ is defined by $T\varphi(A) = \varphi(T^{-1}A)$. It follows from Kakutani's theorem on the equivalence of infinite product measures that T is nonsingular if and only if

$$(3.1) \qquad \Sigma_{i=0}^{\infty}(a_i - a_{i+1})^2 < \infty ,$$

see [3, section 10]. By the same theorem μ is equivalent to ν if and only if

$$(3.2) \qquad \Sigma_{i=1}^{\infty} a_i^2 < \infty .$$

A nonergodic shift T such that μ is invariant on $\mathcal{B}$, but no invariant probability measure $\bar{\mu} \ll \mu$ exists on $\mathfrak{F}$, may be obtained rather easily. Just take $a_i = \frac{1}{4}$ $(i \geq 1)$. It is not difficult to check that this choice of the sequence a_i implies that T is dissipative in $(\Omega, \mathfrak{F}, \mu)$. Dissipative transformations, however, are of little interest in ergodic theory, and they frequently play an exceptional role. Professor Sucheston has therefore raised the question whether a conservative T with the mentioned properties can be found. For this we have to chose the real numbers a_i differently.

We denote the σ-algebra generated by $X_{-n}, X_{-n+1}, \cdots, X_n$ by $\mathfrak{F}(n)$. If φ_1, φ_2 are two probability measures and the restriction $(\varphi_1|\mathfrak{F}(n))$ of φ_1 to $\mathfrak{F}(n)$ is absolutely continuous with respect to $(\varphi_2|\mathfrak{F}(n))$, we denote $d(\varphi_1|\mathfrak{F}(n))/d(\varphi_2|\mathfrak{F}(n))$ by $d\varphi_1/d\varphi_2|_n$. If $\varphi_1 \ll \varphi_2$ we obtain $d\varphi_1/d\varphi_2|_n \to d\varphi_1/d\varphi_2$ φ_2 - a.e. from the martingale theorem. Elementary computations give the following formula for $dT^k\mu/d\mu|_n$: For any $k \geq 0$ and $n \geq 1$

$$(3.3) \qquad \frac{dT^k\mu}{d\mu}\Big|_n (\omega) = \prod_{i=-n}^{+n} \frac{\mu_{i+k}(X_i(\omega))}{\mu_i(X_i(\omega))} = \prod_{i=-n}^{0} \frac{\mu_{i+k}(X_i(\omega))}{\mu_i(X_i(\omega))} \; .$$

We shall now inductively define numbers $\epsilon_j > 0$, $m_j, n_j, k_j, \ell_j \in \mathbb{N} = \{1,2,\cdots\}$ such that

$$(3.4) \qquad n_j = m_j + k_j \; ; \; m_{j+1} = n_j + \ell_j \; .$$

The numbers a_i $(i \geq 1)$ are defined by

$$(3.5) \qquad \begin{array}{ll} a_i = \epsilon_j & (i = m_j, m_j + 1, \cdots, n_j - 1) \\ a_i = 0 & (i = n_j, n_j + 1, \cdots, m_{j+1} - 1) \; . \end{array}$$

We start with $\epsilon_1 = \frac{1}{4}$, $m_1 = 1$, $k_1 = 1$, $n_1 = 2$. This defines μ_{-1} and μ_{-2}.

Let $\mu_i^{(1)} = \mu_i$ $(i \geq -2)$, $\mu_i^{(1)} = \nu_i$ $(i < -2)$ and form all expressions

$$(3.6) \qquad \prod_{i=-n}^{0} \frac{\mu_{i+k}^{(1)}(\eta_i)}{\mu_i^{(1)}(\eta_i)}$$

for all $n,k \in \mathbb{N}$ and all $(\eta_{-n}, \eta_{-n+1}, \cdots, \eta_0) \in \{0,1\}^{n+1}$. There exists a positive lower bound β_1 for the set of all products (3.6), because at most 2 of the factors can be different from 1 and the factors can assume only finitely many values, each of them positive. Find $r_1 \in \mathbb{N}$ such that $r_1\beta_1 > 2$ and let $\ell_1 = 5r_1$. This completes step 1 of the construction.

Let $\delta_1 \geq \delta_2 \geq \cdots > 1$ be a decreasing sequence of real numbers greater than 1 such that $\prod_{i=1}^{\infty} \delta_i < 2$. At the end of step t of the construction we have defined natural numbers $m_1 < n_1 < m_2 < \cdots < m_t < n_t$, $\ell_1 < \ell_2 < \cdots < \ell_t$, $k_1 < k_2 < \cdots < k_t$ such that (3.4) holds. We have further chosen $\epsilon_1 \geq \epsilon_2 \geq \cdots \geq \epsilon_t > 0$.

At the beginning of step t + 1 find $\epsilon_{t+1} > 0$ such that $\epsilon_{t+1} < \epsilon_t$, $\epsilon_{t+1} < 2^{-(t+1)}$ and

$$(3.7) \qquad 1 < \left(\frac{1}{2} + \epsilon_{t+1}\right)^{2m_{t+1}} \left(\frac{1}{2} - \epsilon_{t+1}\right)^{-2m_{t+1}} < \delta_t.$$

(Note that $m_{t+1} = n_t + \ell_t$ is defined!) Find $k_{t+1} \in \mathbb{N}$ with

$$(3.8) \qquad k_{t+1} > k_t; \quad k_{t+1}\epsilon_{t+1}^2 \geq 1; \quad k_{t+1} > 5r_t.$$

Let $n_{t+1} = m_{t+1} + k_{t+1}$. This determines a_i for $i < n_{t+1}$. Therefore

μ_i is now defined for $i > -n_{t+1}$. Let

$$\mu_i^{(t+1)} = \mu_i \ (i > -n_{t+1}); \quad \mu_i^{(t+1)} = \nu_i \ (i \leq -n_{t+1}).$$

Form all expressions

$$\prod_{i=-n}^{0} \frac{\mu_{i+k}^{(t+1)}(\eta_i)}{\mu_i^{(t+1)}(\eta_i)} \tag{3.9}$$

for all $n,k \in \mathbb{N}$ and all $(\eta_{-n},\cdots,\eta_0) \in \{0,1\}^{n+1}$. The infimum β_{t+1} of the products (3.9) is positive, because at most $2n_{t+1}$ factors can be different from 1 and all $\mu_j^{(t+1)}(\{\eta\})$ are from a fixed finite set of positive numbers. Let $r_{t+1} > 2r_t$ be such that

$$r_{t+1}\beta_{t+1} > 2 \tag{3.10}$$

and let $\ell_{t+1} = 5r_{t+1} + n_t$. This completes step t + 1. The inductive construction is complete.

The shift is nonsingular because a_i differs from a_{i+1} only for numbers i of the form $i = m_t - 1$ or $i = n_t - 1$. In both cases $|a_i - a_{i+1}| = \epsilon_t < 2^{-t}$, so that $\Sigma_{i=0}^{\infty}(a_i - a_{i+1})^2 = 2\ \Sigma_{t=1}^{\infty} \epsilon_t^2 < \infty$.

For each $t \geq 1$ there are k_t values of i with $a_i = \epsilon_t$. Therefore $\Sigma_{i=1}^{\infty} a_i^2 \geq \Sigma_{t=2}^{\infty} k_t \epsilon_t^2 = \infty$ by (3.8). Kakutani's theorem [3] implies that μ and ν are singular with respect to each other. This implies that T does not have an invariant probability measure $\bar{\mu} \ll \mu$. (Assume the contrary. Then $(\bar{\mu}|\mathcal{B}) \ll (\mu|\mathcal{B}) = (\nu|\mathcal{B})$. Since T in $(\Omega,\mathcal{B},\nu)$ is the unilateral 2-shift and hence ergodic, $\nu|\mathcal{B}$ is the only invariant probability measure absolutely continuous with respect to $\nu|\mathcal{B}$. Thus $\bar{\mu}|\mathcal{B} = \nu|\mathcal{B}$. As $\bar{\mu}$ is invariant this implies $\bar{\mu} = \nu$, contradicting $\bar{\mu} \ll \mu$.) Essentially the same argument can be used to prove that there exists no infinite invariant $\bar{\mu}$, for which $\bar{\mu}|\mathcal{B}$ is σ-finite. If T has a σ-finite invariant measure $\bar{\mu} \ll \mu$ the $\mathcal{B}$-measurable sets must have $\bar{\mu}$-measure 0 or ∞.

Next we prove that T is conservative. Let $(\eta_j)_{j=-\infty}^{+\infty}$ be an arbitrary sequence of zero's and one's. We want to consider $dT^k\mu/d\mu$ for $k \geq 1$. If t is such that $k \leq r_1 + r_2 + \cdots + r_t$ $(\leq 2r_t)$ and $i \geq -n_t - 2r_t$ we have $\mu_i = \mu_i^{(t)}$ and $\mu_{i+k} = \mu_{i+k}^{(t)}$. This and the choice of β_t implies for $n \leq n_t + 2r_t$ the inequality

$$(3.11) \qquad \prod_{i=-n}^{0} \frac{\mu_{i+k}(\eta_i)}{\mu_i(\eta_i)} \geq \beta_t .$$

For $i < -n_t - 2r_t$ the ratio $\mu_{i+k}(\eta_i)/\mu_i(\eta_i)$ can be different from 1 only if i belongs to one of the disjoint sets

$$I_s = \{-m_s, -m_s - 1, \cdots, -m_s - k + 1, -n_s, -n_s - 1, \cdots, -n_s - k + 1\}$$

$(s > t)$. If $i \in I_s$ we have

$$(3.12) \qquad \frac{\frac{1}{2} - \epsilon_s}{\frac{1}{2} + \epsilon_s} \leq \frac{\mu_{i+k}(\eta_i)}{\mu_i(\eta_i)} \leq \frac{\frac{1}{2} + \epsilon_s}{\frac{1}{2} - \epsilon_s} .$$

Observe that I_s has only $2k \leq 2m_s$ elements. It follows that for all n

$$(3.13) \qquad \prod_{i=-n}^{0} \frac{\mu_{i+k}(\eta_i)}{\mu_i(\eta_i)} \geq \beta_t \cdot \prod_{s=2}^{\infty} \left(\frac{\frac{1}{2} - \epsilon_s}{\frac{1}{2} + \epsilon_s} \right)^{2k} \geq 2^{-1}\beta_t .$$

We have proved $dT^k\mu/d\mu|_n \geq 2^{-1}\beta_t$ everywhere for $k = r_1 + \cdots + r_{t-1} + j$ $(j = 1, \cdots, r_t)$. The inequality (3.10) and the convergence of $dT^k\mu/d\mu|_n$ to $dT^k\mu|d\mu$ $(n \to \infty)$ now imply $\Sigma_{k=1}^{\infty}\, dT^k\mu/d\mu = \infty$. Therefore T is conservative.

For the proof of the ergodicity of T we use a similar idea as in [6]. Recall that $\mathfrak{F}(k,\ell)$ is the σ-algebra $\sigma(X_i, k \leq i \leq \ell)$ generated by the coordinate variables X_i $(k \leq i \leq \ell)$. Let $p \in \mathbb{N}$. If φ is a product measure $\varphi = \prod_{i=-\infty}^{\infty}{}^{\times} \varphi_i$ in Ω such that $\varphi_i = \mu_i$ for $i \notin \{-p,-p+1, \cdots, p\}$ we obtain for $k \geq 0$ and sufficiently large $n = n(k)$

$$\frac{dT^k\varphi}{d\mu}\Big|_n(\omega) = \prod_{i=-n}^{p} \frac{\varphi_{i+k}(X_i(\omega))}{\mu_i(X_i(\omega))} .$$

It follows from $dT^k\varphi/d\mu|_n \to dT^k\varphi/d\mu$ that $dT^k\varphi/d\mu$ is $\mathfrak{F}(-\infty,p)$-measurable for all k. Passing to linear combinations of such product measures φ we see that $dT^k\varphi/d\mu$ is $\mathfrak{F}(-\infty,p)$-measurable for all k whenever $\varphi \ll \mu$ is such that $d\varphi/d\mu$ is $\mathfrak{F}(-p,p)$-measurable. Let $\mathcal{J} \subseteq \mathfrak{F}$ denote the σ-algebra of invariant sets. The Chacon-Ornstein theorem implies for finite measures $\varphi \ll \mu$

$$(3.14) \qquad \lim_{n\to\infty} \frac{d(\Sigma_{k=0}^{n} T^k\varphi)}{d(\Sigma_{k=0}^{n} T^k\mu)} = \frac{d(\varphi|\mathcal{J})}{d(\mu|\mathcal{J})} .$$

Assume that $d\varphi/d\mu$ is $\mathfrak{F}(-p,p)$-measurable. Then the measurability considerations above imply that the limit $d(\varphi|\mathcal{J})/d(\mu|\mathcal{J})$ is $\mathcal{J} \cap \mathfrak{F}(-\infty,p)$-measurable. The σ-algebra $\mathcal{J} \cap \mathfrak{F}(-\infty,p)$ is contained in $\mathfrak{F}(-\infty,q)$ for all $q \in \mathbb{Z}$. By the Kolmogorov-0-1-law $\mathcal{J} \cap \mathfrak{F}(-\infty,p)$ must be the trivial σ-algebra $\{\Omega,\emptyset\}$ mod μ. It follows that $d(\varphi|\mathcal{J})/d(\mu|\mathcal{J})$ is a constant.

Now let $0 \leq \varphi \ll \mu$ be an arbitrary μ-continuous probability measure. Find numbers $p_k \in \mathbb{N}$ and measures $\varphi_k \ll \mu$ such that $d\varphi_k/d\mu$ is $\mathfrak{F}(-p_k,p_k)$-measurable and $\Sigma_{k=1}^{\infty}\|\varphi - \varphi_k\| < \infty$. (The norm is given by the total variation.) Then we have $\Sigma_{k=1}^{\infty}\|(\varphi|\mathcal{J}) - (\varphi_k|\mathcal{J})\| < \infty$ and therefore

$d(\varphi_k|\mathcal{J})/d(\mu|\mathcal{J})$ converges a.e. to $d(\varphi|\mathcal{J})/d(\mu|\mathcal{J})$. Thus $d(\varphi|\mathcal{J})/d(\mu|\mathcal{J})$ is a constant for all $0 \leq \varphi \ll \mu$. This implies $\mathcal{J} = \{\Omega, \emptyset\} \bmod \mu$, i.e. T is ergodic.

4. Complements and remarks: Mrs. A. Rosenberg has recently proved the existence of generating sets for left-amenable groups of nonsingular transformations without finite invariant measure. If G is a left-amenable group of nonsingular transformations of a separable (i.e. countably generated) probability space $(\Omega,\mathfrak{F},\mu)$ such that there exists no G-invariant probability measure $\mu_o \ll \mu$ then there exists a set $A \in \mathfrak{F}$ such that the σ-algebra generated by G(A) is $\mathfrak{F}$. Work on the case of general groups is in progress. Mrs. Rosenberg has also extended my theorem 4.1 of [5] on the existence of strongly generating sets of finite measure in an infinite measure space. Her results will appear in her thesis.

In [5] I have pointed out that the existence of strongly generating sets for measure preserving flows follows from the representation of flows by flows under a function. Recently I have proved a stronger representation theorem and have used it to prove the existence of strongly generating sets in an exhaustive sub-σ-algebra of a flow. These results will appear in my forthcoming paper: "K-flows are forward deterministic, backward completely nondeterministic stationary point processes."

If $(\Omega,\mathfrak{F},\mu)$ is a separable probability space and we identify sets differing by nullsets, $\mathfrak{F}$ is a complete separable metric space with metric $d(A,B) = \mu(A \Delta B)$. It is easy to see that the system of generating sets and the system of strongly generating sets for a fixed but arbitrary nonsingular invertible transformation T are G_δ-sets.

Our theorem therefore implies that the family of strongly generating sets for T is of second category in $\mathfrak{F}$ if there is no finite invariant measure $\mu_o \ll \mu$. The same remark applies to $\mathcal{S}$ and to the result on flows mentioned above.

References

1. K. Jacobs: Neuere Methoden und Ergebnisse der Ergodentheorie. Ergebnisse der Mathematik, N.F., Heft 29, Berlin-Göttingen-Heidelberg: Springer 1960.

2. K. Jacobs: Lecture notes on ergodic theory. Universitet Aarhus, 1962/63.

3. S. Kakutani: On equivalence of infinite product measures. Ann. Math., 49, (1948), 214 - 224.

4. U. Krengel: Classification of states for operators. Proc. Fifth Berkeley Symp. Math. Stat. Probability, Vol II, 2, (1967), 415-429.

5. U. Krengel: On certain analogous difficulties in the investigation of flows in a probability space and of transformations in an infinite measure space, to appear, Proceedings of a symposium in Monterey, (1969).

6. U. Krengel and L. Sucheston: Note on shift-invariant sets. Ann. Math. Stat., 40, (1969), 694-696.

7. W. Krieger: On entropy and generators of measure preserving transformations, to appear, Trans. Amer. Math. Soc.

8. W. Parry: Entropy and generators in ergodic theory. Math. Lecture Note Series, Benjamin, New York, (1969).

9. W. Parry: Aperiodic transformations and generators. J. London Math. Soc., 43, (1968), 191-194.

10. V. A. Rokhlin: New progress in the theory of transformations with invariant measure. Uspehi Mat. Nauk., 15, (1960), 1-26 = Russian Math. Surveys, 15, (4), (1960), 1-22.

11. V. A. Rokhlin: Generators in ergodic theory. Vestnik. Leningrad. Univ. Mat. Meh. Astronom. (1963), 26-32, (Russian).

12. V. A. Rokhlin: Generators in ergodic theory. II. Vestnik Leningrad. Univ. Mat. Meh. Astronom. (1965), 68-72.

13. L. Sucheston: On existence of finite invariant measures, Math. Z., 86, (1964), 327-336.

ON THE ARAKI-WOODS ASYMPTOTIC RATIO SET AND NON-SINGULAR TRANSFORMATIONS OF A MEASURE SPACE

by

Wolfgang Krieger

Ohio State University

1. Introduction

By an isomorphism of a Lebesgue measure space $(X, \mathcal{B}, \mu)$ onto a Lebesgue measure space $(X', \mathcal{B}', \mu')$ we mean a 1-1 mapping $T : X \to X'$ that together with its inverse is measurable and non-singular with respect to $(\mathcal{B},\mu)$ and $(\mathcal{B}',\mu')$. If here $(X,\mathcal{B},\mu) = (X',\mathcal{B}',\mu)$ then we say that T is an **automorphism** of $(X,\mathcal{B},\mu)$. We say that two countable groups $\mathcal{S}$ and $\mathcal{S}'$ of automorphisms of $(X, \mathcal{B}, \mu)$ resp. of $(X', \mathcal{B}', \mu')$ are weakly equivalent, $\mathcal{S} \overset{w}{\sim} \mathcal{S}'$, if there exists an isomorphism $U : (X, \mathcal{B}, \mu) \to (X', \mathcal{B}', \mu')$ such that

$$\{US\, x : S \in \mathcal{S}\} = \{SU\, x : S \in \mathcal{S}'\},\ \text{f.a.a. } x \in X,$$

(comp. [7]). We say that two automorphisms are weakly equivalent if the groups they generate are weakly equivalent, and we say that a group is weakly equivalent to an automorphism if it is weakly equivalent to the group generated by the automorphism.

Let for $n \in \mathbb{N}$ Ω_n be a finite set, and let p_n be a probability measure on Ω_n, $p_n(\omega) > 0$, $\omega \in \Omega_n$. Denote

$$(X_p, \mathcal{B}_p, \mu_p) = \prod_{n=1}^{\infty} (\Omega_n, \mathcal{P}(\Omega_n), p_n),\ p = (p_n)_{n=1}^{\infty}.$$

We denote cylinder sets in X_p by

$$Z_{\mathcal{A}} = \{x \in X_p : (x_n)_{n \in \Theta} \in \mathcal{A}\},\ \mathcal{A} \subset \prod_{n \in \Theta} \Omega_n,\ \Theta \subset \mathbb{N}.$$

Let $\mathcal{S}_p$ be the group that is generated by $\{S_n : n \in \mathbb{N}\}$ where with cyclic permutations π_n of Ω_n for $x \in X_p$

$$(S_n x)_m = \begin{cases} x_m, & \text{if } m \neq n, \\ \pi_n x_n, & \text{if } m = n. \end{cases}$$

These $\mathcal{S}_p$ are weakly equivalent to automorphisms ([7] §3, we call groups with this property hyperfinite). H. Araki and E. J. Woods [1] have associated with every p a closed subset $r_\infty(p)$ of $[0, \infty)$ which they called the asymptotic ratio set. $r_\infty(p)$ is the set of all $\alpha \geq 0$ with the following property: There exists a partition

$$\mathbb{N} = \bigcup_{i=1}^{\infty} \Theta_i$$

of $\mathbb{N}$ into finite sets, sets

$$\mathcal{K}_i, \mathcal{L}_i \subset \prod_{n \in \Theta_i} \Omega_n, \mathcal{K}_i \cap \mathcal{L}_i = \emptyset ,$$

and 1-1 mappings φ_i of $\mathcal{K}_i$ onto $\mathcal{L}_i$, such that

$$\sum_{i=1}^{\infty} \mu_{\mathfrak{p}} (Z_{\mathcal{K}_i}) = \infty ,$$

and

$$\lim_{i \to \infty} \max_{a \in \mathcal{K}_i} | \alpha - \mu_{\mathfrak{p}} (Z_{\varphi_i a}) \mu_{\mathfrak{p}} (Z_a)^{-1} | = 0 .$$

$r_\infty(\mathfrak{p})$ is a weak equivalence invariant of $\mathcal{G}_{\mathfrak{p}}$. Following closely the ideas of Araki and Woods we define in §2 of the present paper a ratio set $r(T)$ for every automorphism T and investigate its properties, thereby obtaining a series of results on the weak equivalence of ergodic automorphisms.

Let us say that an automorphism is of infinite product type if it is weakly equivalent to one of the groups $\mathcal{G}_{\mathfrak{p}}$. For automorphisms T that are of infinite product type $r(T)$ is almost always equal to $r_\infty(T)$, the only exception arising if T admits a σ-finite invariant measure, in which case $r(T) = \{1\}$ and $r_\infty(T) = \{0,1\}$. We do not know if there are ergodic automorphisms that are not of infinite product type. Hence it is not clear that the theory that we present in this paper is more general than the theory of Araki and Woods. We shall see that an ergodic automorphism T is of infinite product type if $r(T) \neq \{0,1\}$.

Denote for $\alpha > 0$

$$\mathcal{G}_\alpha = \mathcal{G}(p_\alpha)_{n=1}^{\infty}, \; p_\alpha(0) = (1 + \alpha)^{-1}, \; p_\alpha(1) = \alpha(1 + \alpha)^{-1} .$$

From every countable ergodic group $\mathcal{G}$ of automorphisms there arises a factor $\mathcal{A}(\mathcal{G})$ by the group measure space construction. Denote

$$\mathcal{A}_\alpha = \mathcal{A}(\mathcal{G}_\alpha) , \; \alpha > 0 .$$

In §3 we shall prove that for all ergodic automorphisms T and all $\alpha > 0$

$$\mathcal{A}_T \otimes \mathcal{A}_\alpha \sim \mathcal{A}_T$$

if and only if $\alpha \in r(T)$ (comp. [1] § 5).

Finally, again following the example of Araki and Woods, we consider in §4 the invariant ρ that is defined by

$$\rho(T) = \{\alpha > 0 : \mathcal{G}_\alpha \times \{T^i : i \in \mathbb{Z}\} \overset{W}{\sim} \mathcal{G}_\alpha \} .$$

(We set for automorphism groups $\mathcal{G}$ and $\mathcal{G}'$ $\mathcal{G} \times \mathcal{G}' = \{S^i \times T^j : S \in \mathcal{G}, T \in \mathcal{G}', i,j \in \mathbb{Z}\}$).

2. The ratio set

All sets and mappings that appear in this paper are measurable by assumption or construction. We need more terminology and notation. T_A will be the automorphism that is induced by the conservative automorphism T of $(X, \mathcal{B}, \mu)$ on $A \subset X$, $\mu (A) > 0$. If $U: (X, \mathcal{B}, \mu) \to (X', \mathcal{B}', \mu')$ is an isomorphism then $U\mu$ will be the measure on $(X', \mathcal{B}')$ that is given by

$$U\mu(B) = \mu(U^{-1}B), \ B \subset X' .$$

The full group $[\mathcal{G}]$ of a countable group $\mathcal{G}$ of automorphisms of $(X, \mathcal{B}, \mu)$ consists of all automorphisms S such that

$$Sx \in \mathcal{G}x, \quad \text{f.a.a.} \ x \in X .$$

We set for an automorphism T

$$[T] = [\{T^i : i \in \mathbb{Z}\}] .$$

A group $\mathcal{G}$ acting on $(X, \mathcal{B}, \mu)$ and a group $\mathcal{G}'$ acting on $(X', \mathcal{B}', \mu')$ are weakly equivalent if and only if there exists an isomorphism $U : (X, \mathcal{B}, \mu) \to (X', \mathcal{B}', \mu')$ such that $[\mathcal{G}'] = U \circ [\mathcal{G}] \circ U^{-1}$. We say that $\mathcal{G}$ contains the σ-finite measure $\nu \sim \mu$ if the group $\{S \in [\mathcal{G}] : S\nu = \nu\}$ is ergodic and if there exists for all $T \in \mathcal{G}$ a partition

$$X = \bigcup_{\vartheta \in \Theta_T} A_T,$$

and $\alpha_{T,\vartheta} > 0$ such that

$$\frac{dT^{-1}\nu}{d\nu} (x) = \alpha_{T,\vartheta} , \quad \text{f.a.a.} \ x \in A_{T,\vartheta} , \vartheta \in \Theta_T, T \in \mathcal{G} .$$

In this situation we denote by $\Delta(\mathcal{G}, \nu)$ the subgroup of the positive reals that is generated by $\bigcup_{T \in \mathcal{G}} \{\alpha_{T,\vartheta} : \vartheta \in \Theta_T\}$ (see for these notions [3] and [7]). All ergodic automorphisms that admit a finite invariant measure are weakly equivalent, and all ergodic automorphisms that admit an infinite σ-finite invariant measure are weakly equivalent ([3] Theorem 5, p 154, and [7] Theorem (6.5)). $\mathcal{G}_\alpha$ contains μ_α and

$\Delta(\mathcal{G}_\alpha, \mu_\alpha) = \{\alpha^i : i \in \mathbb{Z}\}$ ([7] §3), $\alpha > 0$. Every automorphism T that contains a measure ν such that $\Delta(T, \nu) = \{\alpha^i : i \in \mathbb{Z}\}$ is weakly equivalent to $\mathcal{G}_\alpha$, $\alpha > 1$ ([8] Theorem (4.1)). Moreover, all hyperfinite groups $\mathcal{G}$ that contain a measure ν such that $\Delta(\mathcal{G}, \nu)$ is a dense subgroup of the positive reals are weakly equivalent ([8] §5). In the sequal $\mathcal{G}_\infty$ will stand for such a group.

We say that an isomorphism $U : A \to B$, $A, B \subset X$, is compatible with the automorphism T if

$$Ux \in [T]\, x, \qquad \text{f.a.a. } x \in A.$$

We shall use lemma (2.1) of [9] : If T is an ergodic automorphism that does not possess a σ-finite invariant measure then there exists for all sets $A, B \subset X$ of positive measure an isomorphism $U : A \to B$ that is compatible with T.

Let now T be an automorphism of $(X, \mathcal{B}, \mu)$ and let ν be a σ-finite measure equivalent to μ. Let us define the set $r_\nu(T)$ as the set of all $\alpha \in [0,\infty)$ with the following property: For all $A \subset X$ of positive measure, and all $\epsilon > 0$ there exists a set $B \subset A$ of positive measure and an $S \in [T]$, $SB \subset A$, - or, equivalently, an isomorphism S of B onto a subset of A that is compatible with T - such that

$$e^{-\epsilon} < \frac{dS^{-1}\nu}{d\nu}(x)\ \alpha^{-1} < e^{\epsilon}, \qquad \text{f.a.a. } x \in B.$$

(2.1) <u>Lemma</u>. $r_\nu(T) = r_\mu(T)$.

<u>Proof</u>. Let $\alpha \in r_\nu(T)$, and let $A \subset X$, $\mu(A) > 0$, $\epsilon > 0$. Then choose a set $C \subset A$, $\mu(C) > 0$, such that for some $\gamma > 0$

$$\text{(1)} \qquad e^{-\frac{1}{3}\epsilon} < \frac{d\nu}{d\mu}(x)\ \gamma < e^{\frac{1}{3}\epsilon}, \qquad \text{f.a.a. } x \in C.$$

By the definition of $r_\nu(T)$ there is a $B \subset C$, $\mu(B) > 0$, and an $S \in [T]$ such that $SB \subset C$ and

$$\text{(2)} \qquad e^{-\frac{1}{3}\epsilon} < \frac{dS^{-1}\nu}{d\nu}(x)\ \alpha^{-1} < e^{\frac{1}{3}\epsilon}, \qquad \text{f.a.a. } x \in B.$$

It is $SB \subset A$ and we have from (1) and (2) that f.a.a. $x \in B$

$$e^{-\epsilon} < \frac{dS^{-1}\mu}{d\mu}(x)\ \alpha^{-1} = \frac{d\mu}{d\nu}(Sx)\ \frac{dS^{-1}\nu}{d\nu}(x)\ \alpha^{-1}\ \frac{d\nu}{d\mu}(x) < e^{\epsilon}. \qquad \text{Q.e.d.}$$

Since $r_\nu(T)$ does not depend on the choice of ν we can denote it by $r(T)$. We refer to $r(T)$ as the ratio set of T. $r(T)$ is a closed subset of $[0,\infty)$. It is an invariant of weak equivalence. For a hyperfinite group $\mathcal{G}$ we set $r(\mathcal{G}) = r(T)$

where $T \overset{W}{\sim} \mathcal{S}$. A ratio set can be defined for any group of automorphisms.

We set

$$\Lambda_{\mu}^{T}(x) = \{\log \frac{d\,T^{i}\mu}{d\mu}(x) : i \in \mathbb{Z}\} .$$

(2.2) Lemma. Let T be an ergodic automorphism of $(X, \mathcal{B}, \mu)$ that does not admit a σ-finite invariant measure, and let $\alpha > 1$, $\alpha \notin r(T)$. Then there exists an aperiodic automorphism $S \in [T]$, a finite measure $\nu \sim \mu$ that is preserved by S, and a $\xi > 0$ such that

$$\Lambda_{\nu}^{T}(x) \cap (0, \xi) = \emptyset , \qquad \text{f.a.a. } x \in X .$$

Proof. Since $\alpha \notin r(T)$ it follows that there is an $\eta > 0$ and an $A \subset X$, $\mu(A)>0$, such that

(3) $$\Lambda_{\mu}^{T_A}(x) \cap (\log \alpha - \eta , \log \alpha + \eta) = \emptyset , \qquad \text{f.a.a. } x \in A .$$

Hence we can define f.a.a. $x \in A$

$$q_{+}(x) = \min\{s \geq 0 : \Lambda_{\mu}^{T_A}(x) \cap (s, s+\eta) = \emptyset\}$$

$$q_{-}(x) = \max\{s \leq 0 : \Lambda_{\mu}^{T_A}(x) \cap (s-\eta, s) = \emptyset\} .$$

We find from (3) that

(4) $$q_{+}(x) , -q_{-}(x) \leq \log \alpha, \qquad \text{f.a.a. } x \in A .$$

We have

(5) $$\{x \in A : \log \frac{dT_A^{-i}\mu}{d\mu}(x) > q_{+}(x)\} \subset$$

$$\{x \in A : \log \frac{dT_A^{-i}\mu}{d\mu}(x) + q_{-}(T^{i}x) - q^{+}(x) \geq \eta\} , \ i \in \mathbb{Z}.$$

We claim that

(6) $$A = \{x \in A : |\{i \in \mathbb{N}\ q_{-}(x) \leq \log \frac{dT_A^{-i}\mu}{d\mu}(x) \leq q_{+}(x)\}| = \infty\} \cap \{x \in A : |\{i \in \mathbb{N}\ q_{-}(x) \leq \log \frac{dT_A^{i}\mu}{d\mu}(x) \leq q_{+}(x)\}| = \infty\} .$$

Indeed, had e.g. the set

$$B = \{x \in A : |\{i \in \mathbb{N} : q_{-}(x) \leq \log \frac{dT_A^{-i}\mu}{d\mu}(x) \leq q_{+}(x)\}| < \infty\}$$

positive measure, then the set

$$C = \bigcap_{i=1}^{\infty}\{x \in B : \log \frac{dT_A^{-i}\mu}{d\mu} \notin [q_{-}(x), q_{+}(x)]\}$$

would also have positive measure, and T could not induce an ergodic transformation on C, which is absurd.

It follows from (6) that by setting f.a.a. $x \in X$

$$i(x) = \min\{i \in \mathbb{N} : q_{-}(x) \leq \log \frac{dT_A^{-i}\mu}{d\mu}(x) \leq q_{+}(x)\},$$

$$U_x = T^{i(x)}\, x ,$$

we define an aperiodic automorphism in $[T_A]$. It follows from (4) that the measures $U^i \mu$, $i \in \mathbb{Z}$, are uniformly absolutely continuous. We can therefore apply a theorem of Markov ([5] p. 99) and find that U admits a finite invariant measure $\lambda \sim \mu$

$$\lambda\,(D) = \lim_{n\to\infty} \frac{1}{n} \sum_{m=0}^{n-1} \mu\,(U^m D), \qquad C \subset A .$$

This together with

$$q_-\,(x) \leq \log \frac{dU^m\mu}{d\mu}\,(x) \leq q_+\,(x), \text{ f.a.a. } x \in A, m \in \mathbb{Z} ,$$

implies that

$$q_-\,(x) \leq \log \frac{d\lambda}{d\mu}\,(x) \leq q_+\,(x) , \quad \text{f.a.a. } x \in A .$$

Hence we have from (5) that f.a.a. $x \in A$

$$\log \frac{d\, T_A^{-i}\, \mu}{d\mu}\,(x) > q_+\,(x)$$

implies that

$$\log \frac{d\, T_A^{-i}\lambda}{d\lambda}\,(x) \geq q_-(T_A^{\,i}\, x) + \log \frac{d\, T_A^{-i}\, \mu}{d\mu}\,(x) - q_+\,(x) \geq \eta .$$

By a similar argument we find that f.a.a. $x \in A$

$$\log \frac{d\, T_A^{-i}\, \mu}{d\mu}\,(x) < q_-\,(x)$$

implies that

$$\log \frac{d\, T_A^{-i}\, \lambda}{d\lambda}\,(x) \leq -\,\eta .$$

An application of lemma (2.1) of [9] concludes now the proof. Q.e.d.

(2.3) <u>Corollary</u>. For all ergodic automorphisms T $r(T) \cap (0, \infty)$ is a closed subgroup of $(0, \infty)$.

<u>Proof</u>. Let $\alpha, \beta, \in r\,(T) \cap (0, \infty)$, and let $A \subset X$, $\epsilon > 0$. There exist $B \subset A$ and $U \subset [T]$ such that $U B \subset A$ and

$$e^{-\frac{1}{2}\epsilon}\, \alpha \leq \frac{d\, U^{-1}\, \mu}{d\mu}\,(x) \leq e^{\frac{1}{2}\epsilon}\, \alpha , \quad \text{f.a.a. } x \in B$$

and there exist $C \subset UB$ and $V \subset [T]$ such that $VC \subset UB$ and

$$e^{-\frac{1}{2}\epsilon}\, \beta \leq \frac{d\, V^{-1}\, \mu}{d\mu}\,(x) \leq e^{\frac{1}{2}\epsilon}\, \beta , \quad \text{f.a.a. } x \in C .$$

It follows that

$$e^{-\epsilon}\,\alpha^{-1}\,\beta \le \frac{d\,V^{-1}\,U\,\mu}{d\mu}\,(x) \le e^{\epsilon}\,\alpha^{-1}\,\beta\,, \qquad \text{f.a.a. } x \in C\,.$$

Hence $\alpha^{-1}\,\beta \in r\,(T)$.

We infer from lemma (2.2) that if $r(T) \cap (0,1) = \emptyset$ then $1 \in r\,(T)$. Q.e.d.

(2.4) Theorem. Let $\alpha > 1$, and let T be an ergodic automorphism such that

$$(7) \qquad r\,(T) = \{0\} \cup \{\alpha^i : i \in \mathbb{Z}\}\,.$$

Then $T \overset{w}{\sim} \mathcal{S}_\alpha$.

Proof. By lemma (2.2) there exists a finite measure $\nu \sim \mu$, and a $\xi > 0$ such that

$$(8) \qquad \Lambda_\nu^T\,(x) \cap (0,\,\xi) = \emptyset\,, \qquad \text{f.a.a. } x \in X\,.$$

We claim that

$$(9) \qquad \log\alpha \in \Lambda_\nu^T\,(x)\,, \qquad \text{f.a.a. } x \in X\,.$$

Indeed, had the set

$$E = \{x \in X : \log\alpha \notin \Lambda_\nu^T\,(x)\}$$

positive measure, then (7) would imply that

$$\Lambda_\nu^{T_E}\,(x) \cap (\log\alpha - 2^{-n}\,\xi\,,\ \log\alpha + 2^{-n}\,\xi) \neq \emptyset, \qquad \text{f.a.a. } x \in X\,,\ n \in \mathbb{N}\,.$$

But (8) shows that f.a.a. $x \in X$

$$\Lambda_\nu^T\,(x) \cap (\log\alpha - \tfrac{1}{2}\,\xi\,,\ \log\alpha + \tfrac{1}{2}\,\xi)$$

can contain at most one point. Hence we have a contradiction and (9) is proved. We define inductively a sequence h_n of functions

$$h_0\,(x) = 0\,, \quad \text{f.a.a. } x \in X\,,$$

$$h_n(x) = \min\ \Lambda_\nu^T\,(x) \cap (h_{n-1}(x),\,\infty)\,, \quad \text{f.a.a. } x \in X,\ n \in \mathbb{N}\,.$$

We know from (8) that

$$h_n(x) - h_{n-1}\,(x) \ge \xi\,, \qquad \text{f.a.a. } x \in X\,,\ n \in \mathbb{N}\,.$$

Since T is ergodic we can conclude from this and from (9) that for some $N \in \mathbb{N}$

$$(10) \qquad h_N(x) = \log\alpha\,, \qquad \text{f.a.a. } x \in X\,.$$

We define f.a.a. $x \in X$ $(b_n(x))_{n=1}^N \in \mathbb{R}^N$ by

$$\{b_n\,(x) : 1 \le n \le N\} = \{h_n\,(x) - h_{n-1}\,(x) : 1 \le n \le N\}\,,$$

$$b_{n-1}\,(x) \le b_n\,(x)\,,\ 1 \le n \le N\,.$$

According to (9) $x \to (b_n(x))_{n=1}^N$ is a T-invariant function. The ergodicity of T implies that there is a $(\beta_n)_{n=1}^N \in \mathbb{R}^N$ such that

$b_n(x) = \beta_n$, f.a.a. $x \in X$, $1 \leq n \leq N$.

As a consequence of (7) there exists a set $A \subset X$, $\mu(A) > 0$, such that f.a.a. $x \in A$ $\Lambda_\nu^{T_A}(x)$ does not contain any positive number smaller than $\log \alpha$ that is a sum of some of the β_n . This means that

$$\Lambda_\nu^{T_A}(x) = \{i \log \alpha : i \in \mathbb{Z}\} , \qquad \text{f.a.a. } x \in A .$$

We apply lemma (2.5) of [9] and see that T_A contains ν . Application of lemma (2.1) of [9] and Theorem (4.1) of [7] concludes the proof. Q.e.d.

A theorem of L. K. Arnold ([2] Theorem 1) tells us that for an ergodic automorphism T $r(T) = \{1\}$ if and only if T admits a σ-finite invariant measure.

(2.5) Lemma. Let T be an ergodic automorphism, and let $\alpha \in r(T)$, $\varepsilon > 0$. Then there exist for every $A \subset X$ of positive measure, disjoint $B, C \subset X$ of positive measure and a $U \in [T]$ such that $UB = C$ and

$$e^{-\varepsilon} < \frac{d\,U^{-1}\mu}{d\mu}(x)\,\alpha^{-1} < e^{\varepsilon} , \qquad \text{f.a.a. } x \in B .$$

Proof. If $r(T) = [0, \infty)$ then the result follows from the ergodicity of T . If $r(T) = \{0,1\}$, then we appeal to lemma (2.2) . For $r(T) = \{1\}$ we apply Theorem 1 of [2], and for $r(T) = \{0\} \cup \{\alpha^i : i \in \mathbb{Z}\}$, $\alpha > 1$, we apply proposition (2.4).

Q.e.d.

(2.6) Proposition. If $\mathcal{S}_\mathfrak{p}$ does not admit an infinite σ-finite invariant measure then

$$r(\mathcal{S}_\mathfrak{p}) = r_\infty(\mathcal{S}_\mathfrak{p}) .$$

If $\mathcal{S}_\mathfrak{p}$ admits an infinite σ-finite invariant measure then

$$r(\mathcal{S}_\mathfrak{p}) = \{1\} , \qquad r_\infty(\mathcal{S}_\mathfrak{p}) = \{0,1\} .$$

Proof. It follows from lemma (2.5) that

$$r(\mathcal{S}_\mathfrak{p}) \subset r_\infty(\mathcal{S}_\mathfrak{p}) ,$$

and as a consequence of the Lebesgue density theorem we have that

$$r(\mathcal{S}_\mathfrak{p}) \supset (0,\infty) \cap r_\infty(\mathcal{S}_\mathfrak{p}) .$$

Hence theorem 1 of [2] and the results of [1] yield the proof. Q.e.d.

Necessary and sufficient conditions on $\mathfrak{p}$ for $\mathcal{S}_\mathfrak{p}$ to admit a σ-finite invariant measure have been given by D. G. B. Hill [4] and O. Takenouchi [10]. In general the computation of the ratio sets seems to be a difficult problem (comp. [1] §9) .

(2.7) Lemma. Let $A, B \subset X$, let T be an automorphism such that $r(T) = [0,\infty)$, and let $\epsilon > 0$. Then there exists an $S \in [T]$ such that

$$SA = B,$$

and

$$(1-\epsilon)\,\mu(B)\,\mu(A)^{-1} \leq \frac{d\,S^{-1}\mu}{d\mu}(x) \leq (1+\epsilon)\,\mu(B)\,\mu(A)^{-1}, \qquad \text{f.a.a. } x \in A\,.$$

Proof. Let

$$A = \bigcup_{n=1}^{\infty} A_n$$

be a partition of A,

$$\mu(A_n) = 2^{-n}\,\mu(A)\,.$$

For all sets $E, F \subset X$ and $0 < \rho < \mu(F)$ we can find a $U \in [T]$ such that

$$U E \subset F$$

and

$$\rho\,\mu(E)^{-1} \leq \frac{d\,U^{-1}\mu}{d\mu}(x) \leq \mu(F)\,\mu(E)^{-1}, \qquad \text{f.a.a. } x \in E\,.$$

Using this fact we can find inductively $S_n \in [T]$ such that

$$S_n A_n \subset B - \Big(\bigcup_{i=1}^{n-1} S_i A_i\Big), \quad n \in \mathbb{N}$$

and

$$2^n\,\mu(B)\,\mu(A)^{-1}\Big(1 - 2^{-n} - \sum_{i=1}^{n-1} \mu(S_i A_i)\,\mu(B)^{-1}\Big) \leq \frac{d\,S_n^{-1}\mu}{d\mu}(x) \leq$$

$$2^n\,\mu(B)\,\mu(A)^{-1}\Big(1-2^{-n} + \epsilon 2^{-n-1} - \sum_{i=1}^{n-1} \mu(S_i A_i)\,\mu(B)^{-1}\Big), \text{f.a.a. } x \in A_n,\ n \in \mathbb{N}\,.$$

Setting

$$S\,x = S_n\,x\,, \qquad x \in A_n\,,$$

produces an isomorphism S of A onto B that is compatible with T such that

$$\mu(A)\mu(B)^{-1}(1-\epsilon) \leq \frac{dS^{-1}\mu}{d\mu}(x) \leq \mu(A)\,\mu(B)^{-1}(1+\epsilon), \quad \text{f.a.a. } x \in A\,.$$ Q.e.d.

To formulate the proof of the next theorem we shall employ the language of T-arrays (comp. §3 of [7]). A T-array of $A \subset X$ is a system

$$\tau = (A_{\vartheta},\ U_{\vartheta',\vartheta''})_{\vartheta,\vartheta',\vartheta'' \in \Theta}$$

where Θ is a finite set,

$$A = \bigcup_{\vartheta \in \Theta} A_{\vartheta}$$

is a partition of A and the $U_{\vartheta', \vartheta''} : A_{\vartheta'} \to A_{\vartheta''}$ are isomorphisms that are compatible with the automorphism T such that for all $\vartheta, \vartheta', \vartheta'' \in \Theta$

$$U_{\vartheta,\vartheta} = 1,$$

$$U_{\vartheta',\vartheta''} \circ U_{\vartheta,\vartheta'} = U_{\vartheta,\vartheta''} .$$

If, moreover, $\nu \sim \mu$ is a finite measure such that

$$\frac{dU_{\vartheta',\vartheta}\nu}{d\nu}(x) = \nu(A_{\vartheta'})\, \nu(A_{\vartheta})^{-1} \quad \text{f.a.a. } x \in A \;, \; \vartheta, \vartheta' \in \Theta ,$$

then we say that τ is a (T, μ) - array of A. We set f.a.a. $x \in A_{\vartheta}$, $\vartheta \in \Theta$,

$$[x]_{\tau} = \{U_{\vartheta,\vartheta'}\, x : \vartheta' \in \Theta\}$$

With a T-array

$$\xi = (B_{\omega}, V_{\omega',\omega''})_{\omega,\ \omega',\omega'' \in \Omega}$$

of an $A_{\vartheta_o}, \vartheta_o \in \Theta$, we construct a T-array

$$\zeta = (C_{(\vartheta,\omega)}, W_{(\vartheta',\omega'),\ (\vartheta'',\omega'')})_{(\vartheta,\omega),\ (\vartheta',\omega'),\ (\vartheta'',\omega'') \in \Theta \times \Omega}$$

of A by setting for all $(\vartheta,\omega), (\vartheta',\omega'), (\vartheta'',\omega'') \in \Theta \times \Omega$

$$C_{(\vartheta,\omega)} = U_{\vartheta_o,\vartheta}\, B_{\omega},$$

$$W_{(\vartheta',\omega'),\ (\vartheta'',\ \omega'')}\, x = U_{\vartheta_o,\vartheta''}\, W_{\omega',\omega''}\, U_{\vartheta',\vartheta_o}\, x , \qquad \text{f.a.a. } x \in C_{(\vartheta',\omega')}.$$

We call ζ the extension of τ by ξ.

(2.8) Theorem. If for an ergodic automorphism T $r(T) = [0,\infty)$ then $T \overset{W}{\sim} \mathcal{R}_{\infty}$.

Proof. 1. We show first that $r(T) = [0,\infty)$ implies that T is of infinite product type. For this purpose we construct a sequence Ω_n of finite sets, a sequence ν_n of probability measures, $\nu_n \sim \mu$, and (T, ν_n) - arrays

$$\xi_n = (A_a, S_{a',\ a''})_{a,\ a',\ a'' \in \prod_{m=1}^{n} \Omega_m}$$

such that for all $n \in \mathbb{N}$ ξ_{n+1} extends ξ_n, and

(11) $\mu(\{x \in X : 2^{-2^{-n}} < \frac{d\nu_{n+1}}{d\nu_n}(x) < e^{2^{-n}}\}) > 1 - 2^{-n}$,

(12) $[T]\, x = \bigcup_{n=1}^{\infty} [x]_{\xi_n}$, f.a.a. $x \in X$,

(13) $\nu_{n+k}(A_a) = \nu_n(A_a)$, $a \in \prod_{m=1}^{n} \Omega_m$, $k \in \mathbb{N}$,

and such that $\mathcal{B}$ is generated by

$$\bigcup_{n=1}^{\infty} \{A_a : a \in \prod_{m=1}^{n} \Omega_m\} .$$

For the construction recall that there exists a sequence U_n of a.e. periodic automorphisms, such that

(14) $[U_{n+1}]\, x \supset [U_n]\, x\ ,\ n \in \mathbb{N},\ [T]\, x = \bigcup_{n=1}^{\infty} [U_n]\, x\ ,\qquad$ f.a.a. $x \in X$,

([7] §4). Let also $(D_n)_{n=1}^{\infty}$ be a sequence of sets that generate $\mathcal{B}$ such that every entry appears infinitely often in $(D_n)_{n=1}^{\infty}$. The construction is inductive. Let us indicate how ν_{n+1} and ξ_{n+1} can be obtained from ν_n and ξ_n. Using lemma (2.1) of [9] we first construct a T-array

$$\eta = (B_i\ ,\ V_{i',i''})_{1 \leq i,\ i',\ i'' \leq I}$$

of an $A_{a^{(o)}}$, $a^{(o)} \in \prod_{m=1}^{n} \Omega_m$, such that for the extension

$$\zeta = (C_b\ ,\ Q_{b',\ b''})_{b,\ b',\ b'' \in \{1,\ \ldots,\ I\} \times \prod_{m=1}^{n} \Omega_m}$$

of ξ_n by η

(15) $\mu(\{x \in X : [x]_\zeta \supset [U_n]\, x\}) > 1 - 2^{-n}$,

and such that for some $\Gamma \subset \{1,\ \ldots,\ I\} \times \prod_{m=1}^{n} \Omega_m$

$$\mu(D_n \,\Delta\, (\bigcup_{b \in \Gamma} C_b)) < 2^{-n} .$$

Further there exists a partition

$$B_1 = \bigcup_{\ell=1}^{L} E_{1,\ell}$$

and $\rho_{i,\ell} > 0$, $1 \leq i \leq I,\ 1 \leq \ell < L$, such that

(16) $\displaystyle\sum_{i=1}^{I} \mu\,(V_{1,i}\, E_{1,L}) < (1 - e^{-2^{-n-2}})\ \mu\,(A_{a^{(o)}})$,

(17) $\displaystyle\sum_{a \in \prod_{m=1}^{n} \Omega_m}\ \sum_{i=1}^{I}\ \mu\,(S_{a^{(o)},\ a}\, V_{1,i}\, E_{1,L}) < 2^{-n}$,

(18) $I\ \mu\,(E_{1,L}) < (e^{2^{-n-1}} - e^{2^{-n-2}})\ \mu\,(A_{a^{(o)}})$,

(19) $\displaystyle e^{-2^{-n-3}} < \frac{d\, V_{i,1}\, \nu_n}{d\nu_n}\,(x)\ \rho_{i,\ell}^{-1} < e^{2^{-n-3}}$,$\qquad$ f.a.a. $x \in E_{1,\ell}$, $1 \leq \ell < L$,

and by lemma (2.7) there exist isomorphisms

$$R_{(1,1),\ (1,\ell)} : E_{1,1} \to E_{1,\ell}$$

that are compatible with T such that

$$(20)\qquad e^{-2^{-n-3}} < \nu_n(E_{1,1})\,\nu_n(E_{1,\ell})\,\frac{d\,R_{1,\ell}^{-1}\,\nu_n}{d\nu_n}(x) < e^{2^{-n-3}},\quad \text{f.a.a. } x \in E_{1,1}\,.$$

Set

$$E_{i,\ell} = V_{i,e}\,E_{1,\ell}\,,\ 1 \le i \le I\,,\ 1 \le \ell \le L\,,\ R_{(1,1),\ (i,1)}\,x = V_{i,1}\,x\,,\ x \in E_{1,1}\,.$$

Define a measure λ on $A_{a(o)}$ by

$$\lambda(H) = \nu_n(E_{1,\ell})\,\nu_n(E_{1,1})^{-1}\,\lambda(R_{1,\ell}^{-1}H)\,,$$

$$1 \le \ell \le L,\quad R_{1,1} = 1\,,$$

$$\lambda(H) = \rho_{i,\ell}\,\lambda(V_{i,\ell}^{-1})\,,$$

$$H \subset E_{i,\ell}\,,\quad V_{1,1} = 1\,,\quad \rho_{i,\ell} = 1,\ 1 \le i \le I,$$

$$1 \le \ell \le L.$$

We know from (19) and (20) that

$$e^{-2^{-n-2}} < \frac{d\lambda}{d\nu_n}(x) < e^{2^{-n-2}},\quad \text{f.a.a. } x \in A_{a(o)} - \bigcup_{i=1}^{I} E_{i,L}\,.$$

Therefore by (16), (18) and (19)

$$e^{-2^{-n-1}} < \lambda(A_{a(o)})\,\nu_n(A_{a(o)})^{-1} < e^{2^{-n-1}}\,.$$

Hence, if we define ν_{n+1} by

$$\nu_{n+1}(H) = \nu_n(A_{a(o)})\,\lambda(A_{a(o)})^{-1}\,\lambda(H)\,,\ H \subset A_{a(o)}\,,$$

$$(21)\qquad \nu_{n+1}(H) = \nu_n(A_a)\,\nu_n(A_{a(o)})^{-1}\,\nu_{n+1}(S_{a,a(o)}H),\ H \subset A_a,\ a \in \prod_{m=1}^{n} \Omega_m\,,$$

then (11) holds by (16) . We set $\Omega_{n+1} = \{1, \ldots, I\,L\}$ and we set ξ_{n+1} equal to the extension of ξ_n by the array

$$(E_{i,\ell},\ R_{(i',\ \ell'),\ (i'',\ \ell'')})\ 1 \le i',\ i'' \le I,\ 1 \le \ell, \ell', \ell'' \le L\,.$$

(12) holds by (14) and (15), and (13) follows from (21).

Let

$$p_1(k) = \nu_1(A_k)\,,\ k \in \Omega_1,$$

and

$$p_{n+1}(k) = \nu_{n+1}(A_a)\,\nu_n(A_{(a_1,\dots,a_n)})^{-1},$$

$$a \in \prod_{m=1}^{n} \Omega_n ,\ n \in \mathbb{N} .$$

It follows from (11) that there exists a measure $\nu \sim \mu$

$$\nu(H) = \lim_{n\to\infty} \nu_n(H) ,\ H \subset X ,$$

and we see from (12), (13) and from the fact that $\mathcal{B}$ is generated by

$$\bigcup_{n=1}^{\infty} \{A_a : a \in \prod_{m=1}^{n} \Omega_m\}$$

that there exists an isomorphism of $(X, \mathcal{B}, \nu)$ onto $(X_p, \mathcal{B}_p, \mu_p)$ that carries ν into μ_p and $[T]$ into $[\mathcal{S}_p]$.

2. Let $0<\alpha<1$. We show that all $\mathcal{S}_p$ such that $r(\mathcal{S}_p) = [0,\infty)$ are weakly equivalent to $\mathcal{S}_\alpha \times \mathcal{S}_p$. Indeed, if $\alpha \in r(\mathcal{S}_p)$ then we can find a partition

$$\mathbb{N} = \bigcup_{i=1}^{\infty} \Theta_i$$

of $\mathbb{N}$ into finite sets, $\mathcal{K}_i, \mathcal{L}_i \subset \prod_{\vartheta \in \Theta_i} \Omega_\vartheta$, $\mathcal{K}_i \cap \mathcal{L}_i = \emptyset$, and 1-1 mappings φ_i of $\mathcal{K}_i$ onto $\mathcal{L}_i$ such that

$$\sum_{i=1}^{\infty} (1 - \mu_p(Z_{\mathcal{M}_i})) < \infty ,\ \mathcal{M}_i = \mathcal{K}_i \cup \mathcal{L}_i ,$$

and such for all $i \in \mathbb{N}$

(22) $|\alpha - \mu_p(Z_{\varphi a})\,\mu_p(Z_a)^{-1}| < \alpha\, 2^{-i},\ a \in \mathcal{K}_i$.

Define probability measures ν_i on $\mathcal{M}_i$ by

$$\nu_i(a) = \mu_p(Z_a)\,\mu_p(Z_{\mathcal{M}_i})^{-1} ,\ a \in \mathcal{M}_i .$$

We have

$$\mathcal{S}_p \overset{w}{\sim} \mathcal{S}(\nu_i)_{i=1}^{\infty} .$$

Further define probability measures λ_i on $\mathcal{M}_i$ by

$$\lambda_i(a)\,\lambda_i(b)^{-1} = \mu_p(Z_a)\,\mu_p(Z_b)^{-1} ,\ a, b \in \mathcal{K}_i ,$$

$$\lambda_i(a) = \alpha\,\lambda_i(\varphi^{-1} a) ,\ a \in \mathcal{L}_i .$$

We have from (22) that

$$|1 - \lambda_i(a)^{1/2}\,\nu_i(a)^{-1/2}| < 2^{-i} ,\ a \in \mathcal{M}_i,\ i \in \mathbb{N} .$$

This means that

$$\sum_{i=1}^{\infty} \sum_{a \in \mathcal{M}_i} \left| 1 - \lambda_i(a)^{\frac{1}{2}} \nu_i(a)^{-\frac{1}{2}} \right| \nu_i(a) < \infty .$$

Hence by a theorem of Katutani ([6], p. 453)

$$\prod_{i=1}^{\infty} \lambda_i \sim \prod_{i=1}^{\infty} \mu_i .$$

It follows that

$$\mathcal{G}_{(\nu_i)_{i=1}^{\infty}} \overset{w}{\sim} \mathcal{G}_{(\lambda_i)_{i=1}^{\infty}} .$$

Let λ'_i be the probability measure on $\mathcal{K}_i$ that is given by

$$\lambda'_i(a) = \lambda_i(a)\, \lambda_i(\mathcal{K}_i)^{-1} , \; a \in \mathcal{K}_i .$$

We have for the isomorphism

$$U : (\{0,1\}^{\mathbb{N}} \times \prod_{i=1}^{\infty} \mathcal{K}_i , \mu_\alpha \times \prod_{i=1}^{\infty} \lambda'_i) \to (\prod_{i=1}^{\infty} \mathcal{M}_i , \prod_{i=1}^{\infty} \lambda_i)$$

that is given by

$$(U(x,y))_i = \begin{cases} y_i , & \text{if } x_i = 0 , \\ \varphi\, y_i , & \text{if } x_i = 1 , \end{cases} \qquad (x,y) \in \{0,1\}^{\mathbb{N}} \times \prod_{i=1}^{\infty} \mathcal{K}_i ,$$

$$U(\mu_\alpha \times \prod_{i=1}^{\infty} \lambda'_i) = \prod_{i=1}^{\infty} \lambda_i .$$

and

$$[\mathcal{G}_\alpha \times \mathcal{G}_{(\lambda'_i)_{i=1}^{\infty}}] = U^{-1} \circ [\mathcal{G}_{(\lambda_i)_{i=1}^{\infty}}] \circ U .$$

Hence, since $\mathcal{G}_\alpha \times \mathcal{G}_\alpha \overset{w}{\sim} \mathcal{G}_\alpha$

$$\mathcal{G}_p \overset{w}{\sim} \mathcal{G}_\alpha \times \mathcal{G}_{(\lambda'_i)_{i=1}^{\infty}} \overset{w}{\sim} \mathcal{G}_\alpha \times \mathcal{G}_p .$$

Let now $\alpha, \beta > 1$ be such that $\log \alpha (\log \beta)^{-1}$ is irrational. We know that

$$\mathcal{G}_p \overset{w}{\sim} \mathcal{G}_\alpha \times \mathcal{G}_\beta \times \mathcal{G}_p .$$

Again applying Kakutani's theorem on the equivalence of product measures we find from this that

$$\mathcal{G}_p \overset{w}{\sim} \mathcal{G}_\alpha \times \mathcal{G}_\beta \times \mathcal{G}_q$$

where q_n is a probability measure on Ω_n such that all the ratios $q_n(\omega)\, q_n(\omega')^{-1}$ are in the group that is generated by α and β. Theorem (4.1) of [8] yields now

$$\mathcal{G}_\alpha \times \mathcal{G}_\beta \times \mathcal{G}_\sigma \overset{W}{\sim} \mathcal{G}_\alpha \times \mathcal{G}_\beta \ . \qquad\qquad\qquad \text{Q.e.d.}$$

Note that the preceding proof contains a new proof of the fact that all automorphisms T that contain a measure μ such that $\Delta\,(T,\mu)$ is a dense subgroup of $(0,\infty)$ are weakly equivalent.

(2.9) <u>Proposition</u>. For all ergodic automorphisms T

$$T \overset{W}{\sim} \{T^i : i \in \mathbb{Z}\} \times \mathcal{G}_1 \ .$$

<u>Proof</u>. The proposition holds if $T \overset{W}{\sim} \mathcal{G}_\alpha$, $0 < \alpha \leq \infty$. If $r(T) \cap (0,1) = \emptyset$ then we apply lemma (2.2) and find that there is a finite measure $\nu \sim \mu$ that is preserved by an aperiodic automorphism $S \in [T]$. There exists an isomorphism $U : (X, \mathcal{B}, \mu) \to$ $(X, \mathcal{B}, \mu) \times (X_1, \mathcal{B}_1, \mu_1)$ such that

$$U\,\{S^i\,x : i \in \mathbb{Z}\} = \{(S^i \times W)\,U\,x : i \in \mathbb{Z}\ ,\ W \in \mathcal{G}_1\} \ , \quad \text{f.a.a.}\ \ x \in X \ ,$$

(see [3] Theorem 5, p. 154). But then also

$$U\,\{T^i\,x : i \in \mathbb{Z}\} = \{(T^i \times W)\,U\,x : i \in \mathbb{Z}\ ,\ W \in \mathcal{G}_1\} \ . \qquad\qquad \text{Q.e.d.}$$

3. The ratio set and von Neumann algebras

(3.1) <u>Lemma</u>. Let T be an ergodic automorphism of $(X, \mathcal{B}, \mu)$ and let Δ be a countable dense subgroup of the positive reals. Then there exists for all $\epsilon > 0$ a measure $\nu \sim \mu$ such that

$$e^{-\epsilon} < \frac{d\nu}{d\mu}\,(x) < e^\epsilon \ ,\quad \frac{dT^i\nu}{d\nu}\,(x) \in \Delta \ ,\quad \text{f.a.a.}\ \ x \in X \ ,\ i \in \mathbb{Z} \ .$$

<u>Proof</u>. There exists a decreasing sequence of $A_k \subset X$, $A_1 = X$, and commuting $S_k \in [T]$, where S_k has period N_k , such that we have partitions

$$A_k = \underset{n\,=\,0}{\overset{N_k-1}{\bigcup}} S_k^{\,n}\,A_{k+1} \ ,\ k \in \mathbb{N}$$

and such that $[T]$ is equal to the full group of the group generated by $\{S_k : k \in \mathbb{N}\}$ (see [9] Proposition (2.2)). We choose for all $k \in \mathbb{N}$ and $1 \leq \eta < N_k$ partitions

$$A_{k+1} = \underset{\ell\,=\,1}{\overset{\infty}{\bigcup}} B_{k,n,\ell} \ ,$$

and $\rho_{k,n,\ell} \in \Delta$ such that

$$(23) \quad e^{-2^{-k}\epsilon} < \frac{dS_k^{-n}\mu}{d\mu}(x)\, \rho_{k,n,\ell}^{-1} < e^{2^{-k}\epsilon}, \qquad \text{f.a.a. } x \in B_{k,n,\ell} .$$

Then we define a sequence ν_k of measures by

$$\nu_k(C) = \mu(C), \qquad C \subset A_{k+1},$$

$$(24) \quad \nu_k(C) = \sum_{\ell=1}^{\infty} \rho_{m,n,\ell}\, \nu_k(S_m^{-n} \cap B_{m,n,\ell}), \; C \subset S_m^n A_{m+1}, 1 \leq m \leq k, 1 \leq n \leq N_m .$$

It follows from (23) and (24) that

$$e^{-2^{-k}\epsilon} < \frac{d\nu_{k+1}}{d\nu}(x) < e^{2^{-k}\epsilon}, \qquad \text{f.a.a. } x \in X, \; k \in \mathbb{N},$$

and

$$\frac{dS_k^n \nu_{k'}}{d\nu_{k'}}(x) = \frac{dS_k^n \nu_k}{d\nu_k}(x) \in \Delta, \qquad \text{f.a.a. } x \in X,$$

$$1 \leq \eta < N_k, \; k' \geq k, \; k \in \mathbb{N} .$$

Setting

$$\frac{d\nu}{d\mu}(x) = \lim_{k\to\infty} \frac{d\nu_k}{d\mu}(x), \qquad \text{f.a.a. } x \in X .$$

$$\nu(C) = \lim_{k\to\infty} \nu_k(C), \qquad C \subset X,$$

yields

$$\frac{dS_k^{-n}\nu}{d\nu}(x) \in \Delta, \qquad \text{f.a.a. } x \in A_k, \; 1 \leq \eta < N_k . \qquad \text{Q.e.d.}$$

(3.2) <u>Theorem</u>. Let $\alpha > 1$, and let T be an ergodic automorphism of (X, B, μ) such that

$$(25) \quad \mathcal{A}_T \otimes \mathcal{A}_\alpha \sim \mathcal{A}_T .$$

Then $\alpha \in r(T)$.

<u>Proof</u>. 1. Let S be an automorphism of (Y, C, λ), $\lambda(Y) = 1$, that contains λ such that $\Delta(S, \lambda)$ is dense in $(0, \infty)$. Let T be an ergodic automorphism such that $[T]$ contains an aperiodic automorphism that preserves μ. Then there exists for all $\epsilon > 0$ a measure $\nu \sim \mu$, $\nu(X) = 1$, such that

$$e^{-\epsilon} < \frac{d\nu}{d\mu}(x) < e^{\epsilon}, \qquad \text{f.a.a. } x \in X,$$

together with an isomorphism $U : (X, B, \mu) \to (Y, C, \lambda)$

such that $U\nu = \lambda$ and

$$U \circ [T] \circ U^{-1} \subset [S] .$$

To prove this assertion we construct as in the proof of proposition (2.9) an isomorphism

$$V : (X, B, \mu) \to (X, B, \mu) \times (Y, C, \lambda)$$

such that $V\mu = \mu \times \lambda$ and such that

(26) $V \circ [T] \circ V^{-1} = [\{T^i : i \in \mathbb{Z}\} \times \{R \in [S] : R\lambda = \lambda\}] .$

Then we apply lemma (3.1) to find a probability measure $\varkappa \sim \nu$ such that

$$e^{-\epsilon} < \frac{d\varkappa}{d\mu}(x) < e^{\epsilon} , \quad \frac{d\,T\varkappa}{d\varkappa}(x) \in \Delta(S, \lambda) , \quad \text{f.a.a. } x \in X .$$

We set

$$\nu = U^{-1}(\varkappa \times \lambda) .$$

Then also

(27) $e^{-\epsilon} < \frac{d\nu}{d\mu}(x) < e^{\epsilon} , \quad$ f.a.a. $x \in X .$

$\{T^i : i \in \mathbb{Z}\} \times \{S^j : j \in \mathbb{Z}\}$ contains $\varkappa \times \lambda$ and

$$\Delta(\{T^i : i \in \mathbb{Z}\} \times \{S^i : j \in \mathbb{Z}\} , \varkappa \times \lambda) = \Delta(S, \lambda) .$$

By theorem (4.1) of [7] there exists an isomorphism

$$W: (X, \mathcal{B}, \mu) \times (Y, C, \lambda) \to (Y, C, \lambda)$$

such that $W(\varkappa \times \lambda) = \lambda$ and

(28) $W \circ [\{T^i : i \in \mathbb{Z}\} \times \{S^i : j \in \mathbb{Z}\}] \circ W^{-1} = [S] .$

We set

$$U = W \circ V$$

and find from (26) (27) and (28) that ν and U have the asserted properties.

2. Let now T be an ergodic automorphism such that (25) holds. By lemma (2.2) there exists a finite measure $\varkappa$ that is preserved by an aperiodic automorphism in $[T]$, and by lemma (2.1) it is enough to prove that $\alpha \in r_{\varkappa}(T)$. Let $A \subset X$, $\mu(A) > 0$, $\epsilon > 0$. Let also $\mathfrak{p}$ be a sequence of probability measures on $\{0,1\}$ such that $\mathcal{S}_{\mathfrak{p}}$ contains $\mu_{\mathfrak{p}}$ and $\Delta(\mathcal{S}_{\mathfrak{p}}, \mu_{\mathfrak{p}})$ is dense in the positive reals. We apply the first part of the proof and obtain a probability measure $\nu \sim \mu$ on A and an isomorphism

$$U : (A, A \cap \mathcal{B}, \nu) \to (X_{\mathfrak{p}}, \mathcal{B}_{\mathfrak{p}}, \mu_{\mathfrak{p}})$$

such that

(29) $$U\nu = \mu_p \ , \ U \circ [T_A] \circ U^{-1} \subset [\mathcal{S}_p] \ .$$

From (25) and lemma (2.1) of [9] we find that

$$\mathcal{A}_{T_A} \otimes \mathcal{A}_\alpha \sim \mathcal{A}_{T_A} \ .$$

From this we infer that there exist for some $n \in \mathbb{N}$ $a, b \in \{0,1\}^n$, such that

$$e^{-\frac{\varepsilon}{3}} < \alpha \, \mu_p (Z_a) \, \mu_p (Z_b)^{-1} < e^{\frac{\varepsilon}{3}} ,$$

(comp. [1] pp. 78, 79, 84 and the proof of theorem (2.6) of [9]). With $V : Z_a \to Z_b$, $(Vx)_m = x_m$, $m > n$, and $W = U^{-1} \circ V \circ U$, $B = U^{-1} Z_a$ we have then by (29) that $B \subset A$, $W B \subset A$ and

$$e^{-\varepsilon} < \frac{d\, W^{-1} \varkappa}{d \varkappa} (x) \, \alpha^{-1} < e^{\varepsilon} , \qquad \text{f.a.a. } x \in B \ . \qquad \text{Q.e.d.}$$

4. The invariant ρ

On ρ we note the following proposition.

(4.1) Proposition. The following assertions on an ergodic automorphism T of $(x, \mathcal{B}, \mu)$ are equivalent

(a) $\alpha \in \rho(T)$,

(b) There exists an $S \in [\mathcal{S}_\alpha]$ such that $S \overset{W}{\sim} T$,

(c) There exists a $\nu \sim \mu$ such that

$$\left\{\frac{d\, T^i \nu}{d\nu} (x) : i \in \mathbb{Z}\right\} \subset \{\rho^i : i \in \mathbb{Z}\}, \qquad \text{f.a.a. } x \in X \ .$$

Proof. We can use proposition (2.9) and the fact that $\mathcal{S}_\alpha$ contains μ_α to show that (a) implies (b). (a) follows from (c) by means of lemma (2.3) of [9] and theorem (4.1) of [7]. Q.e.d.

We note that for every ergodic automorphism T there exists an $S \in [\mathcal{S}_\infty]$ such that $T \overset{W}{\sim} S$. More precisely, as a consequence of lemma (3.1), proposition (2.9) and theorem (4.1) of [7] we know that for every ergodic automorphism T of $(x, \mathcal{B}, \mu)$ and all $\varepsilon > 0$ there exists a measure ν and an isomorphism $U: (x, \mathcal{B}, \mu) \to (x', \mathcal{B}', \mu')$ such that

$$1 - \varepsilon < \frac{d\nu}{d\mu} (x) < 1 + \varepsilon, \qquad \text{f.a.a. } x \in X ,$$

$$U \circ T \circ U^{-1} \in [\mathcal{S}_\infty],$$

$$U\nu = \mu',$$

where $\mathcal{S}_\infty$ acts on $(X', \mathcal{B}', \mu')$ and contains μ'.

REFERENCES

1. Araki, H. and E. J. Woods: A classification of factors, Publ. RIMS, Kyoto University Ser. A, 4 (1968), 51-130.

2. Arnold, L. K.: On σ-finite invariant measures, Z. Wahrscheinlichkeitstheorie verw. Geb. 9 (1968), 85-97.

3. Dye, H. A.: On groups of measure preserving transformations I, Amer. J. Math. 85 (1959), 119-159.

4. Hill, D. G. B: σ-finite invariant measures on infinite product spaces, thesis, Yale University, 1969.

5. Jacobs, K: Neuere Methoden und Ergebnisse der Ergodentheorie, Berlin-Göttingen-Heidelberg: Springer 1960.

6. Kakutani, S.: On equivalence of infinite product measures, Ann. of Math. II. Ser. 49 (1948), 214-224.

7. Krieger W.: On non-singular transformations of a measure space I, Z. Wahrscheinlichkeitstheorie verw. Geb. 11, (1969), 83-97.

8. ______________: On non-singular transformations of a measure space II, Z. Wahrscheinlichkeitstheorie verw. Geb. 11 (1969), 98-119.

9. ______________: On a class of hyperfinite factors that arise from null-recurrent Markov chains, to appear in J. Functional Analysis.

10. Takenouchi, O.: On type classification of factors constructed as infinite tensor products, Publ. RIMS, Kyoto University Ser. A, 4 (1968), 467-482.

Imbedding Bernoulli Shifts in Flows

by

D. S. Ornstein[1]

Stanford University

1. Introduction. The purpose of this paper is to show that Bernoulli shifts can be imbedded in a flow. The flow is the following: the flow, S_t, will be a flow built under a function (see [11, 12]). Let T acting on X be the 2 shift. The function on X will take on 2 values, 1 on A, the set of sequences in X whose 0th coordinate is 0, and $2^{1/2}$ on $X - A$, the set of sequences in X whose 0th coordinate is 1. Let P be the partition into the set of points above A and the set of points above $X - A$. For small t, $\bigvee_{-\infty}^{\infty} (S_t)^i P$ will be the full σ-algebra, and P relative to S_t will satisfy a property very close to "weak Bernoulli" which we will call "very weak Bernoulli." We will make some minor changes in the argument given in [5]*, to show that "very weak Bernoulli" transformations are Bernoulli. Since the above mentioned argument involves a careful analysis of the proof that two Bernoulli shifts with the same entropy are isomorphic, this paper will also serve as an exposition of the main ideas involved there. We also tried to write this paper in a way that will minimize the repetition of arguments in obtaining various applications of this method.

*A joint paper with N. Friedman.

1 Research supported in part by NSF Grant GP-8781

We define a notion of a partition being "finitely determined relative to T " (or F.D.) and show that if T_1 and T_2 have finitely determined generating partitions, and $E(T_1) = E(T_2)$, then T_1 is isomorphic to T_2 .

Two Bernoulli shifts with the same entropy are isomorphic [3] because if T^iP are independent, then P is F.D. Two "weak Bernoulli" [5] or "very weak Bernoulli" shifts with the same entropy are isomorphic because if T^iP is weak Bernoulli or very weak Bernoulli then P is F.D. A factor of a Bernoulli shift with finite entropy is a Bernoulli shift [7] because if T is a Bernoulli shift (of finite entropy) and P any finite partition, then T^iP is F.D. The above notion of F.D. gives a characterization of Bernoulli shifts which is enough to show that roots of Bernoulli shifts are Bernoulli shifts. (T is a Bernoulli shift if and only if every finite partition is F.D. relative to T).

This format does not include the result that Bernoulli shifts with infinite entropy (and possibly continuous state space) are isomorphic [6], or that increasing unions of Bernoulli shifts are Bernoulli shifts [6]; from which it follows that factors of Bernoulli shifts with infinite entropy are Bernoulli shifts [7]. These results require a different modification of the argument in [1].

2. Preliminaries. Let $(X, \mathcal{A}, m)$ denote the measure space consisting of the unit interval with Lebesgue measure. All sets will be in $\mathcal{A}$ either by assumption or construction. We abbreviate $(X, \mathcal{A}, m)$ by X. T will be an invertible measure preserving transformation on X.

Let p_i, $1 \leq i \leq k$, be disjoint sets whose union is X. We consider the partition $P = (p_1, p_2, \ldots, p_k)$ to be the vector consisting of the k sets with a fixed ordering. Thus a partition will always be ordered. We still write $p \in P$ considering P as a set.

Let P have k sets and let Q have ℓ sets. The joint partition of P and Q is

$$P \vee Q = (p_i \cap q_j : 1 \leq i \leq k, \quad 1 \leq j \leq \ell),$$

where the ordering in $P \vee Q$ is lexicographically. Thus $P \vee Q \neq Q \vee P$ in general. Given partitions $P_1, \ldots, P_n$, the associativity of $\vee$ implies we can denote

$$\bigvee_{i=1}^{n} P_i = P_1 \vee P_2 \vee P_3 \vee \ldots \vee P_n.$$

Given a partition P and a transformation T, we denote

$$\bigvee_{i=0}^{n} T^i P = P \vee T P \vee \ldots \vee T^n P.$$

We let $\bigvee_{-\infty}^{\infty} T^i P$ denote the smallest σ-algebra (together with all sets of measure 0) containing all the sets in $T^i P$, $i = 0, \pm 1, \ldots$. The measure space $(X, \bigvee_{-\infty}^{\infty} T^i P, m)$ is denoted by X_P.

Given a set A with positive measure, denote

$$m_A(B) = m(A \cap B)/m(A),$$

Given a partition P, the induced partition on A is

$$P/A = (p_i \cap A : 1 \leq i \leq k).$$

The <u>distribution</u> of P/A is the vector

$$d(P/A) = (m_A(p_i) : 1 \leq i \leq k).$$

In particular, $d(P) = d(P/X)$.

Let P and Q be partitions, each with k sets, and let A and B be sets of positive measure. We denote

$$d(P/A,\ Q/B) = \sum_{i=1}^{k} |m_A(p_i) - m_B(q_i)|.$$

In particular, $d(P,Q) = d(P/X,\ Q/X)$. We also denote

$$D(P,Q) = \sum_{i=1}^{k} m(p_i \,\Delta\, q_i). \qquad (p \,\Delta\, q \text{ denotes symmetric difference.})$$

If $\{P_i\}_1^n = \{P_i\}_{i \leq i \leq n}$ and $\{\overline{P}_i\}_1^n$ are sequences of partitions, we will denote $\overline{d}(\{P_i\}_1^n, \{\overline{P}_i\}_1^n) = \inf \frac{1}{n} \sum_{i=1}^{n} D(Q_i, \overline{Q}_i)$ where inf is taken over all $\{Q_i\}_1^n$, $\{\overline{Q}_i\}_1^n$ where $d(\bigvee_{i=1}^{n} Q_i) = d(\bigvee_{i=1}^{n} P_i)$ and $d(\bigvee_{n=1}^{n} \overline{Q}_i) = d(\bigvee_{i=1}^{n} \overline{P}_i)$. Note that $\overline{d}(\{P_i\}_1^n, \{R_i\}_1^n) \leq \overline{d}(\{P_i\}_1^n, \{Q_i\}_1^n) + \overline{d}(\{Q_i\}_1^n, \{R_i\}_1^n)$.

If P_1 is a subclass of sets in P, then we write $P_1 \subset P$. This is the usual meaning in the sense that the sets in P_1 are sets in P.

Given partitions P and Q, we say P contains Q within ε and write $Q \overset{\varepsilon}{\subset} P$ to mean that there is a partition P' of X such that the sets in P' are unions of sets in P and $D(P',Q) < \varepsilon$. We write $Q \subset P$ if $D(P',Q) = 0$. The distinction between $P_1 \subset P$, where P_1 is a subclass of P, and $Q \subset P$, where Q is a partition of X, will be clear from the context

If C is a class of sets, then we let $\cup C$ denote the union of the sets in C.

We say P is <u>ε-independent</u> of Q if there exists a subclass $Q_1 \subset Q$, $m(\cup Q_1) > 1 - \varepsilon$, and

$$d(P/q,P) < \varepsilon \, , \; q \in Q_1 \, .$$

We say that the sequence of partitions $\{P_i\}_1^n$ is ε-independent of the partition Q if there exists a subclass $Q_1 \subset Q$, $m(\cup Q_1) > 1 - \varepsilon$, and

$$\bar{d}(\{P_1/q\}_1^n \, , \, \{P_i\}_1^n) < \varepsilon \, , \; q \in Q_1 \, .$$

<u>Definition 1</u>: A partition P is <u>very</u> <u>weak</u> <u>Bernoulli</u> (V.W.B.) for T if for each ϵ there exists $N = N(\varepsilon)$ such that for all $n > 0$ and $m > 0$ $\{T^i P\}_0^{n+N}$ is ε- independent of $\bigvee_{-m}^{-1} T^i P$. T is a V.W.B. transformation if T has a V.W.B. generator.

<u>Definition 2</u>: We say that a partition P is finitely determined (F.D.) relative to T if given ε there is a $\eta = \eta(\varepsilon)$ and $n_1 = n_1(\varepsilon)$ such that if $\overline{T}$ is any mixing transformation and $\overline{P}$ a partition such that

(1) $\overline{d}(\{T^i P\}_0^{n_1}, \{\overline{T}^i \overline{P}\}_0^{n_1}) < \eta$ and

(2) $|E(\overline{P},\overline{T}) - E(P,T)| < \eta$, then for all n, $\overline{d}(\{T^i P\}_1^n, \{\overline{T}^i \overline{P}\}_1^n) < \varepsilon$.

We will use an equivalent form of the above definition in which we replace (1) by $d(\bigvee_0^{n_1} T^i P, \bigvee_0^{n_1} \overline{T}^i \overline{P}) < \eta$. *

Given P and T, the <u>P-n-name</u> of $x \in X$ is the sequence of integers $f(i)$, $0 \leq i < n$, such that

$$T^i(x) \in p_{f(i)}, \quad 0 \leq i < n.$$

If F is a set, all of whose points have the same P-n-name, then we speak of the P-n-name of F.

Given transformations T_1 and T_2 and partitions P_1 and P_2, we write $(P_1, T_1) \sim (P_2, T_2)$ if

$$d(\bigvee_0^n T_1^i P_1) = d(\bigvee_0^n T_2^i P_2), \quad n = 0,1,2,\ldots .$$

The <u>entropy</u> of P/A is defined as

$$E(P/A) = -\sum_{i=1}^{k} m_A(p_i) \log_2 m_A(p_i).$$

* $\overline{d}(\{T^i P\}_0^{n_1}, \{\overline{T}^i \overline{P}\}_0^{n_1})$ is not the same as $d(\bigvee_0^{n_1} T^i P, \bigvee_0^{n_1} \overline{T}^i \overline{P})$, but by changing η we define the same class of P.

In particular, $E(P) = E(P/X)$. Given partitions P and Q, the <u>conditional entropy</u> of P <u>given</u> Q is

$$E(P/Q) = \sum_{i=1}^{\ell} m(q_i)\, E(P/q_i).$$

A direct verification yields

$$E(P/Q) = E(P \vee Q) - E(Q).$$

The entropy of P relative to T is

$$E(P,T) = \lim_n E(P/\bigvee_1^n T^i P).$$

We now mention some notation used only in Lemma 14. Let T^iF, $0 \leq i \leq n$, be disjoint sets. Let R_i be a partition of T^iF for each i. We refer to the set of pairs

$$G = \{(T^iF,\ R_i) \ : 0 \leq i \leq n\}$$

as a <u>gadget</u>. Note that $T^{-i}R_i$ is a partition of F. Given a gadget

$$G' = \{(T'^iF',\ R'_i) \ : 0 \leq i \leq n\},$$

we say G <u>and</u> G' <u>are isomorphic</u> and write $G \sim G'$ if

$$d(\bigvee_0^n T^{-i}R_i) = d(\bigvee_0^n T'^{-i}R'_i).$$

Let $W = \bigvee_{-n}^{n} T^iP$ where $P = (p_1, \ldots, p_k)$. Thus $w \in W$ implies

$$w = \bigcap_{-n}^{n} T^i p_{j_i}, \quad 1 \leq j_i \leq k, \quad -n \leq i \leq n.$$

We also denote

$$w = (j_{-n}, \ldots, j_o, j_1, \ldots, j_n).$$

Let S_n denote the set of sequences consisting of entries 1, 2, ... , k of length 2n + 1. Thus we can consider $w \in W$ as an element in S_n. A partition L of S_n generates a partition L_P of X as follows. Let

$$L = (\ell_1, \ell_2, \ldots, \ell_r)$$

and define

$$L_P = (\bigcup_{w \in \ell_i} w \quad : 1 \leq i \leq r).$$

Then $W \overset{\epsilon}{\supset} Q$ means there is a partition L of S_n such that $D(L_P, Q) < \epsilon$.

3. In this section we shall prove the following result.

Theorem. Two very weak Bernoulli transformations with the same entropy are isomorphic.

This will be a consequence of Proposition 9 and the following:

Theorem. Two transformations with finitely determined generators and the same entropy are isomorphic.

The proof proceeds by a sequence of lemmas.

Lemma 1. Let P and Q be partitions with k sets and let $\varepsilon > 0$. If

(1.1) $\bar{d}(P,Q) < \varepsilon$,

then there exist partitions P* and Q* of X such that

(1.2) $d(P^*) = d(P)$ and $d(Q^*) = d(Q)$,

(1.3) $D(P^*,Q^*) < \varepsilon$.

Proof. Let A_i be disjoint sets with

$$m(A_i) = \min\{m(p_i), m(q_i)\}, \quad 1 \leq i \leq k.$$

In $X - \bigcup_{i=1}^{k} A_i$ choose disjoint B_i and disjoint C_i such that

$$m(B_i) = m(p_i) - m(A_i), \quad m(C_i) = m(q_i) - m(A_i), \quad 1 \leq i \leq k.$$

Let $P^* = (A_i \cup B_i : 1 \leq i \leq k)$ and $Q^* = (A_i \cup C_i : 1 \leq i \leq k)$. It is easily checked that (1.2-3) are satisfied.

<u>Lemma 2.</u> $\bar{d}(\{P_i\}_1^n , \{Q_i\}_1^n) \le d(\bigvee_1^n P_i , \bigvee_1^n Q_i)$.

<u>Proof.</u> Applying Lemma 1, we get P_i^* and Q_i^* such that

$$d(\bigvee_1^n P_i) = d(\bigvee_1^n P_i^*) , \; d(\bigvee_1^n Q_i) = d(\bigvee_1^n Q_i^*) \text{ and } D(\bigvee_1^n P_i^* , \bigvee_1^n Q_i^*) < \varepsilon .$$

Since

$$D(P_i^* , Q_i^*) \le D(\bigvee_1^n P_i^* , \bigvee_1^n Q_i^*)$$

we have

$$\sum_1^n D(P_i^* , Q_i^*) < \varepsilon n .$$

<u>Lemma 3.</u> Let $\varepsilon > 0$ and let Q_i , Q_i' , $0 \le i \le n$, be partitions such that

(3.1) $\{Q_i\}_1^n$ is ε-independent of Q_o .

(3.2) $\{Q_i'\}_1^n$ is ε-independent of Q_o' .

(3.3) $\bar{d}(\{Q_i\}_1^n , \{Q_i'\}_1^n) < \varepsilon$.

Then there exist partitions P_i , P_i' , $1 \le i \le n$, such that, letting $P_o = Q_o$ and $P_o' = Q_o'$,

(3.4) $d(\bigvee_{i=0}^n Q_i) = d(\bigvee_{i=0}^n P_i)$ and $d(\bigvee_{i=0}^n Q_i') = d(\bigvee_{i=0}^n P_i')$.

(3.5) $\sum_{i=1}^n D(P_i , P_i') < 8n\varepsilon$.

Proof: Let q be an atom of Q_o and q' be an atom of Q'_o. Define P_i and P'_i, $1 \leq i \leq n$ on $q \cap q'$ so that

(1) $d(\bigvee_1^n P_i/q \cap q') = d(\bigvee_1^n Q_i/q)$,

(2) $d(\bigvee_1^n P'_i/q \cap q') = d(\bigvee_1^n Q'_i/q')$ and

(3) $1/n\ D(P_i/q \cap q' , P'_i/q \cap q') < 2\bar{d}(\{Q_i\}_1^n/q , \{Q'_i\}/q')$.

Now 3.1 implies that there is a collection $\tilde{Q}_o \subset Q_o$, $m(\cup \tilde{Q}_o) > 1 - \varepsilon$; and if $q \in \tilde{Q}_o$, then

(4) $\bar{d}(\{Q_i\}_1^n/q , \{Q_i\}_1^n) < \varepsilon$.

3.2 implies the above with Q replaced by Q'. If $q \in \tilde{Q}_o$ and $q' \in \tilde{Q}'_o$, then (3.3), (3), and (4) imply

(5) $1/n\ D(P_i/q \cap q' , P'_i/q \cap q) < 6\ \varepsilon$.

(5), $m(\cup \tilde{Q}_o) > 1 - \varepsilon$ and $m(\cup \tilde{Q}'_o) > 1 - \varepsilon$ imply (3.5). (1) and (2) imply (3.4).

Lemma 4. Let $\{P_i\} = \{P_i\}_{1 \leq i \leq n}$, and let R and Q be partitions such that

(4.1) $\{P_i\}$ is ε-independent of Q .

(4.2) There exists $Q_1 \subset Q$ such that $m(\cup Q_1) > 1 - \varepsilon$ and

$\bigvee_1^n P_i/q$ is ε-independent of R/q , $q \in Q_1$.

Then

(4.3) $\{P_i\}$ is 3ε-independent of $Q \vee R$.

Proof. By (4.1) there exists $Q_2 \subset Q$ such that $m(\cup Q_2) > 1 - \varepsilon$ and

(1) $\bar{d}(\{P_i\}/q , \{P_i\}) < \varepsilon , q \in Q_2$.

Let $Q_3 = Q_1 \cap Q_2$; hence $m(\cup Q_3) > 1 - 2\varepsilon$. Define V as

$$V = \{q \cap r : q \in Q_3 , r \in R \text{ and } d(\bigvee_1^n P_i/q \cap r , \bigvee_1^n P_i/q) < \varepsilon\} .$$

If $q \cap r \in V$, then by Lemma 2,

(2) $\bar{d}(\{P_i\}/q \cap r , \{P_i\}/q) < \varepsilon$.

(4.2) implies

(3) $m(\cup V) = \sum_V m(q \cap r) \geq \sum_{Q_3} m(q)(1-\varepsilon) > (1-2\varepsilon)(1-\varepsilon) > 1 - 3\varepsilon$.

If $q \cap r \in V$, then (1) and (2) imply $\bar{d}(\{P_i/q \cap r , \{P_i\}) < 2\varepsilon$. This and (3) imply 4.3.

Lemma 5. Let a be a positive integer, $b > 0$, and $c > 0$. There exists $h = h(a,b,c) > 0$ such that if

(5.1) P is a partition with at most a sets,

(5.2) $m(S) \geq b$,

(5.3) $d(P/S, P) \geq c$,

then

(5.4) $E(P/\{S, S^c\}) \leq E(P) - h$.

Proof. Suppose $h > 0$ does not exist. Hence there exists $h_n \downarrow 0$ and corresponding systems (P_n, S_n, h_n) such that (5.1-3) hold but (5.4) does not. We may regard the system as a vector with 2a + 2 variables $d(P_n/S_n)$, $d(P_n/S_n{}^c)$, $m(S_n)$, and h_n. Since all variables are in [0,1], a diagonalization argument yields a system (P, S, O) satisfying (5.1-3) and $E(P/\{S, S^c\}) = E(P)$. This is a contradiction.

<u>Lemma 6</u>. Given a and $\varepsilon > 0$, let $h = h(\varepsilon, \varepsilon^2/2a, \varepsilon^2/2a)$ as in Lemma 5. If P has at most a sets and Q is a finite partition such that $E(P/Q) > E(P)-h$, then P is ε-independent of Q.

<u>Proof</u>. Suppose there exists $Q_1 \subset Q$ and $q \in Q_1$ implies

(1) $d((P/q), P) > \varepsilon$.

If $m(\cup Q_1) > \varepsilon$, then (1) implies

$$(2) \quad \sum_{q\in Q_1} m(q)\, d((P/q), P) > \varepsilon^2$$

$$= \sum_{q\in Q_1} m(q) \sum_{p\in P} \left|\frac{m(pq)}{m(q)} - m(p)\right|$$

$$= \sum_{p\in P} \sum_{q\in Q_1} |m(pq) - m(p)\, m(q)| \cdot$$

Thus for some $p \in P$ we have

$$(3) \quad \sum_{q\in Q_1} |m(pq) - m(p)\, m(q)| > \varepsilon^2/a.$$

Hence there exists $Q_2 \subset Q_1$ such that

$$(4) \quad \sum_{q\in Q_2} m(pq) - m(p)\, m(q) > \varepsilon^2/2a \qquad (\text{or} < -\varepsilon^2/2a) .$$

Let $S = \cup Q_2$; hence (4) implies

(5) $m(pS) - m(p)\, m(S) > \varepsilon^2/2a$.

Now (5) implies

(6) $m(S) > \varepsilon^2/2a$,

(7) $\dfrac{m(pS)}{m(S)} - m(p) > \varepsilon^2/2a$.

Thus (7) implies

(8) $d((P/S), P) > \varepsilon^2/2a$.

By Lemma 5 we conclude

$$E(P/Q) \leq E(P/\{S,S^c\}) \leq E(P) - h,$$

which is a contradiction.

Lemma 7. Let P be a partition with k sets and let L be a positive integer. Let $P_1 = \bigvee_{i=1}^{L} T^i P$, $Q = \bigvee_{-n}^{0} T^i P$, and $R = \bigvee_{-n-m}^{-n-1} T^i P$. Let $\varepsilon > 0$ and let h correspond to $a = k^L$ and ε in Lemma 6. If

(7.1) $E(P_1/Q) < L\, E(P,T) + \varepsilon h$,

then there exists $Q_1 \subset Q$ such that

(7.2) $m(\cup Q_1) > 1 - \varepsilon$,

(7.3) P_1/q is ε-independent of R/q, $q \in Q_1$.

Proof. The definition of E(P,T) implies

(1) $L\, E(P,T) \leq E(P_1/Q \vee R) \leq E(P_1/Q)$.

Lemma 6 implies that either

(2) P_1/q is ε-independent of R/q, or

(3) $E(\,(P_1/q)\,/\,(R/q)\,) < E(P_1/q) - h$.

Suppose (3) holds for $q \in Q_2$, where $m(\cup Q_2) \geq \varepsilon$. Then

$$E(P_1/Q) - E(P_1/Q \vee R)$$

$$= \sum_{q \in Q} m(q) \left[E(P_1/q) - \sum_{r \in R} \frac{m(qr)}{m(q)} E(P_1/qr)\right]$$

$$= \sum_{q \in Q} m(q) \left[E(P_1/q) - E((P_1/q)/(R/q))\right]$$

$$> \sum_{q \in Q_2} m(q)\, h \geq \varepsilon h.$$

This contradicts (7.1) and (1).

Lemma 8. Let P be very weak Bernoulli for T and let $\varepsilon > 0$. Let $N = N(\varepsilon/3)$ as in Definition 1. Then there exists a positive integer n_* and $\eta > 0$ such that if T' and P' satisfy

(8.1) $$d\left(\bigvee_{-n_*}^{N} T^i P \,,\, \bigvee_{-n_*}^{N} T'^i P'\right) < \eta,$$

(8.2) $$|E(P,T) - E(P', T')| < \eta,$$

then for each m

(8.3) $\{T'^i P'\}_0^N$ is ε-independent of $\bigvee_{-m}^{-1} T'^i P'$.

Proof. Let $P_1 = \bigvee_0^N T^i P$, $Q = \bigvee_{-n}^{0} T^i P$, and $R = \bigvee_{-n-m}^{-n-1} T^i P$. The choice of N implies

(1) $\{T^i P\}_0^N$ is $\frac{\varepsilon}{3}$-independent of Q , for any choice of n .

Let h correspond to $a = k^N$ and $\varepsilon/3$ in Lemma 6. Fix $n_* = n$ so large that

(2) $E(P_1/Q) < (\ N\ )\ E(P,T) + \varepsilon h/3$.

As above, consider P_1', Q', and R' corresponding to T' and P'. First choose η so small that (1) and (8.1) imply

(3) $\{T'^i P'\}_0^N$ is $\varepsilon/3$-independent of Q' .

By (2) and (8.1) we can guarantee

(4) $E(P_1'/Q') < (\ N\ )\ E(P, T) + \varepsilon h/3$.

Now (4) and (8.2) for η sufficiently small yields

(5) $E(P_1'/Q') < (\ N\ )\ E(P', T') + \varepsilon h/3$.

Lemma 7 and (5) imply there exists $Q_1' \subset Q'$ so that

(6) $m(\cup Q_1') > 1 - \varepsilon/3$.

(7) P_1'/q is $\varepsilon/3$-independent of R'/q, $q \in Q_1'$.

(3) and (7) imply (8.3) by Lemma 4.

Proposition 9. Let P be very weak Bernoulli for T . Then P is finitely determined for T .

Proof. We must show the following: Let $\varepsilon > 0$. There exist n_1 and $\eta > 0$ so that if T' is a transformation with partition P' satisfying

(9.1) $d(\bigvee_{o}^{n_1} T^i P, \bigvee_{o}^{n_1} T'^i P') < \eta$,

(9.2) $|E(P,T) - E(P',T')| < \eta$,

then there exist partitions P_i and P_i' of X and a positive integer n_2

such that

$$(9.3)\quad d\Big(\bigvee_{o}^{n} P_i\Big) = d\Big(\bigvee_{o}^{n} T^i P\Big), \quad n = 0, 1, 2, \ldots .$$

$$(9.4)\quad d\Big(\bigvee_{o}^{n} P_i'\Big) = d\Big(\bigvee_{o}^{n} T'^i P'\Big), \quad n = 0, 1, 2, \ldots .$$

$$(9.5)\quad \sum_{i=o}^{n} D(P_i, P_i') < \varepsilon n, \qquad n \geq n_2.$$

Apply Lemma 8 with $\varepsilon/8 = \varepsilon$. Choose $n_1 = n_* + N$ of Lemma 8. Keep the same η as in Lemma 8 (we can assume $\eta < \varepsilon/8$).

Assume we have P_i and P_i', $0 \leq i \leq n$ so that (9.3-5) hold. We shall obtain (9.3-5) for $n + N$. By measure preservance, Lemma 8 implies that $\{T^i P'\}_n^{n+N}$ is $\varepsilon/8$-independent of $\bigvee_0^n T^i P'$ and our choice of N and Definition 1 imply $\{T'^i P\}_n^{n+N}$ is $\varepsilon/8$-independent of $\bigvee_0^n T'^i P$. We also have (by 9.1 and Lemma 2)

$$\bar{d}(\{T^i P\}_n^{n+N}, \{T'^i P'\}_n^{n+N}) < \varepsilon/8 .$$

Consider P_o and P_o' replaced by $\bigvee_0^n P_i$ and $\bigvee_0^n P_i'$ in Lemma 3. Then Lemma 3 implies there exist partitions P_i and P_i', $n < i \leq n + N$ such that

$$(7)\quad d\left(\bigvee_{0}^{n} P_i \vee \bigvee_{n+1}^{n+N} P_i\right) = d\left(\bigvee_{0}^{n} T^i P \vee \bigvee_{n+1}^{n+N} T^i P\right) .$$

$$(8)\quad d\left(\bigvee_{0}^{n} P'_i \vee \bigvee_{n+1}^{n+N} P'_i\right) = d\left(\bigvee_{0}^{n} T'^{\,i} P \vee \bigvee_{n+1}^{n+N} T'^{\,i} P'\right) .$$

$$(9)\quad \sum_{n+1}^{n+N} D(P_i, P'_i) < N\varepsilon . \qquad \text{Q.E.D.}$$

<u>Remark</u>. The above proposition implies that if $T^i P$ are independent, then P is finitely determined relative to T with $n_1 = 0$. A direct proof of this is, however, much simpler.

<u>Notation</u>. We now consider a transformation T_1 and a partition $R = (r_1 , r_2 , \ldots , r_k)$. Let $Q = \bigvee_{0}^{u} T_1^i R$. If $q \in Q$, then

$$q = \bigcap_{0}^{u} T_1^i r_{s_i} , \; 1 \le s_i \le k , \; 0 \le i \le u .$$

We denote $q = (s_u, s_{u-1}, \ldots, s_1, s_o)$. Let $\ell = (\ell_o, \ell_1, \ldots, \ell_{n-1})$ be a sequence of length $n > u$, where $1 \leqq \ell_i \leqq k$, $0 \leqq i < n$. Let $N(\ell,q)$ be the number of times that q appears as a consecutive subsequence in ℓ; hence $N(\ell,q) \leqq n - u$.

Let $\varepsilon > 0$. We define ℓ to be an <u>ε-sequence for Q</u> if

$$\left|\frac{N(\ell,q)}{n} - m(q)\right| < \varepsilon,$$

for each $q \in Q$.

<u>Lemma 10</u>. Let R, T_1, and Q be as above and $\varepsilon > 0$. Let T be a transformation such that T^iB_j, $0 \leqq i < n$, $1 \leqq j \leqq J$, are disjoint sets, where $u/n < \varepsilon/3$. Let $X_1 = \bigcup_{i=o}^{n-1} \bigcup_{j=1}^{J} T^iB_j$ satisfy $m(X_1) > 1 - \varepsilon/3$. Let

$$\ell_j = (\ell_{j,i} : 0 \leqq i < n), \ 1 \leqq j \leqq J,$$

be $\varepsilon/3k^{u+1}$-sequences for Q. Let $P = (p_1, \ldots, p_k)$ be the partition defined on X_1 by $T^iB_j \subset p_{\ell_{j,i}}$, $0 \leqq i < n$, $1 \leqq j \leqq J$. Let P be defined arbitrarily on $X - X_1$. Then

$$(10.1) \quad d\left(\bigvee_o^u T^iP, Q\right) < \varepsilon.$$

If the sequences ℓ_j, $1 \leqq j \leqq J$, are distinct, then

$$(10.2) \quad \bigvee_{-n}^{n} T^i\,(P \vee \{B, B^c\}) \supset \{T^iB_j : 0 \leqq i < n, 1 \leqq j \leqq J\},$$

where $B = \bigcup_{j=1}^{J} B_j$.

Proof. Fix $q \in Q$ where

$$q = \bigcap_{i=0}^{u} T_1^{\ i}\, r_{s_i} .$$

The corresponding term $q' \in Q' = \bigvee_0^u T^i P$ is

$$q' = \bigcap_{i=0}^{u} T^i p_{s_i} .$$

We have

$$m(q') = \sum_{j=1}^{J} N(\ell_j, q)\, m(B_j) + \Delta(q'),$$

where

$$\sum_{q \in Q} \Delta(q') \leq u/n + m(X - X_1) < 2\varepsilon/3.$$

Thus we obtain

$$d(Q,Q') = \sum_{q\in Q} \left| m(q) - \sum_{j=1}^{J} N(\ell_j; q)\, m(B_j) - \Delta(q') \right|$$

$$\leq \sum_{q\in Q} \sum_{j=1}^{J} \left| m(q) - \frac{N(\ell_j, q)}{n} \right| n\, m(B_j) + 2\varepsilon/3$$

$$< \sum_{q\in Q} \varepsilon/3k^{u+1} + 2\varepsilon/3 < \varepsilon.$$

Thus (10.1) is verified. (10.2) follows by noting that each C_j is assigned a distinct sequence ℓ_j of length n, $1 \leq j \leq J$.

In the following lemma we consider T_1, R, and Q as before. For $q = \bigcap_0^u T_1^i r_{s_i}$ we write $q = (s_u, \ldots, s_1, s_o)$. Let $L_n = \bigvee_0^{n-1} T_1^{-i} R$

and write $\ell = \bigcap_{0}^{n-1} T_1^{-i} r_{\ell_i} \in L_n$ as $\ell = (\ell_0, \ell_1, \ldots, \ell_{n-1})$.

Lemma 11. Let T_1 be ergodic and measure preserving, $a > 0$, and $b > 0$. There exists n sufficiently large and $L' \subset L_n$ such that $m(\cup L') > 1 - a$ and $\ell \in L'$ implies ℓ is a b-sequence for Q.

Proof. If $x \in \ell$ and $T_1^d(x) \in q$, then

$$q = (\ell_{d-u}, \ldots, \ell_{d-1}, \ell_d).$$

The result follows by applying the ergodic theorem to the characteristic function of each $q \in Q$.

Lemma 12.* Let R have k sets and be finitely determined for T_1 with $E(T_1) = E(R, T_1)$, and fix $\varepsilon > 0$. Let η_1 and η be as in the definition of "finitely determined" for $\varepsilon^2/3$ instead of ε. Let T be a Bernoulli shift** with $E(T) = E(T_1)$. Let P' be a partition with k sets such that

(12.1) $d(\bigvee_{0}^{n_1} T_1^i R, \bigvee_{0}^{n_1} T^i P') < \eta$,

(12.2) $0 < E(T_1) - E(P', T) < \eta$.

Then given $\delta > 0$ and a positive integer u, there exists a partition P with k sets such that

(12.3) $d(\bigvee_{0}^{u} T_1^{i} R, \bigvee_{0}^{u} T^i P) < \delta$.

(12.4) $0 < E(T_1) - E(P, T) < \delta$.

(12.5) $D(P', P) < 6\varepsilon$.

---

* The proof of this lemma contains some ideas of Smorodinsky [8].

** In the special case where $T_1^i R$ are independent we can drop the assumption that T is a Bernoulli shift and can take $n_1 = 0$. Lemma 12 is then the same as Lemma 4 of [3].

<u>Proof</u>. Choose a refinement W of P' such that

(1) $E(T_1) - E(W,T) = \beta > 0$, $\beta < \delta/5$.

Choose $\gamma < \min(\delta, \varepsilon)$ such that $D(W', W) < \gamma$ implies

(2) $E(W', T) > E(W, T) - \delta/5$.

We shall now choose n so large to satisfy several conditions. Applying Lemma 11 to T_1, R, and $Q = \bigvee_0^u T_1^{i} R$ we have, for all n sufficiently large, $L' \subset L_n = \bigvee_0^{n-1} T_1^{-i} R$, such that

(3) $m(\cup L') > 1 - \gamma/10$ and $\ell \in L'$ implies ℓ is a $\delta/2k^{u+1}$-sequence for Q.

The Shannon-McMillan-Breiman theorem will now be applied to T_1 and R and T and W. Choose n so large there exists $L'' \subset L_n$ such that

(4) $m(\cup L'') > 1 - \gamma/10$ and $\ell \in L''$ implies $m(\ell)$ is between $2^{-[E(T_1) \pm \beta/10]n}$.

Choose n so large there exists $W_n \subset \bigvee_0^{n-1} T^{-i} W$ such that

(5) $m(\cup W_n) > 1 - \gamma/10$ and $w \in W_n$ implies $m(w)$ is between $2^{-[E(W,T) \pm \beta/10]n}$.

(6) Choose $n \geq n_2$ such that $u/n < \delta/5$, $n\beta > 10$, and $m(A) \leq 1/n$ implies

$$-[m(A) \log m(A) + (1-m(A)) \log (1-m(A))] < \delta/5.$$

Rohlin's theorem says that we can choose a set F" such that

$T^i F''$, $0 \le i < n$, are disjoint and

$$m(\bigcup_0^{n-1} T^i F'') > 1 - \gamma/20.$$

Let $\xi > 0$. By mixing (hence measure preservance) we can choose K so large that $F' = T^K F''$ satisfies $d(\bigvee_0^{n-1} T^{-i} W, \bigvee_0^{n-1} T^{-i} W / F') \cdot < \xi$.

For ξ sufficiently small we can find a subset F of F' such that

(7) $m(\bigcup_0^{n-1} T^i F) > 1 - \gamma/10.$

(8) $d(\bigvee_0^{n-1} T^{-i} W/F, \bigvee_0^{n-1} T^{-i} W) \cdot = 0.$

Because of (5) we also have

(9) $m(F \cap \cup W_n) > m(F)(1 - \gamma/10).$

(10) $m(w \cap F)$ is between $m(F)\, 2^{-[E(W,T) \pm \beta/10]n}$ for $w \in W_n$.

Now (12.1-2), definition of "finitely determined," X being non-atomic, and (8) imply we can partition $T^i F$ by R_i so that

(11) $d(\bigvee_0^{n-1} T^{-i} R_i/F) = d(L_n) = d(\bigvee_0^{n-1} T^{-i} R)$.

(12) $\sum_0^{n-1} D(R_i, P' / T^i F) < n\, \varepsilon^2/3.$

Let R^* denote the partition of $\bigcup_0^{n-1} T^i F$ such that $R^*/T^i F = R_i$.

Let E denote the set of points in F whose R^*-n-name and P'-n-name differ in more than $n\varepsilon$ places. Then (12) implies

(13) $m(E) < \varepsilon m(F)/3.$

Let $L_n^* = \bigvee_0^{n-1} T^{-i} R^*/F$. Let $L^{*\prime}$ denote those sets $\ell \in L_n^*$ such that

(14) ℓ is a $\delta/2k^{u+1}$-sequence for $Q = \bigvee_0^u T_1^i R$.

Let $L^{*\prime\prime}$ denote those sets $\ell \in L_n^*$ such that

(15) $m(\ell)$ is between $m(F)\, 2^{-[E(T_1) \pm 2\beta/10]n}$.

Then (3) and (4) imply $L = L^{*\prime} \cap L^{*\prime\prime}$ satisfies

(16) $m(F \cap \cup L) > (1 - 2\gamma/10)\, m(F)$.

Let C be the class of $w \in W_n/F$ such that more than half of w is covered by one or many $\ell \in L$ where the R^*-n-name of ℓ differs from the P'-n-name of w in less than ϵn places. Since W is a refinement of P', w has a P'-n-name. If $w \in W_n/F$ and $w \notin C$, then

$$w' = \{x \in w : x \notin \cup L \text{ or } x \in E \cap \cup L\},$$

satisfies $2m(w') \geq m(w)$. Thus (13) and (16) imply

$$\sum_{w \notin C} m(w) \leq 2[m(F - \cup L) + m(E)] \leq 2m(F)\, (2\gamma/10 + \epsilon/3).$$

Thus (9) implies

(17) $m(\cup C) > (1 - \epsilon)\, m(F)$.

We shall now verify

(18) to each $w \in C$ we can assign an $\ell \in L$ such that the R^*-n-name of ℓ differs from the P'-n-name of w in less than ϵn places, and no $\ell \in L$ is assigned to more than one $w \in C$.

To obtain (18), first note that (10) and (15) imply that the measure of any $w \in C$ is greater than twice the measure of any $\ell \in L$.

Hence the definition of C implies that any t elements in C intersect at least t elements in L whose R*-n-name differs from the P'-n-name of one of the t elements in C in less than ϵn places. Thus an application of the marriage lemma yields (18).

We now verify

(19) to each $w \in W_n/F$, $w \notin C$, we can assign a distinct $\ell \in L$ which has not already been assigned to a $w \in C$.

To obtain (19), note that (10) implies that the number of elements in W_n/F .. is less than

$$2^{[E(W,T) + \beta/10]n},$$

and (15) and (16) imply that the number of $\ell \in L$ is more than

$$2^{[E(T_1) - 2\beta/10]n}$$

Hence there are more than twice as many elements in L as in W_n/F, so (19) follows.

(18) and (19) imply each $w \in W_n/F$ is assigned a distinct $\ell(w) \in L$ such that

(20) The R*-n-name of $\ell(w)$ is a $\delta/2k^{u+1}$ sequence for $Q = \bigvee_0^u T_1^i R$ and

(21) if $w \in C$, then the R*-n-name of $\ell(w)$ differs from the P'-n-name of w in less than ϵn places.

P .ill now be defined on $X_1 = \bigcup_0^{n-1} T^i (F \cap \cup W_n)$. Let the R*-n-name of $\ell(w)$ in (20) be written as

$$(\ell_0, \ell_1, \ldots, \ell_{n-1}), \quad 1 \leq \ell_i \leq k, \quad 0 \leq i < n.$$

Then $T^i(w)$ will be in p_{ℓ_i}, $0 \leq i < n$. This defines $p_j \cap X_1$ for $1 \leq j \leq k$. Define P any way on $X-X_1$. Let $\Lambda = F \cap \cup W_n$; hence $m(\Lambda) \leq 1/n$.

We shall now verify that (12.3-5) hold. First of all, (7) and (9) imply

(22) $m(X_1) > 1 - 2\gamma/10 > 1 - \delta/2$.

Thus (20, (22), and Lemma 10.1 with $\varepsilon = \delta$ imply (12.3). Lemma 10.2 implies

$$P^* = \bigvee_{-n}^{n} T^i (P \vee \{A, A^c\}) \supset \{T^i(w) : \quad w \in W_n/F,\ 0 \leq i < n\}.$$

Thus (22) implies P^* contains a partition W' such that $D(W,W') < 4\gamma/10$. Hence (2) implies

$$E(P \vee \{A,A^c\},T) = E(P^*,T) \geq E(W',T) > E(W,T) - \delta/5.$$

Thus (6) and (1) imply

$$E(P,T) > E(T_1) - 3\,\delta/5 > E(T_1) - \delta.$$

We have $E(P,T) \leq E(T) = E(T_1)$. Before completing (12.4) we shall check (12.5). By (7), (21), and (17)

$$D(P,P') < 2[\gamma/10 + n\,\varepsilon\, m(F) \;+\; n\, m(F\text{-}UC)]$$

$$< 2[\varepsilon + \varepsilon + \varepsilon\; n\, m(F)] \;<\; 6\varepsilon.$$

Lastly, suppose $E(P,T) = E(T_1)$. Then we can make an arbitrarily small change in P and lower $E(P,T)$, still preserving the estimates for P. For let B be a generator for T. Given $a > 0$, there exists k such that $\bigvee_{-K}^{K} T^{i}B \supset^{a/10} P$. Since T is a Bernoulli shift, we can choose B' such that $D(B',B) < a/10\,(2K+1)$ and $E(B',T) \leq E(B') < E(B) = E(T)$.

Now $\bigvee_{-K}^{K} T^{i}B'$ contains a partition P_1 such that $D(P_1,P) < 2a/10$ and $E(P_1,T) \leq E(B',T)$. Choosing a sufficiently small, the above estimates hold with P replaced by P_1.

If $T_1{}^{i} R$ are independent then we can vary P continuously getting P_t, $0 \leq t \leq 1$ so that $P_o = P$, $d(P_1,R) = 0$, $D(P_t,P) < \delta$ and $d(P_t, R) < \delta$. If $E(P_1, T) = E(T,1 = E(R,T_1)$ then we are finished (since we have the conclusion of Proposition 13 and Lemma 12 is only used to prove this). If not we can find a t such that $d(R, P_t) < \delta$, $0 < E(T_1) - E(P_t, T) > \delta$, $D(P_t, P^1) < 6\,\epsilon + \delta$.

<u>Proposition 13</u>. Let (R,T_1) be finitely determined and $E(R,T_1) = E(T_1)$. Given $\varepsilon > 0$, there exists $\delta > 0$ and a positive integer u such that if T is a Bernoulli shift* with $E(T_1) = E(T)$ and if P' satisfies

(13.1) $d(\bigvee_{o}^{u} T_1{}^{i} R, \ \bigvee_{o}^{u} T^{i}P') < \delta$,

(13.2) $0 < E(T_1) - E(P',T) < \delta$,

then there exists P such that

(13.3) $D(P',P) < \epsilon$.

(13.4) $(P,T) \sim (R,T_1)$.

In case (R,T_1) is a Bernoulli shift, then we only need $d(R,P') < \delta$ in (13.1) as in [2]. Proposition 13 follows by induction from Lemma 12.

To get started, one can apply the method in Lemma 12 to construct P' satisfying (13.1) and (13.2). Thus, given (R,T_1) and T as in Proposition 13, we can find P such that $(P,T) \sim (R,T_1)$.

---

* In the special case where $T_1{}^{i}R$ are independent we can drop the assumption that T is a Bernoulli shift and can take $u = 0$. Proposition 13 is then Lemma 5 of [3].

Lemma 14. Let (R,T_1) be finitely determined. Let (P,T) be a Bernoulli shift, where P is a generator for T and $E(T) = E(P) = E(R,T_1)$. Let Q be a partition such that

$$(14.1)\quad (Q,T) \sim (R,T_1).$$

Given $\varepsilon > 0$, there exist Q_1 and K such that

$$(14.2)\quad (Q_1,T) \sim (R,T_1).$$

$$(14.3)\quad \bigvee_{-K}^{K} T^i Q_1 \overset{\varepsilon}{\supset} P.$$

$$(14.4)\quad D(Q_1,Q) < \varepsilon.$$

Proof. Since P is a generator for T, we can choose K_1 such that

$$(1)\quad \bigvee_{-K_1}^{K_1} T^i P \overset{\varepsilon/10}{\supset} Q.$$

Applying Proposition 13 (for the case of a Bernoulli shift) to T acting in X_Q, we get δ such that if P' is a partition in X_Q satisfying

$$(2)\quad d(P',P) < \delta,$$

$$(3)\quad 0 < E(T) - E(P',T) < \delta,$$

then there exists P_1 in X_Q such that

$$(4)\quad D(P_1,P') < \varepsilon/30\, K_1$$

$$(5)\quad (P_1,T) \sim (P,T).$$

Choose $\varepsilon_1 < \delta_1 \wedge \varepsilon$ such that if Q' is a partition with the same number of sets as Q, then

(6) $D(Q',Q) < 2\varepsilon_1$ implies $|E(Q',T) - E(Q,T)| < \delta$.

Choose $K_2 > K_1$ such that

(7) $\bigvee_{-K_2}^{K_2} T^i P \overset{\varepsilon_1/10}{\supset} Q.$

Choose n_1 such that

(8) $K_2/n_1 < \varepsilon_1/100$.

By Rohlin's. Theorem we obtain a set F in X_Q such that $T^i F$, $0 \leqq i \leqq n_1$, are disjoint and $X_1 = \bigcup_0^{n_1} T^i F$ satisfies

(9) $m(X_1) > 1 - \varepsilon_1/100$.

Let G be the gadget formed from $T^i F$, $0 \leqq i \leqq n_1$, by partitioning each $T^i F$ by Q. Let G_1' denote G regarded as a gadget in X and let G_2' denote G regarded as a gadget in X_Q; hence $G_1' \sim G_2'$. Form the gadget G_1 from $T^i F$, $0 \leqq i \leqq n_1$, by partitioning each $T^i F$ by $Q \vee P$; hence G_1 is a gadget in X. Now X_Q is non-atomic because T is mixing. Thus we can pick a partition P' in X_Q so that if we form the gadget G_2 from $T^i F$, $0 \leqq i \leqq n_1$, by partitioning each $T^i F$ by $Q \vee P'$, then

(10) $G_1 \sim G_2$.

This defines P' on X_1. We can now define P' on $X - X_1$ so that $E(P') < E(P)$. To see this, note that we could first define P' on $X - X_1$ so that $d(P') = d(P)$. Since $E(P')$ has no local minimum, we could change P' on an arbitrarily small set and lower its entropy. Furthermore, the change could be made on $X - X_1$ if each atom in P has non-empty intersection with $X-X_1$. This can be guaranteed since T is mixing and we may substitute $T^n F$ for F, where n is sufficiently large. Thus we can assume

(11) $E(P',T) \leq E(P') < E(P) = E(T)$.

Now (1) implies there exists a partition L of S_{K_1} (see definitions) such that

(12) $D(L_P, Q) < \varepsilon/10$.

(12), (10), and (9) imply

(13) $D(L_{P'}, Q) < 2\varepsilon/10$.

(7), (8), (9), and (10) imply

(14) $\bigvee_{-K_2}^{K_2} T^i P' \overset{2\varepsilon/10}{\supset} Q$.

(10) and (9) imply

(15) $d(P,P') < \varepsilon_1'/100 < \delta$,

Thus (15) implies (2), and (14) and (6) imply (3).

Hence we obtain P_1 in X_Q satisfying (4) and (5). Now (4) and (13) imply

(16) $D(L_{P_1}, Q) < 3\varepsilon/10$.

We next choose $K_3 > K_2$ such that

$$(17) \quad \bigvee_{-K_3}^{K_3} T^i Q \overset{\varepsilon/10}{\supset} P_1.$$

By Proposition 13 there is a $\delta_2 > 0$ and a positive integer u so that if Q^* satisfies

$$(18) \quad d(\bigvee_{0}^{u} T^i Q^*, \bigvee_{0}^{u} T^i Q) < \delta_2,$$

$$(19) \quad 0 < E(T) - E(Q^*,T) < \delta_2, \quad (E(Q,T) = E(T)) ;$$

then there exists Q_1 in X_Q such that

$$(20) \quad (Q_1, T) \sim (R, T_1) ,$$

$$(21) \quad D(Q_1, Q^*) < \varepsilon/30 K_3 .$$

Choose $\varepsilon_2 < \delta_2 \wedge \varepsilon$ such that if P_2 and P have the same number of sets, then

$$(22) \quad D(P_2, P) < \varepsilon_2 \text{ implies } |E(P_2, T) - E(P,T)| < \delta_2.$$

Choose $K_4 > K_3$ such that

$$(23) \quad \bigvee_{-K_4}^{K_4} T^i Q \overset{\varepsilon_2/10}{\supset} P_1.$$

Choose n_2 so that

$$(24) \quad K_4/n_2 < \varepsilon_2/100 \text{ and } u/n_2 < \varepsilon_2/100.$$

By Rohlin's Theorem we can find a set E_1' such that $T^i E_1'$, $0 \leq i \leq n_2$, are disjoint and

$$(25)\quad m\Big(\bigcup_{0}^{n_2} T^{i} E_1'\Big) > 1 - \varepsilon_2/100.$$

Since T is mixing, we have

$$\lim_{n} d\Big(\bigvee_{0}^{n_2} T^{-i}P_1/T^{n}E_1'\Big) = d\Big(\bigvee_{0}^{n_2} T^{-i}P_1\Big).$$

Choosing n sufficiently large, we can remove a set Z_1 from $T^{n}E_1'$ so that $E_1 = T^{n}E_1' - Z_1$ satisfies

$$(26)\quad d\Big(\bigvee_{0}^{n_2} T^{-i}P_1/E_1\Big) = d\Big(\bigvee_{0}^{n_2} T^{-i}P_1\Big).$$

(27) $T^{i}E_1$, $0 \leqq i \leqq n_2$, are disjoint.

$$(28)\quad X_2 = \bigcup_{0}^{n_2} T^{i}E_1 \quad \text{satisfies} \quad m(X_2) > 1 - 2\varepsilon_2/100.$$

Now repeat the same argument to obtain E such that

$$(29)\quad d\Big(\bigvee_{0}^{n_2} T^{-i}P/E\Big) = d\Big(\bigvee_{0}^{n_2} T^{-i}P\Big).$$

(30) $T^{i}E$, $0 \leqq i \leqq n_2$ are disjoint.

$$(31)\quad X_3 = \bigcup_{0}^{n_2} T^{i}E \quad \text{satisfies} \ m(X_3) > 1 - 2\varepsilon_2/100.$$

Let G_3' be the gadget formed from $T^{i}E_1$, $0 \leqq i \leqq n_2$, by partitioning each $T^{i}E_1$ by P_1. Let G_4' be the gadget formed from $T^{i}E$, $0 \leqq i \leqq n_2$, by partitioning each $T^{i}E$ by P. Hence (5), (26), and (29) imply $G_3' \sim G_4'$.

Let G_3 be the gadget formed from $T^i E_1$, $0 \leq i \leq n_2$, by partitioning each $T^i E_1$ by $P_1 \vee Q$. Choose Q^* so that if G_4 is the gadget formed from $T^i E$, $0 \leq i \leq n_2$, by partitioning each $T^i E$ by $P \vee Q^*$, then

(32) $G_3 \sim G_4$.

The same method as at the end of the proof of Lemma 12 can be utilized to guarantee

(33) $E(Q^*, T) < E(T)$.

(32), (31), and (28) imply (18). (17), (23), and (24) imply

(34) $$\bigvee_{-K_3}^{K_3} T^i Q^* \overset{2\varepsilon/10}{\supset} P.$$

(35) $$\bigvee_{-K_4}^{K_4} T^i Q^* \overset{2\varepsilon_2/10}{\supset} P.$$

(35) and (22) imply (19). Thus we obtain Q_1 satisfying (20) and (21). (21) and (34) imply

(36) $$\bigvee_{-K_3}^{K_3} T^i Q_1 \overset{3\varepsilon/10}{\supset} P.$$

Thus (36) implies (14.3) with $K = K_3$. (14.2) holds by (20). To obtain (14.4), we note that (16), (32), (28), and (31) imply

(37) $D(L_P, Q^*) < 4\varepsilon/10$.

(37) and (21) imply

(38) $D(L_p,Q_1) < 5\varepsilon/10$.

Thus (38) and (12) yield (14.3).

<u>Proposition 15</u>. Let (R,T_1) be finitely determined. Let (P,T) be a Bernoulli shift where P is a generator for T and $E(T) = E(P) = E(R,T_1)$. Let Q be a partition such that $(Q,T) \sim (R,T_1)$. Then given ε there is a partition Q^* such that

(15.1) $(Q^*,T) \sim (R,T_1)$,

(15.2) $\bigvee_{-\infty}^{\infty} T^i Q^* \supset P$,

(15.3) $D(Q,Q^*) < \varepsilon$.

<u>Proof</u>. Lemma 14 says that for $\varepsilon_1 < \varepsilon 2^{-1}$ we can find Q_1 and K_1 such that

(1) $(Q_1, T) \sim (R,T_1)$.

(2) $D(Q, Q_1) < \varepsilon_1$.

(3) $\bigvee_{-K_1}^{K_1} T^i Q_1 \overset{2^{-1}}{\supset} P$.

Choose $\varepsilon_2 < 2^{-2}$ so that (3) and

(4) $D(Q_1, Q_2) < \varepsilon_2$

imply

(5) $\bigvee_{-K_1}^{K_1} T^i Q_2 \overset{2^{-1}+2^{-2}}{\supset} P$.

Apply Lemma 14 to obtain Q_2 satisfying (4),

(6) $(Q_2, T) \sim (R, T_1)$,

and there exists K_2 such that

$$(7)\quad \bigvee_{-K_2}^{K_2} T^i Q_2 \overset{2^{-2}}{\supset} P.$$

Suppose we have Q_n and $K_1, \ldots, K_n$ such that

$$(8)\quad (Q_n, T) \sim (R, T_1).$$

$$(9)\quad \bigvee_{-K_j}^{K_j} T^i Q_n \overset{2^{-j}+\cdots+2^{-n}}{\supset} P, \quad 1 \leq j \leq n.$$

Choose $\varepsilon_{n+1} < 2^{-n-1}$ such that (9) and

$$(10)\quad D(Q_n, Q_{n+1}) < \varepsilon_{n+1}$$

imply

$$(11)\quad \bigvee_{-K_j}^{K_j} T^i Q_{n+1} \overset{2^{-j}+\cdots+2^{-n-1}}{\supset} P, \quad 1 \leq j \leq n.$$

Apply Lemma 14 to obtain Q_{n+1} satisfying (10),

$$(12)\quad (Q_{n+1}, T) \sim (R, T_1),$$

and there exists K_{n+1} such that

$$(13)\quad \bigvee_{-K_{n+1}}^{K_{n+1}} T^i Q_{n+1} \overset{2^{-n-1}}{\supset} P.$$

Thus (11) and (13) imply (9) holds with n replaced by n+1. Proceeding inductively, we obtain $Q^* = \lim_n Q_n$ satisfying (15.1-2).

Proof of Theorem. Let (R_1, T_1) and (R_2, T_2) be finitely determined with $E(R_1, T_1) = E(R_2, T_2)$. Let (P, T) be a Bernoulli shift with $E(P,T) = E(R_1, T_1)$. By the remark after Proposition 13 we can find $(Q_j, T) \sim (R_j, T_j)$, $j = 1, 2$. By Proposition 15 we obtain Q_1^* and Q_2^* such that

(1) $(Q_j^*, T) \sim (R_j, T_j)$, $j = 1, 2$.

(2) $\bigvee_{-\infty}^{\infty} T^i Q_j^* \supset P$, $j = 1, 2$.

The theorem follows by (1), (2), and the fact that P generates.

SECTION 2

In this section we will show that if S_t is the flow described in the introduction, then for each fixed t the transformation S_t has a very weak Bernoulli generator and hence is a Bernoulli shift.

Let us recall some notation. Let T acting on X be the 2-shift. Let $Q = \{Q_1, Q_2\}$ be a partition such that $T^i Q$ are independent and generate and $m(Q_1) = m(Q_2) = \frac{1}{2}$. Let f take the value β_1 on Q_1 and β_2 on Q_2 where β_1/β_2 is irrational and $\frac{1}{2}(\beta_1+\beta_2) = 1$. Let Y be the part of $X \times R$ that lies below the graph of f. Let $P = \{P_1, P_2\}$ be the partition of Y where P_1 is the part of Y above Q_1, and P_2 the part of Y above Q_2. The flow S_t moves each point y straight up until it hits the graph of f, say at $(x, f(x))$. It then jumps to $(Tx, 0)$ and continues to move up. (That is, if we identify $(x, f(x))$ with $(Tx, 0)$ the vertical lines gives us orbits and S_t moves each point t units along its orbit.)

The idea of the proof will be to get the regularity we need by applying the renewal theorem; see [2, p. 347]. For each x in X we consider the first or smallest $t > 0$ such that $S_t(x) \in X$. This can be thought of as a random variable on X that takes on values β_1 and β_2 with probability $\frac{1}{2}$. If we consider the nth, $t > 0$ such that $S_t \in X$, then this is a random variable which is the sum of n independent identically distributed random variables. We thus have a random walk to which we can apply the renewal theorem. (The random walk jumps either β_1 or β_2 ahead with probability $\frac{1}{2}$.)

If we started with any subset E of X in $\bigvee_{-\infty}^{0} T^{i}Q$ (instead of X), and normalized E to have measure 1, then we would also get a random walk. If $E \subset Q_1$, then we get the same walk as above except that we start with a jump of β_1. The corresponding statement holds if E is in Q_2.

Lemma 1. If $0 < \alpha < \frac{1}{4}\min(\beta_1, \beta_2)$, then $\bigvee_{i=-\infty}^{\infty} S_{\alpha}^{i}P$ generates the full σ-algebra of Y.

Proof. For each $y \in Y$ we get a partition of the line, L_y, into two sets a_1 and a_2 according to whether $S_t(y)$ is in P_1 or P_2. (a_1 and a_2 will each be a collection of intervals, the length of each interval in a_1 is a multiple of β_1 and the length of each interval in a_2 is a multiple of β_2.)

If $y_1 \neq y_2$, then L_{y_1} and L_{y_2} will be different. (This is obvious if y_1 and y_2 are in X and the general statement follows from this.)

The partition of the line, L_y, induces a partition, I_y, on the points of the form $n\alpha$, $n = \ldots 1, 0, 1, \ldots$. It is easy to see that I_y determines L_y up to a translation of magnitude $\leq \alpha$.

We will now use the renewal theorem to show that for a. e. y I_y determines L_y. To do this it will be enough to show that for each ϵ (of the form $\frac{1}{n}$) and a. e. y there is an n and an m such that each of the intervals $n\alpha$, $n\alpha+\epsilon$, and $m\alpha-\epsilon$, $m\alpha$, intersects both sets of L_y. Let $y = S_t(x)$, $x \in X$. Then we must find, for each rational t and a. e. x, two intervals, $(t+n\alpha\ ,\ t+n\alpha+\epsilon)$ and $(t+m\alpha-\epsilon\ ,\ t+m\alpha)$, each of which intersects both sets in L_x. The renewal theorem says that there is a $\gamma > 0$ such that if I is an interval of length ϵ and if the left end point of I is large enough, then, for a set of x of measure $> \gamma$, there is a t in I such that $S_t(x) \in X$ and hence for a set of x of measure $> \frac{1}{2}\gamma$, I intersects both sets of L_x. Repeated application of this gives our desired result.

To show that P is very weak Bernoulli relative to S_α, it is easy to see that it is enough to prove the following:

<u>Lemma</u> 2. Given ϵ, there is an N such that if C and $\overline{C}$ are subsets of X in $\bigvee_{-\infty}^{0} T^i Q$, then for all $n > N$ and $0 \leq s \leq \beta_1+\beta_2$, $0 \leq \overline{s} \leq \beta_1+\beta_2$ we have

$$\overline{d}(\{S_{-s}S_\alpha^{-i}P/C\}_{i=0}^n\ ,\ \{S_{-\overline{s}}S_\alpha^{i}P/\overline{C}\}_{i=0}^n) < \epsilon\ .$$

(Note that $S_{-1}S_\alpha^{-i}P$ induces a partition on C. C is regarded as a measure space with the measure induced on it by X.)

<u>Remarks</u>. (1) $\text{dist} \bigvee_0^n S_{-s}S_\alpha^{-i}P/C = \text{dist} \bigvee_0^n S_\alpha^{i}P/S_t(C)$ and this is why Lemma 3 implies P is very weak Bernoulli.

(2) We can regard the above partition as the partition we get by sampling the random walk (with path space C) at the time $s+i\alpha$, $0 \leq i \leq n$.

<u>Proof</u> <u>of</u> <u>Lemma</u> 2. We first note that

$$\text{(A)}\quad \overline{d}(\{S_{-s_1}S_\alpha^{i}P/C\}_{i=0}^n\ ,\ \{S_{-s_2}S_\alpha^{i}P/C\}_{i=0}^n) < \frac{|s_1-s_2|}{\alpha}\ ,$$

(A) says that if we sample our random walk at time $s_1+i\alpha$ or $s_2+i\alpha$, $0 \leq i \leq n$, then the expected number (relative to the measure on C) of i such that $S_{s_1}S_\alpha^{\,i}(x)$ and $S_{s_2}S_\alpha^{\,i}(x)$ are in different atoms of P is $< \frac{|s_1-s_2|}{\alpha}$ $(x \in C)$ and this is so because the expected number of returns to X in intervals of the form $(s_1+i\alpha, s_2+i\alpha)$ is $< \frac{|s_1-s_2|}{\alpha}$ by the renewal theorem.

To prove Lemma 2 it is enough to get the conclusion for i running from N to n (instead of 0 to n) since n can be taken much larger than N. To do this we will partition C into sets C_i where C_i is the set of all x such that the largest $t < s + N\alpha$ for which $S_t(x) \in X$ is t_i (i.e., all x whose last return to X before $s + N\alpha$ occurs at the same point, t_i). It is easy to see that $\bigvee_N^n S_{-s}S_\alpha^{-i}P/C_i$ has the same distribution as the partition we get by sampling our original walk at times $(s+N\alpha-t_i) + j\alpha$, $0 \leq j \leq n-N$.

Now let $\bar{t}_i$ be the numbers corresponding to the t_i when $\bar{C}$ replaces C. The renewal theorem says that if N is large enough, the distribution of the $(s+N\alpha-t_i)$ is very close to the distribution of the $(\bar{s}+N\alpha-\bar{t}_i)$. This fact and (A) gives Lemma 2.

REFERENCES

[1] Billingsley, P., Ergodic Theory and Information (1965), Wiley, New York.

[2] Feller, W., An Introduction to Probability Theory and Its Applications, Vol. II (1966), Wiley, New York.

[3] Ornstein, D. S., Bernoulli shifts with the same entropy are isomorphic, to appear. (Advances in Math.)

[4] Parry, W., Entropy and Generators in Ergodic Theory (1969), Benjamin, New York.

[5] Friedman, N. and Ornstein, D. S., An isomorphism of weak Bernoulli transformations, to appear. (Advances in Math.)

[6] Ornstein, D. S., Bernoulli shifts with infinite entropy are isomorphic, to appear. (Advances in Math.)

[7] _____________, Factors of Bernoulli shifts are Bernoulli shifts, to appear. (Advances in Math.)

[8] Smorodinsky, M., An exposition of Ornstein isomorphism theorem, to appear. (Advances in Math.)

[9] Shields, P. and McCabe, R., A class of Markov operators which dilate to a shift, to appear. (Advances in Math.)

[10] Azencott, R., Difféomorphismes d'Anosov et schémas de Bernoulli, Comptes Rendus, Acad. Sciences, Paris.

[11] Ambrose, W., Representation of ergodic flows, Ann. Math. 42 (1941), 723-739.

[12] Ambrose, W. and Kakutani, S., Structure and continuity of measurable flows. Duke Math. J. 9, (1942) 25-42.

[13] Smorodinsky, M., A partition on a Bernoulli shift which is not "weak Bernoulli," to appear.

[14] Feldman, J. and Smorodinsky, M., Bernoulli flows with infinite entropy, to appear.

ON THE EXISTENCE OF A σ-FINITE INVARIANT MEASURE UNDER A GENERALIZED HARRIS CONDITION.[1]

DONALD S. ORNSTEIN - STANFORD UNIVERSITY

and

LOUIS SUCHESTON - OHIO STATE UNIVERSITY

Summary

A Markov transition probability function was shown by Harris [3] to admit a σ-finite invariant measure, under a certain probabilistic recurrence condition which was later given an essentially equivalent measure-theoretic form (see [2], [4], [5], and [8]). The latter includes the assumption that if T is the L_∞ operator induced by the system, then the L_∞ norm of T is one. The present paper weakens this assumption replacing it by: $\liminf T^n h < \infty$ a.e.

[1] Research supported by the National Science Foundation, Grants GP 8781 and GP 7693.

1. Invariant measure and bounded sets.

Let X be an abstract set, $\mathcal{A}$ a σ-field of subsets of X, m a σ-finite measure on $\mathcal{A}$. Statements a.e. = "almost everywhere," "null set," etc., refer to m; such statements are however sometimes omitted. All considered sets and functions are assumed measurable. Let L be a linear space of measurable functions on $(X, \mathcal{A}, m)$ and a lattice under pointwise operations: if f, g are in L, then also $\sup(f,g)$ is in L. In particular, $\sup(f,0)$, written f^+, is in L if f is. L^+ is the class of non-negative elements of L. A function $\bar{f} \in L^+$ is called a modification of a function $f \in L^+$ if there exists an $h \in L^+$ such that $\bar{f} = f - h + Th$. If T is an operator on L, $D_n(f,g)$ is the ratio $\sum_{i<n} T^i f / \sum_{i<n} T^i g$ (i runs over non-negative integers), T_∞ is the operator $I + T + T^2 + \cdots$. A starting point for us will be the following theorem due to Ornstein [11]:

Theorem 1. Let T be a positive linear operator on L. If $f,g \in L^+$ and $D_n(f,g)$ fails to converge to a finite limit on a set $E \subset [T_\infty g > 0]$, then there exists a sequence e_n of modifications of $f + g$ such that $e_n(x)$ converges to ∞ for a.e. x in E.

Given a positive linear operator T on L and an $h \in L^+$, we denote by S_h the class of functions $f \in L$ such that $|f| < K \sum_{i<N} T^i h$ for some positive number K and some integer N. Then S_h is a linear space and a lattice. We call a function $e \in L^+$ small if $e \in S_h$ for each $h \in L^+$ with support intersecting the support of e; we call a set E bounded if 1_E (indicator function of E) is a small function.

Note that if $f \in S_g^+$ and $g \in S_h^+$, then $f \in S_h^+$. Indeed, if $f < K \sum_{i<N} T^i g$ and $g < K' \sum_{i<N'} T^i h$, then $h < K'' \sum_{i<N''} T^i h$, where $K'' = KK'$ and $N'' = N + N'$.

Proposition 1. Assume that there is a non-null small function $h \in L^+$ such that: (a) If $h_1 \in S_h^+$, then $\liminf T^n h_1 < \infty$ a.e. If $f, g \in S_h^+$, then (b) $D_n(f,g)$ converges to a finite limit on the set $[T_\infty g > 0]$ and (c) $\lim D_n(Tf,g) = \lim D_n(f,g)$ on the set $[T_\infty g = \infty]$.

Proof. Suppose that the assumptions of the theorem hold but (b) fails for some functions f, g. Then by Theorem 1 applied to the space S_h there is some non-null subset E of $[T_\infty g > 0]$ and a sequence e_n of modifications of $f + g$ such that e_n converges to infinity on E. By Egorov's theorem there exists a non-null subset F of E such that on F $e_n \to \infty$ uniformly; replacing if need be e_n by a subsequence, we may assume that $e_n > n$ on F for every positive integer n. Since h is small, $h \in S_{1_F}$, and since $f + g \in S_h$, $f + g \in S_{1_F}$. There are positive integers K and N such that

$$K \sum_{i<N} T^i 1_F > f + g,$$

hence $1_F < e_n/n$ now implies that for each n

$$\frac{1}{N} \sum_{i<N} T^i e_n > \frac{n}{KN} (f + g) .$$

The left hand side is a modification of $f + g$ for each n ; thus choosing n sufficiently large we obtain a modification of $f + g$, $e = f + g - h_1 + Th_1$, $h_1 \in S_h^+$, with $e > 2(f + g)$; hence $f + g < -h_1 + Th_1$. Now for all n

$$\sum_{i<n} T^i(f + g) \leq -h_1 + T^n h_1 \leq T^n h_1 .$$

Since $D_n(f,g)$ fails to converge on E, $T_\infty(f + g) = \infty$ on E, hence $\lim T^n h_1 = \infty$ on E. This contradicts (a).

It remains to prove (c). We have by (b) that

$$\lim [D_n(Tf,g) - D_n(f,g)] = \lim \frac{T^n f - f}{\sum_{i<n} T^i g} \quad \text{exists on} \quad [T_\infty g > 0],$$

hence by (a) this limit must be zero on $[T_\infty g = \infty]$.

Now let T be a positive linear operator on L_∞ of a σ-finite space $(X, \mathcal{A}, m)$. T is assumed <u>countably additive</u>; i.e., $f_i \uparrow f$ implies $T f_i \uparrow T f$ for $f_i, f \in L_\infty^+$. (This is true if and only if T is the adjoint of an L_1 operator.) We are searching for a σ-finite equivalent invariant measure.

<u>Theorem 2</u>. Assume that T is a positive linear countably additive operator on L_∞ of a σ-finite measure space $(X, \mathcal{A}, m)$ and assume:

(a) $\lim\inf T^n h < \infty$ a.e. for each $h \in L_\infty^+$;

(b) $T_\infty h = \infty$ a.e. on X for each non-null $h \in L_\infty^+$;

(c) There is a bounded non-null set H.

Then there exists a σ-finite equivalent measure v such that $h \in L_\infty^+$ implies $\int h\, dv = \int Th\, dv$. v is unique modulo multiplication by constants.

Proof. The existence of a bounded non-null set implies the existence of small non-null functions in L_∞^+ (and vice versa). Let h be such a function. Let $f \in L_\infty^+$ be arbitrary, but such that $\operatorname{supp} f \cap \operatorname{supp} T^i h \neq \emptyset$ where i is fixed. By (b) applied to f there is an integer k such that the function $f' = \inf (T^k f, h)$ is not null.

Since h is small, $h \in S_{f'} \subset S_{T^k f} \subset S_f$; therefore $T^i h \in S_f$.
This proves that $T^i h$ is small. The support of a small function g may be written as a countable union of bounded sets, e.g. the sets $[1/i \leq g < 1/(i-1)]$, $i = 1,2,\cdots$. Since by (b) $X = \bigcup_i \operatorname{supp} T^i h$, it follows that X is a countable union of bounded sets. A subset of a bounded set is bounded and the measure m is σ-finite; therefore we may and do assume that X is a disjoint union of bounded sets X_i, $i = 1,2,\cdots$, and $m(X_i) < \infty$ for all i. By Proposition 1 applied with $L = L_\infty$, $h = g = 1_{X_i}$ (i fixed), $\lim D_n(f,1_{X_i}) = \lim D_n(Tf,1_{X_i})$ exists a.e. on X_i. Let

$$(1.1) \qquad v^i(f) = \int_{X_i} \lim D_n(f,1_{X_i})\, dm ,$$

then, by the countable additivity of T and the Vitali-Hahn-Saks theorem, v^i is a countably additive measure on measurable subsets of X_i, v^i is T invariant in the sense that $v^i(f) = v^i(Tf)$, and clearly $v^i \ll m$. The converse is also true because the set X_i is bounded: indeed, if $A \subset X_i$ and

$$1_{X_i} < K \sum_{k<N} T^k 1_A ,$$

then $v^i(A) = \frac{1}{N} \sum_{k<N} v^i(T^k 1_A) > 1/(KN)$. Hence the measure $v = \sum_i v_i$ satisfies the conditions of the theorem; the invariance of v follows from the countable additivity of T.

Finally, we prove the uniqueness of v. T is a positive linear contraction operator on the space $L_1(X, \mathcal{A}, v)$. The assumption (b) implies that T is conservative and there exist no non-trivial T-closed sets A : no sets A such that $f \in L_1(X, \mathcal{A}, v)$, $\operatorname{supp} f \subset A$ implies $\operatorname{supp} Tf \subset A$. (Equivalently, there exist no non-trivial

T*-invariant sets.) This follows from (b) for f in L_∞, and holds for f in $L_1(X, \mathcal{A}, v)$, as may be seen by an approximation argument. If v' is another σ-finite equivalent invariant measure, then T has the same properties as an operator on $L_1(X, \mathcal{A}, v')$. It suffices to compare v and v' on sets of finite positive v and v' measure, because X is a countable union of such sets. If A and B are two such sets, then by the identification of limit part of the Chacon-Ornstein theorem

$$\lim D_n(1_A, 1_B) = \frac{v(A)}{v(B)} = \frac{v'(A)}{v'(B)} \quad \text{a.e. on } X ;$$

hence the ratio $v(A) / v'(A)$ does not depend upon the set A. This completes the proof of the theorem.

2. Existence of bounded sets under a non-singularity condition.

In this section the operator T is assumed to be induced by a transition measure: a function $T = T(x,A)$ of two variables $x \in X$, $A \in A$, such that

$T(x,\cdot)$ is a measure on $\mathcal{A}$ for each fixed $x \in X$,

$T(\cdot,A)$ is an $\mathcal{A}$-measurable bounded real-valued function on X for each fixed $A \in \mathcal{A}$.

Define inductively transition measures T^n as follows: $T^o(x,A) = 1_A(x)$, and

$$(2.1)\qquad T^n(x,A) = \int T^{n-1}(x,dy)\, T(y,A) \qquad n = 1,2,\cdots .$$

Thus $T^1(x,A) = T(x,A)$. We assume that T is null-preserving, that is such that if $A \in \mathcal{A}$, $m(A) = 0$, then $T(x,A) = 0$ a.e. (m); the exceptional null set where $T(x,A) \neq 0$ may depend on A. This assumption guarantees that the transition measure T defines an L_1 operator (written on the right), acting on L_1 identified with the space of finite signed m-continuous measures:

$$(2.2)\qquad \gamma T(A) = \int T(x,A)\gamma(dx) \qquad \gamma \in L_1,\ A \in \mathcal{A} .$$

The adjoint operator, written on the left, is a countably additive operator acting on L_∞, to which the results of the previous section will apply. Its action is given by the relation

$$(2.3)\qquad Th(x) = \int T(x,dy)\, h(y) \qquad h \in L_\infty,\ x \in X.$$

To see that (2.3) holds, verify it for h of the form 1_A, then approximate a function in L_∞ by a linear combination of such functions.

The Lebesgue theorem allows us to write, for each fixed $n > 0$ and x,

$$(2.4) \qquad T^n(x,\cdot) = T^n_c(x,\cdot) + T^n_s(x,\cdot)$$

where T^n_c is absolutely continuous with respect to m, T^n_s is singular. Let $S_{n,x}$ be the singular set of $T^n(x,\cdot)$: $m(S_{n,x}) = 0$, and $T^n_s(x,X) = T^n_s(x,S_{n,x})$. For each x and each $A \in \mathcal{A}$ we may write, by the Radon-Nikodým theorem,

$$(2.5) \qquad T^n_c(x,A) = \int_A d_n(x,y)\, m(dy) ,$$

where $d_n(x,y)$ is the n-step <u>density function</u>. It will be convenient to be able to assume that the densities are measurable, as functions of (x,y), with respect to the product σ-field $\mathcal{A} \times \mathcal{A}$, and this is possible if the σ-field $\mathcal{A}$ is generated by a countable collection of sets. The result is known if T is Markovian, and the proof given in Doob ([1], p. 612) extends to the general case. The idea is the following: Since $\mathcal{A}$ is countably generated, we may find a sequence of <u>finite</u> fields $\mathcal{A}_n$ increasing to $\mathcal{A}$. On finite fields the densities appearing in (2.5) are of course jointly measurable; the density on $\mathcal{A} \times \mathcal{A}$ is naturally (supermartigale theorem) their limit, hence it is measurable.

We show that the densities d_n may be chosen so that for <u>each</u> x and y

$$(2.6) \quad d_{m+n}(x,y) \geq \int T^m(x,dz)\, d_n(z,y) \geq \int d_m(x,z)\, d_n(z,y)\, m(dz).$$

We have for each $h \in L_\infty$

$$\int T^{m+n}(x,dy)\ h(y) \geq \int T^{m}(x,dz) \int d_n(z,y)\ h(y)\ m(dy)$$

$$= \int [\ \int T^{m}(x,dz)\ d_n(z,y)\ ]\ h(y)\ m(dy).$$

Since $S_{m+n,x}$ is a null set, we may and do assume that it does not intersect the support of h; the left hand side of the last inequality now becomes $\int d_{m+n}(x,y)\ h(y)\ m(dy)$, while the right hand side remains unchanged. Since h was arbitrary, it follows that (2.6) holds for each fixed x, outside of a set of y which is null, but may depend on x. Actually, we modify the definition of $d_n(x,y)$ so that (NS) continues to hold and (2.6) is valid for every x and y. We follow ([1], p. 196) and [6], replacing d_n by e_n, defined inductively by

$$e_n(x,y) = \max[d_n(x,y),\ \sup_{k<n} \int T^{k}(x,dz)\ e^{n-k}(z,y)]\ .$$

$e_n(x,y)$ are $\mathcal{A} \times \mathcal{A}$ measurable and (2.6) holds for each x and y if d_n is replaced by e_n. In the sequel, we will continue to write d_n rather than e_n and we will assume (2.6). The action of T is assumed to be given by

(2.7) $\quad T^n 1_A(x) = \int_A d_n(x,y)\ m(dy) + T^n_s(x,A), \qquad A \in \mathcal{A},\ n = 1,2,\cdots,$

where $d_n(x,y)$ are the densities satisfying (2.6), measurable on the space $(X \times X, \mathcal{A} \times \mathcal{A})$, and $T^n_s(x,\cdot)$ is for each x and n a measure singular with respect to m. An important particular case arises when T is an integral operator: then the singular parts T^n_s vanish. Another important particular case is the "essential Harris case": $\|T\| = 1$ and T possesses a certain degree of non-singularity; more precisely,

(NS) $\begin{cases} \text{There exists a non-null set } B \text{ and an integer } n_o > 0 \\ \text{such that for each } x \in B, \ m[y: d_{n_o}(x,y) > 0] > 0. \end{cases}$

Here we weaken the assumption $\|T\| = 1$, replacing it by (a).

Theorem 3. Assume that

(a) $\liminf T^n h < \infty$ a.e. for each $h \in L_\infty^+$;

(b) $T_\infty h = \infty$ a.e. for each $h \in L_\infty^+$, $h \not\equiv 0$;

(c) The condition (NS) holds.

Then there exists a σ-finite equivalent measure v such that for each $h \in L_\infty^+$, $\int h \, dv = \int Th \, dv$. v is unique modulo multiplication by constants.

Proof. It will suffice to establish the existence of a bounded set: Theorem 3 will then follow from Theorem 2. Most arguments are known from the Markovian case; the point is to show that there exists a combination of arguments which does not depend on the assumption $\|T\| = 1$.

Lemma 1. Assume that T satisfies (b) above and there exists non-null sets D and E, an integer N and a positive number a such that

(2.8) $$\sum_{i<N} d_i(x,y) > a \qquad x \in D, \ y \in E.$$

Then the set D is bounded.

Proof. Let $f \in L_\infty^+$ be non-null and such that $\operatorname{supp} f \subset D$. Then by (b) there is an integer k such that $f' = \inf (T^k f, 1_E) \not\equiv 0$. For each $x \in D$,

$$\sum_{i<N+k} T^i f(x) \geq \sum_{i<N} T^i f'(x) \geq \int_E \sum_{i<N} d_i(x,y) f'(y) \, m(dy)$$

$$\geq a \int_E f'(y) \, m(dy) > 0.$$

This proves the lemma.

Lemma 2. Under the assumptions (b) and (c) of Theorem 3,

$$(2.9) \qquad \sum_{i<\infty} \int_A d_i(x,y)\, m(dy) = \infty$$

for each non-null set A and at each point $x \in B$.

Proof. We have for each set A and at every point x

$$(2.10) \qquad T_c^{m+n}(x,A) \geq \int d_m(x,y)\, T^n(y,A)\, m(dy).$$

Indeed, $T^n(y,A) = 0$ a.e. if $m(A) = 0$. Thus for each x $\int d_m(x,y)\, T^n(y,\cdot)\, m(dy)$ is an m-continuous measure dominated by

$$T^{m+n}(x,\cdot) = \int T^m(x,dy)\, T^n(y,\cdot).$$

The maximality of $T_c^{m+n}(x,\cdot)$ implies (2.10). Now for each $x \in B$, each A

$$\sum_{i<n} T_c^{n_o+i}(x,A) \geq \int d_{n_o}(x,y) \left[\sum_{1\leq i<n} T^i(y,A) \right] m(dy) \to \infty ,$$

the inequality being a consequence of (2.10) and the convergence to infinity following from the assumptions (b) and (c) of Theorem 3. This proves the lemma.

Proposition 1. Assume that there exists a set B with $0 < m(B) < \infty$, and a positive number δ such that for each $x \in B$,

$$m \left[y : y \in B, \ \sum_{i<\infty} d_i(x,y) = 0 \right] < (1/2 - \delta)\, m(B).$$

Then there exists a non-null set $D \subset B$ and an integer N such that (2.8) holds with $E = D$. (Hence by Lemma 1 D is bounded, if also the assumption (b) of Theorem 3 holds.)

Proof. Set for each $x \in B$, $j = 2,3,\cdots,$

$$B_j(x) = [\ y : y \in B,\ \sum_{i<j} d_i(x,y) > 1/j\ ].$$

The sequence of sets $B_j(x)$ is increasing for each x, and for each x there is a smallest integer $i(x)$ such that

$$m[B_{i(x)}(x)] > (1/2 + \delta)\ m(B).$$

Let $C_j = [\ x : x \in B,\ i(x) = j\ ]$. Then $B = \Sigma\, C_j$, hence there is an integer M such that

$$m(C_1 + \cdots + C_M) > (1 - \delta/2)\ m(B).$$

Let $A = C_1 + C_2 + \cdots + C_M$, then for $x \in A$

(2.9) $$\sum_{i<M} d_i(x,y) > 1/M$$

for y in a subset of B of measure $> (1/2 + \delta)\ m(B)$. $m(A) > (1 - \delta/2)\ m(B)$ now implies that (2.9) holds for each $x \in A$ and for y in a subset of A of measure $> (1/2 + \delta - \delta/2)\ m(B) \geq m(A)/2 + \delta\ m(A)/2$. Now let

$$H = [(x,y) : (x,y) \in A \times A,\ \sum_{i<M} d_i(x,y) > 1/M],$$

$$H_1(x) = [\ y : (x,y) \in H\ ],$$

$$H_2(y) = [\ x : (x,y) \in H\ ].$$

Let $a = m(A)$; if $\epsilon = \delta m(A)/2$ then $m[H_1(x)] \geq (1/2)a + \epsilon$. From Fubini's theorem we now have

$$\int_A m[H_1(x)]\ m(dx) = \int_A m[H_2(y)]\ m(dy) \geq a\left(\frac{1}{2}\,a + \epsilon\right).$$

Let

$$D = [\ y : m[H_2(y) > \frac{1}{2}\,a\ ],$$

then

$$\frac{1}{2} a^2 + a\epsilon \leq \int_D m[H_2(y)]\, m(dy) + \int_{A-D} m[H_2(y)]\, m(dy)$$

$$\leq am(D) + \frac{1}{2} a[a - m(D)].$$

Hence $m(D) \geq 2\epsilon$. If $x,y \in D \subset A$, then $m[H_1(x)] > \frac{1}{2} m(A) + \epsilon$, $m[H_2(y)] > \frac{1}{2} m(A)$, hence $m[H_1(x) \cap H_2(y)] > \epsilon$.

Now if $x,y \in D$, $N = 2M$, then applying (2.6) we have that for some constant c

$$\sum_{i<N} d_i(x,y) \geq c \int [\sum_{i<M} d_i(x,z)][\sum_{j<M} d_j(z,y)]\, m(dz)$$

$$\geq c \int_{H_1(x) \cap H_2(y)} \cdots \quad m(dz) \geq c\ \epsilon\ 1/M^2 > 0.$$

This proves that the set D is bounded.

We now conclude the proof of the theorem. Let for arbitrary fixed $z \in B$

$$A(z) = [\ y : y \in B, \quad \sum_{i<\infty} d_i(z,y) = 0\ ].$$

Applying Lemma 2 with $A = A(z)$ we obtain that $m[A(z)] = 0$, for each $z \in B$. Proposition 1 is now applicable and it establishes the existence of a bounded non-null set. This permits to deduce Theorem 3 from Theorem 2.

References

1. J. L. Doob, Stochastic Processes, New York, Wiley and Sons, 1953.

2. J. Feldman, "Integral kernels and invariant measures for Markov transition functions," Ann. Math. Stat., 36, (1965), 517-523.

3. T. E. Harris, "The existence of stationary measures for certain Markov processes," Proc. Third Berkeley Sumposium on Mathematical Statistics II (1956), 113-124.

4. R. Isaac, "Non-singular Markov processes have stationary measures," Ann. Math. Stat., 35, (1964), 869-871.

5. N. C. Jain, "A note on invariant measures," Ann. Math. Stat., 37, (1966), 729-732.

6. N. Jain and B. Jamison, "Contributions to the Doeblin's theory of Markov processes," Z. Wahrscheinlichkeitstheorie verw. Geb. 8, (1967), 19-40.

7. B. Jamison and S. Orey, "Markov chains recurrent in the sense of Harris," Z. Wahrscheinlichkeitstheorie verw. Geb. 8, (1967), 41-48.

8. M. Metivier, "Existence of an invariant measure and an Ornstein's ergodic theorem," Ann. Math. Stat., 40, (1969), 79-96.

9. S. T. C. Moy, "The continuous part of a Markov operator," J. Math. Mech., 18, (1968), 137-142.

10. J. Neveu, "Mathematical Foundations of the Calculus of Probability," Holden-Day, San Francisco, 1965.

11. D. S. Ornstein, "The sums of iterates of a positive operator," To appear.

12. D. S. Ornstein and L. Sucheston, "An operator theorem on L_1 convergence to zero, with applications to Markov kernels," Ann. Math. Stat., to appear.

THE AMBROSE-KAKUTANI THEOREM AND THE POISSON PROCESS

by

Fredos Papangelou

Ohio State University

§ 1. Introduction. One way to describe probabilistically point processes on the real line R is the following (see [7]). Let Ω be the space of all countably infinite sets of real numbers which are unbounded both from above and from below and are finite in every finite interval. If $\omega \in \Omega$ and $Q \in \mathcal{B}$ ($\mathcal{B}$ is the σ-field of Borel sets in R) then $N(\omega,Q)$ will denote the number of points of ω in Q. Let $\mathfrak{F}$ be the σ-field generated by the functions $N(\omega,Q)$, $Q \in \mathcal{B}$ in Ω. A probability measure P on the space $(\Omega,\mathfrak{F})$ "gives rise" to a point process on the real line without multiple points. We write $N(Q)$ for the random variable $N(\omega,Q)$. In the sequel we shall only deal with probabilities P such that the measure

$$\mu(Q) \equiv E(N(Q)) = \text{expected number of points in } Q$$

is finite whenever Q is bounded. If $X \subseteq R$ and $t \in R$ we denote by $X + t$ the set $\{x + t : x \in X\}$. A point process is called stationary if

$$P(N(Q_1) = K_1,\dots, N(Q_n) = K_n) = P(N(Q_1 + t) = K_1,\dots, N(Q_n + t) = K_n)$$

for any Borel sets $Q_1,\dots, Q_n$ any non-negative integers $K_1,\dots, K_n$ and any real t.

In [6] Palm introduced the conditional probability of the non-existence of points in the interval $(0, t)$ given that there is a point at 0. Later Khintchine [4] proved by analytic methods the existence of a whole series of similar conditional probabilities. A measure-theoretic basis for these probabilities was given in [7] where the conditional probability $P(A|t)$ of an event $A \in \mathfrak{F}$ given that there is a point at t is defined as a Radon-Nikodym derivative:

$$\int_A N(\omega,Q)\, P\,(d\omega) = \int_Q P(A|t)\, \mu\,(dt)$$

For stationary processes Neveu [5] indicated another approach to $P(A|t)$. (In this case $P(A|t) = P(A - t \mid 0)$ when the right version is chosen). There is a close connection between Neveu's approach and the Ambrose-Kakutani theorem on the representation of flows ([1], [2]), which we indicate briefly. To be precise we define a flow in Ω by

(1) $$T_t\omega = \omega - t \qquad -\infty < t < \infty$$

This is the group of shift transformations. Let $\Omega_o = \{\omega \in \Omega : 0 \in \omega\}$; Ω_o is a natural cross-section of Ω . For each $\omega \in \Omega$ let $-\tau$ be the greatest non-positive point in ω and define the mapping

(2) $$\omega \to (\omega + \tau , \tau) \in \Omega_o \times R_+$$

This is a one-to-one mapping of Ω onto the space $\bar{\Omega} = \{(\omega_o, t) : \omega_o \in \Omega_o,$ $0 \leq t < F(\omega_o)\}$ where for $\omega_o \in \Omega_o$ $F(\omega_o)$ denotes the smallest positive point in ω_o . All the conditions of [1, Theorem 1] for $\bar{\Omega}$ are satisfied and it follows from that theorem (or from the direct treatment of [5]) that there is a finite measure π on Ω_o such that the mapping (2) is an isomorphism between (Ω, P) and $(\bar{\Omega}, \pi \otimes \lambda)$ (λ is the Lebesgue measure). The probability $P(\cdot|0)$ is then the normalization of π . The induced transformation on Ω_o is the shift of the discrete time process of interpoint distances $\ldots, X_{-1}, X_o, X_1, \ldots$ defined on Ω_o (cf. [7] and [5]) . The flow (1) becomes in this representation a flow under the function F .

§ 2. Past-dependent changes of time. The main result of this section is Theorem 3 below which indicates for a large class of point processes a natural past-dependent time change that will send them onto the Poisson process. No proofs are given in the present paper. These, together with more details, will appear elsewhere. First we begin with a characterization of the Poisson process.

If Q_o is a Borel subset of the real line, we say that an event A happens in Q_o if it belongs to the σ-field generated by the random variables $N(Q)$ with $Q \subseteq Q_o$, $Q \in \mathcal{B}$. For each $t \in R$ let $\mathcal{F}_t$ be the σ-subfield of $\mathcal{F}$ generated by the events which happen in $(-\infty, t)$. The intensity measure of a not necessarily stationary point process is the measure $\mu(Q) = E(N(Q))$ on $\mathcal{B}$. Though the definition of a point process given above excludes the possibility of multiple points we repeat this in the statements of the first two theorems.

<u>Theorem 1.</u> Suppose that a not necessarily stationary point process satisfies the following conditions:

(i) There are no multiple points

(ii) The measure $\mu(Q) = E(N(Q))$ is non-atomic and finite for bounded sets

(iii) If $A \in \mathfrak{F}_s$ then $P(A|t) = P(A)$ for almost all $t \geq s$ ($P(A|t)$ is definable because of the second half of condition (ii)).

Then the process is a (not necessarily homogeneous) Poisson process with intensity measure μ.

A mixed Poisson process is one constructed as follows. A random positive number X is chosen with distribution function $F(x)$ such that $\int_0^\infty x \, dF(x) < \infty$ and a Poisson sample is built with rate X. Equivalently, define the random rate of a stationary process with $E(N(0, 1)) < \infty$ by

$$X(\omega) = \lim_{n\to\infty} \frac{N(\omega,[0, n])}{n} \qquad \text{a.s.} ;$$

then the process is mixed Poisson if and only if conditional on $X = x$ it is a Poisson process with rate x. In ergodic terms : its ergodic components are Poisson (with different rates).

<u>Theorem 2.</u> Assume for a not necessarily stationary process that

(i) There are no multiple points

(ii) $E(N(Q)) = a\lambda(Q)$ where λ is the Lebesgue measure and $a > 0$

(iii) If A happens in the complement of Q then $P(A|t_1) = P(A|t_2)$ for almost all pairs $(t_1, t_2) \in Q \times Q$.

Then the process is stationary and is in fact a mixed Poisson process.

The proof proceeds by establishing exchangeability (cf. [3]).

Consider now a stationary point process. In this case $\mu = a \cdot \lambda$ where λ is the Lebesgue measure. We can choose a version of $P(A|t)$ such that $P(A|t) = P(A - t|0)$ (see [7]). The probabilities $P(\cdot)$ and $P(\cdot\,|0)$ are singular to each other, for if $\Omega_0 = \{\omega \in \Omega : 0 \in \omega\}$ then $P(\Omega_0) = 0$, $P(\Omega_0\,|0) = 1$ ([7]). However it is possible that $P(\cdot\,|0) \ll P(\cdot)$ on the σ-field $\mathfrak{F}_0$. If this is true let $X(\omega)$ be the Radon-Nikodym derivative

$$P(A|0) = \int_A X(\omega)\, P(d\omega) \qquad A \in \mathcal{F}_0 .$$

X is $\mathcal{F}_0$-measurable. Then

$$P(A|t) = \int_A X(\omega - t)\, P(d\omega) \qquad A \in \mathcal{F}_t$$

Setting $X(t, \omega) = X(\omega - t)$ $(t \in R, \omega \in \Omega)$ we obtain a stationary and measurable stochastic process adapted to the σ-fields $\mathcal{F}_t$, $-\infty < t < \infty$. The next theorem roughly speaking states the following: Suppose that starting at 0 say, we trace the positive half-line $[0, +\infty)$ in such a way that at the time we are passing position t our speed is $\frac{1}{X(t)}$ (which can be $+\infty$). (The value of $X(t)$ is determined by the observation of the past, i.e. of what happened in $(-\infty, t)$). Then the time instants at which we shall meet all the non-negative points of the process form a homogeneous Poisson process.

For a more precise formulation define for each $\omega \in \Omega$ the function

$$\Phi_\omega (t) = \int_0^t X(\tau, \omega)\, d\tau \qquad t \geq 0$$

<u>Theorem 3.</u> For a stationary process assume $P(\cdot\,|0) \ll P(\cdot)$ on $\mathcal{F}_0$. If

$$0 \leq t_1(\omega) < t_2(\omega) < t_3(\omega) < \dots$$

are the non-negative points of a sample ω, we define the points

$$(\Pi) \qquad 0 \leq \tau_1(\omega) \leq \tau_2(\omega) \leq \tau_3(\omega) \leq \dots$$

by

$$\tau_n(\omega) = \Phi_\omega(t_n(\omega)) = \int_0^{t_n(\omega)} X(u, \omega)\, du .$$

Under the probability P the sequence (Π) is a.s. strictly increasing and is in fact a homogeneous Poisson process with the same intensity measure $\mu = a\lambda$ as the original one.

<u>Theorem 4.</u> Suppose that in Theorem 3 the random variable X is invariant (i.e. $X(t_1) = X(t_2)$ a.s. for any t_1, t_2). Then X and the process (Π) are independent and the original process is mixed Poisson with random rate aX.

This is really another way of stating (and proving) Theorem 2 in the case where stationarity is assumed.

§ 3. A problem of R. Davidson on random sets of lines. We are here interested in random sets of lines in the plane which satisfy the following two conditions: (i) the expected number of lines in the random set intersecting any given circle is finite and (ii) the "finite-dimensional distributions" of the random set are stationary under the group G of Euclidean motions. Such random sets were studied by R. Davidson in [3].

Let L be the space of all oriented lines in the plane. Choose for a natural reference system a fixed line $\ell_o \in L$ and a fixed point O on ℓ_o. The normal coordinates for an oriented line ℓ are (θ, p) where θ is the angle it makes with ℓ_o and p its signed distance from O $(0 \leq \theta < 2\pi, -\infty < p < \infty)$. If we identify ℓ with (θ, p) then we see that we are really considering random sets of points on the cylinder $C \times R$ $(C = \{\theta : 0 \leq \theta < 2\pi\})$, whose distributions are stationary under a three- parameter group acting on $C \times R$. It is well-known that the measure $d\nu = d\theta dp$ is invariant under the Euclidean group. Hence, by stationarity there is an $a > 0$ such that $E(N(Q)) = a \cdot \nu(Q)$ for every Borel subset Q of L.

Davidson has asked [3] whether a stationary random set with a.s. no parallel lines is a doubly stochastic Poisson one (i.e. it is a "Poisson set" built on a random but stationary measure in L). We shall give a partial answer by determining the structure of such random sets under a condition similar to that of Theorem 3.

It can be proved that one can define conditional probabilities $P(A|\ell)$ $(\ell \in L)$ in the same way as in [7] and that in the stationary case they can be chosen so that $P(TA|T\ell) = P(A|\ell)$ for every Euclidean transformation T. Write $\ell_1 || \ell_2$ whenever ℓ_1, ℓ_2 are parallel with the same orientation.

<u>Lemma</u> (R. Davidson). Suppose $X(\ell)$, $\ell \in L$ is a stochastic process parametrized by the elements of L, which is stationary under G and continuous in the mean. If $\ell_1 || \ell_2$ then $X(\ell_1) = X(\ell_2)$ a.s.

In fact fix a point S on ℓ_1 and let $\bar{\ell}$ be the line passing through S and forming an angle ϵ with ℓ_1. Then $E\,|\,X(\ell_1) - X(\ell_2)\,| \leq$

$\leq E \mid X(\ell_1) - X(\bar{\ell}) \mid + E \mid X(\bar{\ell}) - X(\ell_2) \mid = 2E \mid X(\ell_1) - X(\bar{\ell}) \mid$ by stationarity, and this is small when ϵ is small.

Suppose now $P(\cdot|\ell) \ll P(\cdot)$ on the σ-field of events happening in $L - \{\ell\}$, with Radon-Nikodym derivative $X(\ell, \omega)$. Here $X(\ell, \omega)$ is a stationary process with $EX(\ell) = 1$. There is an obvious measurable version and using standard techniques one can show it is continuous in the mean. By the above lemma the process $X(\ell, \omega)$ is essentially a process $X(\theta, \omega)$ parametrized by the first coordinate θ of $\ell = (\theta, p)$, i.e. a stochastic process on the circle $0 \leq \theta < 2\pi$, stationary under rotations. Further $P(A|\ell_1) = P(A|\ell_2)$ whenever $\ell_1 || \ell_2$ and A happens in $L - \{\ell_1, \ell_2\}$.

<u>Theorem 5.</u> Suppose that for some (and then for all) $\ell \in L$ $P(\cdot|\ell) \ll P(\cdot)$ on the σ-field of events happening in $L - \{\ell\}$. Then the process has the following structure: On the circle C we put the (stationary under rotations) random measure $m(\omega)$ whose density is $X(\theta, \omega)$, $0 \leq \theta < 2\pi$, form the product measure $m \otimes \lambda$ where λ is the Lebesgue measure, and pick a random "Poisson set" from the measure space $(L, a(m \otimes \lambda))$.

REFERENCES

1. W. Ambrose, Representation of ergodic flows, Ann. Math 42, 723-739 (1941)

2. W. Ambrose and S. Kakutani, Structure and continuity of measurable flows, Duke Math J. 9, 25-42 (1942).

3. R. Davidson, Thesis (Chapter 6: Stochastic processes of flats; Chapter 7: Exchangeable stochastic point processes), University of Cambridge (1968).

4. A. Y. Khintchine, Mathematical methods in the theory of queueing, Griffin's Statistical Monographs and Courses, No. 7, 1960.

5. J. Neveu, Sur la structure des processus ponctuels stationnaires, C. R. Acad. Sc. Paris 267 Serie A, 561-564, (1968).

6. C. Palm, Variation in intensity in telephone conversations, Ericsson Technics 1-189, 1943-44.

7. C. Ryll-Nardzewski, Remarks on processes of calls, Proc. of Fourth Berkeley Symposium, Vol. 2, 455-465 (1960).

GENERALIZED MARTINGALES*

by

M. M. Rao

Carnegie-Mellon University

1. Introduction. At least from the middle 1940's, it was believed that martingale and ergodic theories, being essentially theories of integration in infinitely many variables, are closely related to each other. The first explicit formulation of such a relation seems to be due to Jerison [10] in 1959 who showed that the Hopf-Dunford-Schwartz ergodic theorem and a martingale theorem for the decreasing index, on a σ-finite measure space, are equivalent. Similar equivalence also holds between the Hurewicz ergodic theorem and a martingale theorem. In either of these results the measure space for the martingale theory cannot be taken to be finite and the known convergence theory ([10],[4],[9]) for decreasing indexed martingales is found to be inadequate. This incidentally shows the need for a development of the martingale theory in this direction. Some new techniques seem desirable here. For an account of the ergodic theory, until 1956, see [7].

The connection between the ergodic and martingale theories indicated the possibility of developing the necessary (global) maximal theorems (i.e. inequalities) that give the pointwise convergence of both the theories. This point of view has been worked out fully by Tulcea [9], in 1963, who then deduced the corresponding martingale and ergodic theorems. On the other hand, a different point of view of a unified theory of these two studies, which perhaps contains other novelties, is possible, and can be stated as follows.

Since martingales are defined in terms of a family of commuting

*Supported under the NSF Grant GP-15632.

conditional expectation operators, which are by definition also contractive projections (say on the Lebesgue spaces), and since also the operators associated with the ergodic theorems (e.g. those arising from measure preserving transformations and their generalizations) are contractions with certain additional properties, it is natural to look for the existence of any operator limit theorems which unify both the above mentioned cases. Such a unified theory, through a class of what are called the Reynold's operators, was discovered by Rota [20] in 1961, under the name of generalized martingales, who then presented a basic pointwise convergence theorem for such martingales on L^p, $p > 1$. In the context of a class of Orlicz spaces, including the above spaces, the author [14] has given in 1966 a mean convergence theorem for the generalized martingales of Rota. This study depends crucially on the structure of Reynold's operators [22]. The technical problems were such that the underlying measure space in thses studies was finite which still unifies the corresponding classical ergodic and martingale cases.

The purpose of this paper is to pursue this latter point of view and develop the convergence theory for the generalized martingales on a broad class of Banach function spaces, on a σ-finite measure space, including the earlier study. This involves, first, an extension of Rota's representation theorem [22] which is given in Section 3 below after presenting the necessary preliminary material in Section 2. The convergence theory is included in Section 4 and the final section contains some remarks on certain other extensions and related problems.

2. Preliminaries. In this section various concepts used in the Introduction together with some necessary auxiliary results for later use, will be given. It is convenient to start with a description of Banach function spaces in a form suitable for the work here. The

general terminology follows Dunford-Schwartz, [5].

Let (Ω,Σ,μ) be a (positive) measure space and L^ρ be the subspace of equivalence classes of scalar measurable functions on Ω such that $\rho(f) < \infty$ where $\rho(\cdot)$ is a function norm, i.e., (i) $\rho(f) = \rho(|f|)$, (ii) $0 \leq f_1 \leq f_2$, a.e., implies $\rho(f_1) \leq \rho(f_2)$, (iii) $\rho(\cdot)$ is a norm, and (iv) $0 \leq f_n \uparrow f$ a.e., implies $\rho(f_n) \uparrow \rho(f)$. This last property is called the Fatou property of the norm. Under these conditions L^ρ is a Banach (function) space where functions of the same equivalence class are identified here and hereafter. The L^ρ need not be complete if ρ verifies only (i) to (iii). For an account of the basic facts of L^ρ-spaces, see [25]. f in L^ρ is said to have an absolutely continuous norm (a.c.n) if $\rho(f\chi_{A_n}) \downarrow 0$ for all $A_n \in \Sigma$ with $A_n \downarrow \emptyset$. Let $L^\rho_a \subset L^\rho$ be the collection of all elements with a.c.n. It is easily checked that the L^p, $p \geq 1$ and more generally the Orlicz spaces L^Φ are subsumed under this set up. They have all their elements with a.c.n., if $1 \leq p < \infty$ and $\Phi(2x) \leq c\Phi(x)$ for $x \geq 0$, $0 < c < \infty$, but the L^ρ spaces can be more inclusive.

Even if $\mu(\Omega) < \infty$, an L^ρ space need not have constants in it. Consequently it will be assumed that each L^ρ considered below has a weak unit f_0 in the following sense. A weak unit is any elementary f $(= \sum_{i=1}^{\infty} a_i\chi_{A_i})$ in L^ρ such that $f > 0$ a.e. on Ω, $A_i \in \Sigma$ are disjoint and $\rho(\chi_{A_i}) < \infty$. It is no restriction to assume that f is also bounded. Let $\Sigma_i = \sigma\{\{A_i\} : f = \sum_{i=1}^{\infty} a_i\chi_{A_i}, f \text{ a weak unit}\}$, i.e., Σ_i is the σ-field determined by $\{A_i\}$. If $\mathfrak{F} = \{\Sigma_i \subset \Sigma : \Sigma_i$ determined by a weak unit$\}$, then $\mathfrak{F}$ is partially ordered by $\Sigma_i < \Sigma_j$ iff $\Sigma_i \supset \Sigma_j$. If μ is σ-finite, then it was shown in [12] that a weak unit always exists in any L^ρ. In this case $\mathfrak{F}$ is non-empty. By Zorn's lemma, $\mathfrak{F}$ has a maximal element Σ_0. [In the L^p or L^Φ

cases, if $\mu(\Omega) < \infty$, then $\Sigma_o = \{\emptyset,\Omega\}$, the trivial σ-field.] Let f_o be the weak unit determined by Σ_o. In what follows a weak unit signifies such a (non-unique) minimal f_o. Note that $\Sigma_o = \sigma(f_o)$. Hereafter μ is assumed σ-finite; the $\{A_i\}$ of f_o also can be $\mu(A_i)<\infty$, [12].

The following facts on L^ρ will be used. (For a proof, see [25].) The set $L^\rho_a \subset L^\rho$ is a Banach space. If $f_o \in L^\rho_a$, then the adjoint space $(L^\rho_a)^*$ can be identified with $L^{\rho'}$ on (Ω,Σ,μ), where ρ' is the associate norm of ρ defined by

$$\rho'(f) = \sup\{ |\int_\Omega fg d\mu| : \rho(g) \leq 1, g \in L^\rho\}. \tag{1}$$

Also under the Fatou property of ρ and σ-finiteness of μ, it is true that $(\rho')' = \rho'' = \rho$. By removing a certain maximal "unfriendly set" from the measure space (Ω,Σ,μ), it may be assumed that the essentially bounded functions of L^ρ_a also belong to $L^{\rho'}$, the associate space defined above. In what follows an L^ρ-space is assumed to have been readjusted to possess the above structure. All the Lebesgue and Orlicz spaces automatically have this structure.

A linear contraction $R : L^\rho \mapsto L^\rho$ is said to be a Reynold's operator if it verifies the algebraic identity:

$$R(fg) = (Rf)(Rg) + R[(f-Rf)(g-Rg)], \quad f,g \in L^\rho \cap L^\infty. \tag{2}$$

A linear contractive projection $P : L^\rho \mapsto L^\rho$ is termed an averaging operator if the following algebraic identity holds:

$$P(fPg) = (Pf)(Pg), \quad f,g \in L^\rho \cap L^\infty. \tag{3}$$

Thus every averaging is also a Reynold's operator and every conditional expectation is an averaging. The relation between the last two operators on L^ρ-spaces, is determined in [17]. Finally a generalized martingale on L^ρ is a family of pairwise commuting Reynold's operators $\{R_t, t > 0\}$ on L^ρ which satisfies the identity:

$$(sR_t - tR_s)R_s f = (s-t)R_t R_s^2 f, \quad 0 < t < s, \; f \in L^\rho \cap L^\infty. \qquad (4)$$

This concept is due to Rota [20]. It is immediate that, for $\mathcal{B}_t \subset \Sigma$, a filtering (to the left) family of σ-fields such that μ on $\mathcal{B}_t$ is σ-finite, if $R_t = E^{\mathcal{B}_t}$ (the conditional expectation operator) then (4) holds automatically and $\{R_t f, t > 0\}$ is a decreasing martingale in the classical sense (and an increasing one is obtained if s and t are interchanged in the identity of (4)). It was noted in [20] that the classical ergodic averages also are subsumed under (4).

It will be illuminating at this point to note that, formally, Jerison's [10] formulation of the ergodic theorems as martingales, satisfies (4). Thus let $\mathbb{N}$ denote the non-negative integers, $\mathfrak{h}$ the power set of $\mathbb{N}$ and ν be the counting measure. Let $\mathcal{G}_n = \sigma\{(0,1,\ldots,n-1),\{k\},k \geq n\}$ be the σ-algebra generated by the sets shown and let $(S,\mathcal{S},\zeta)$ be the product measure space of (Ω,Σ,μ) and $(\mathbb{N},\mathfrak{h},\nu)$ so that ζ is σ-finite. If $\mathfrak{F}_n \subset \mathcal{S}$ is the product σ-field of Σ and $\mathcal{G}_n$, then $\mathfrak{F}_n \supset \mathfrak{F}_{n+1}$ and ζ on $\mathfrak{F}_n$ is σ-finite for all n. Hence $E^{\mathfrak{F}_n}$, the conditional expectation operator, exists for each n, [4]. If $T : L^\rho \mapsto L^\rho$ is a bounded linear operator, and $f \in L^\rho$, let $h(\omega,k) = (T^k f)(\omega) : \Omega \times \mathbb{N} \mapsto \mathbb{R}$, so that h is $\mathcal{S}$-measurable, and if $h_n = E^{\mathfrak{F}_n}(h)$, then, as noted in [10], it can be checked that $h_n = \frac{1}{n}\sum_{k=0}^{n-1} T^k f$, on $\Omega \times \{0,1,\ldots,n-1\}$, and $= T^k f$ on $\Omega \times \{k \geq n\}$. Thus $\{h_n, \mathfrak{F}_n, n \geq 1\}$ is a decreasing martingale and $h_n \to h_0$ a.e., iff $\frac{1}{n}\sum_{k=0}^{n-1} T^k f \to h_0$, a.e. Since $E^{\mathfrak{F}_n}$ is a projection operator, it is clear that $E^{\mathfrak{F}_n}$ formally verifies (4). However, even if T is induced by a measure preserving transformation, neither h nor h_n belongs to L^ρ on $(S,\mathcal{S},\zeta)$ except in trivial cases. This statement holds true even if $\mu(\Omega) < \infty$, and L^{ρ} is replaced by L^{p}, because ζ is always non-finite. The counter examples of ([4], p. 272) and of [10] show that the martingale of the type $\{h_n, \mathfrak{F}_n, n \geq 1\}$ need not generally converge a.e. when $\int_S |h_1| d\zeta = \int_{\mathbb{N}} \int_{\Omega} |h| d\mu d\nu < \infty$ is false. In the present case this integral is always infinite, but the Hopf-Dunford-Schwartz theorem shows that the martingale converges a.e. whenever $f \in L^p$, $1 \leq p < \infty$, and T is a contraction on both L^1 and L^{∞}. No martingale theory that applies here (and such a result must exist, as abundently suggested by the Dunford-Schwartz theory) is available at this time. As shown in [10], the Hurewicz ergodic theorem also gives another class of martingales. These results show a need to develop the corresponding convergence theory of decreasing martingales on σ-finite measure spaces. On the other hand, the operators $\{R_t, t > 0\}$ verifying (4) do unify the ergodic and martingale theories to a large extent, as noted earlier, and thus the terminology 'generalized martingales' may be considered as justified. The convergence theory of the latter is the subject of this paper.

For the above stated theory, however, it is essential that the structure theory of R_t on L^{ρ} be worked out beforehand. Thus an integral representation of R_t will be given in the next section for a large class of L^{ρ}-spaces, and it will be utilized in the following section for the limit theorems. It also has some independent interest.

3. Representation. A general characterization of Reynold's operators on a large class of L^{ρ}-spaces is given in the following result.

Theorem 1. Let $L^{\rho}(\Sigma) = L^{\rho}_a(\Sigma)$ be a Banach function space on (Ω, Σ, μ), a σ-finite measure space, as defined above. Let f_o be a weak unit which may (and will) be taken to be in $L^{\rho}(\Sigma) \cap L^{\rho'}(\Sigma) \cap L^{\infty}(\Sigma)$, where

ρ' is the associate norm of ρ given by (1). Let $R : L^{\rho}(\Sigma) \mapsto L^{\rho}(\Sigma)$ be a weakly compact (contractive) Reynold's operator such that (1) $Rf_o = f_o$, and (2) $R(L^{\rho} \cap L^{\infty}) \subset L^{\rho} \cap L^{\infty}$. Then there exist uniquely (i) a σ-field $\mathcal{B} \subset \Sigma$ relative to which f_o is measurable, (ii) a conditional expectation $E^{\mathcal{B}} : L^{\rho}(\Sigma) \mapsto L^{\rho}(\mathcal{B})$, and (iii) a strongly continuous semi-group $\{V(t), t \geq 0\}$ induced by a measure preserving transformation on $\mathcal{B}$, in terms of which the following representation holds (as a Bochner integral):

$$Rf = \int_0^{\infty} e^{-t} V(t) E^{\mathcal{B}}(f)\,dt, \quad f \in L^{\rho}(\Sigma), \tag{5}$$

where (a) $R(L^{\rho}(\mathcal{B})) \subset L^{\rho}(\mathcal{B})$ and is dense in the latter, (b) R and $E^{\mathcal{B}}$ commute, so that $RE^{\mathcal{B}} = E^{\mathcal{B}}R = R$.

Remark. This result, for $L^{\rho} = L^2$ and $R1 = 1$, was obtained by Rota in [22]. The proof of the above theorem is long and involved. The main idea is to reduce the result to the last half of Rota's proof in [22]. The needed work is to find substitute results for the arguments of [22] where a theorem of Nagy on the identity of fix points of a contraction and its adjoint in a Hilbert space was used. Another form of the above result was given in [19] where a point of view of vector measures is employed. For the L^{Φ}-spaces, a result of this type was given in [18], which still needs several auxiliary propositions.

For the proof of the following result, which is a special case of one proved in [18], is required.

Proposition 2. Let $L^{\rho}(\Sigma) = L^{\rho}_a(\Sigma)$ be a real Banach function space with a weak unit f_o on (Ω, Σ, μ) as in Theorem 1. Then a subspace $\mathfrak{m} \subset L^{\rho}(\Sigma)$ is a measurable subspace (i.e. is of the form $\mathfrak{m} = L^{\rho}(\mathcal{B})$, $\mathcal{B} \subset \Sigma$ and $\mu|\mathcal{B}$ is σ-finite) iff either (i) $\mathfrak{m}$ is a Banach lattice containing a weak unit (can be taken as f_o), or (ii) the bounded functions of $\mathfrak{M}$ form a (norm) dense subalgebra containing a **weak** unit.

The proof of this result is based on a Stone-Weierstrass type argument (cf. [15], Thm. 2.1) and, since a slightly more general form is given in [18], it will be omitted here.

Proof of Theorem. The first part of the proof is, under the present hypotheses, to reduce the result to the L^2-case, i.e., to show that R is also defined (and a contractive operator) on $L^2(\Sigma)$, and then the proof follows from that of [22]. However, this reduction involves many details and computations. The details can be outlined as follows.

Let $\mathfrak{M}_o = R(L^\rho(\Sigma))$. Then $f_o \in \mathfrak{M}_o$ and if $\mathfrak{M}$ is the L^ρ-closure of $\mathfrak{M}_o$, then from the hypothesis that $R(L^\rho \cap L^\infty) \subset L^\rho \cap L^\infty$, it is easily seen that the bounded functions of $\mathfrak{M}$ form an algebra which is dense. Since ρ is an a.c.n., the above proposition implies $\mathfrak{M} = L^\rho(\mathcal{B})$ for a σ-field $\mathcal{B} \subset \Sigma$, and the fact that $f_o \in \mathfrak{M}$ yields that μ on $\mathcal{B}$ $(= \mu_{\mathcal{B}})$ is also σ-finite. It is first claimed that $P = E^{\mathcal{B}}(\cdot) : L^\rho(\Sigma) \mapsto L^\rho(\mathcal{B})$, the conditional expectation (which exists), is a contractive projection [16], and secondly that P and R commute on $\mathfrak{M}$.

To see the truth of the first statement, let $f \in L^\rho(\Sigma)$ be arbitrary. Consider $\nu_f : \mathcal{B} \mapsto \mathbb{R}$, the line, by $\nu_f(A) = \int_A f d\mu$, $A \in \mathcal{B}$. Then ν_f is $\mu_{\mathcal{B}}$-continuous and, by the Radon-Nikodým theorem, there is a (a.e.) unique $\mathcal{B}$-measurable $\tilde{f}$ such that $\nu_f(A) = \int_A \tilde{f} d\mu_{\mathcal{B}}$, $A \in \mathcal{B}$, and the map $E^{\mathcal{B}} : f \mapsto \tilde{f}$ is seen to be the conditional expectation. The only less evident fact is that $\rho(E^{\mathcal{B}}(f)) \leq \rho(f)$, and this is noted thus. For this it is sufficient to consider $f \geq 0$ so that, then, $\tilde{f} = E^{\mathcal{B}}(f) \geq 0$, a.e. As noted in Section 2, the second associate norm $\rho'' = \rho$. Let $\tilde{\nu}_f(A) = \int_A f d\mu$, $A \in \Sigma$, and consider

$$\rho''(f) = \sup\{|\int_\Omega fgd\mu| : \rho'(g) \leq 1, g\in L^{\rho'}(\Sigma)\}$$

$$= \sup\{|\int_\Omega gd\tilde{\nu}_f| : \rho'(g) \leq 1, g\in L^{\rho'}(\Sigma)\}$$

$$= \rho''(\tilde{\nu}_f), \text{ by definition of } \rho'' \ (= \rho)\text{-variation of } \tilde{\nu}_f,$$

(cf. e.g. [6]). But $\nu_f = \tilde{\nu}_f|\mathcal{B}$, the restriction of $\tilde{\nu}_f$ to $\mathcal{B}$. Then $\rho''(\nu_f) \leq \rho''(\tilde{\nu}_f)$. However the mapping $\lambda : f \mapsto \tilde{\nu}_f$, by $\lambda(f)(A) = \tilde{\nu}_f(A)$, $A\in\Sigma$, is an injection of L^ρ into the space of additive set functions of ρ $(= \rho'')$-bounded variation vanishing on μ-null sets. This was noted in ([13], Lemma 5) for Orlicz spaces, and was systematically used and extended in [24]. The needed special result in the context of L^ρ-spaces is easy. A quick proof can also be constructed from the work of [6]. Thus

$$\rho(f) = \rho''(f) = \rho''(\tilde{\nu}_f) \geq \rho''(\nu_f) = \rho''(\tilde{f}) = \rho(\tilde{f}) = \rho(E^{\mathcal{B}}(f)).$$

This proves the first assertion.

It is clear that on $\mathfrak{m}$, $PR = R$ with $P = E^{\mathcal{B}}$. The complete statement is related to other facts and hence $PR = RP$ comes out only after using the further hypothesis and with considerable work which, however, will be needed in the proof. Thus the weak compactness of the contractive R on $L^\rho(\Sigma)$ implies, by ([5], VIII.8.6), $\frac{1}{n}\sum_{i=0}^{n-1} R^i$ converges strongly to a projection (= Q, say) onto $\mathfrak{m}_1 = \{f : Rf = f\} \subset \mathfrak{m}$, and $f_o\in\mathfrak{m}_1$. Moreover $RQ = QR = R$ on $\mathfrak{m}_1$. Consequently the adjoints verify $R^* = R^*Q^* = Q^*R^*$ so that R^* is also reduced by the projection Q^*. Since R^* is also weakly compact (cf. [5], p. 485) it follows that $\frac{1}{n}\sum_{i=0}^{n-1}(R^*)^i \to \overline{Q}$ (say), strongly in $(L^\rho)^* = L^{\rho'}$, as earlier, and $\overline{Q}$ is a contractive projection. However, considering the weak operator topology in the above (together with the second adjoints) one easily obtains $\overline{Q} = Q^*$ on $L^{\rho'}$. If $\mathfrak{n}_1 = (I-Q)(L^\rho)$, it follows that the range of Q^* is $\mathfrak{n}_1^\perp$, the annihilator of $\mathfrak{n}_1$, and the null space of Q^* is $\mathfrak{m}_1^\perp$. Thus $\mathfrak{n}_1^\perp$ is the set of fix points of R^*. On the other hand $\mathfrak{m}_1^* \subset \mathfrak{n}_1^\perp$, and $f_o \in \mathfrak{m}_1$. But the hypothesis (2) on the Reynold's operator R again implies that the bounded functions of $\mathfrak{m}_1$ form an algebra and if $\mathfrak{m}_2$ is the norm closure of this algebra then, by the proposition, it is of the form $L^\rho(\mathcal{B}_1)$ for some σ-field $\mathcal{B}_1 \subset \Sigma$. Clearly $f_o \in L^\rho(\mathcal{B}_1) \subset \mathfrak{m}_1$ so that $\mu|\mathcal{B}_1$ is σ-finite, and also $f_o \in (L^\rho(\mathcal{B}_1))^* = L^{\rho'}(\mathcal{B}_1) \subset \mathfrak{m}_1^* \subset \mathfrak{n}_1^\perp$. It follows therefore that $R^* f_o = f_o$. This is a key reduction in the proof.

Next consider any $f, g \in L^\rho(\Sigma) \cap L^\infty(\Sigma)$, and the Reynold's identity (2) in the form

$$\int_\Omega f_o R(fRg + gRf)\,d\mu = \int_\Omega f_o[Rf\cdot Rg + R(Rf\cdot Rg)]\,d\mu. \tag{6}$$

This equation is well-defined since the bounded functions of L^ρ belong to $L^{\rho'}$ also. Since $(L^\rho)^* = L^{\rho'}$, noted already, the adjoint R^* of R verifies $\int_\Omega g(Rh)\,d\mu = \int_\Omega (R^* g)h\,d\mu$ for all $g \in L^{\rho'}$, $h \in L^\rho$. Thus (6) can be written, on taking adjoints appropriately, as follows.

$$\int_\Omega (R^* f_o)(fRg + gRf)\,d\mu = \int_\Omega [R^* f_o\cdot(Rf\cdot Rg) + f_o(Rf\cdot Rg)]\,d\mu. \tag{7}$$

Since $R^* f_o = f_o$, and since by the Reynold's identity, for any $h \in L^\rho$, one has $R(f_o h) = f_o Rh$, the equation (7) can be written as

$$\int_\Omega (fR(gf_o) + (f_o g)Rf)\,d\mu = 2\int_\Omega Rf\cdot R(gf_o)\,d\mu. \tag{8}$$

But $Rf \in L^\rho \cap L^\infty \subset L^{\rho'}$, by hypothesis. Hence taking adjoints appropriately in (8), one has

$$\int_\Omega (R^* f + Rf)gf_o\,d\mu = 2\int_\Omega R^*(Rf)\cdot gf_o\,d\mu. \tag{9}$$

Taking $g = \chi_A$, with $\rho(\chi_A) < \infty$, and noting such functions are dense in L^ρ, (9) yields the important relation (since $f_o > 0$),

$$(R^* + R)f = 2R^*Rf, \quad f \in L^{\rho} \cap L^{\infty}. \tag{10}$$

This is another key reduction in the proof.

The point now is to show that R is also defined in $L^2(\Omega,\Sigma,\mu)$ and has a bounded extension onto the whole space, then the last half of the proof of [22] applies. For this, let $U = I - 2R$ on L^{ρ}. Then by (10), for any $h \in L^{\rho} \cap L^{\infty}$, $U^*Uh = h$. Moreover for such h

$$\int_{\Omega} (Uh)^2 d\mu = \int_{\Omega} U^*Uh \cdot h d\mu = \int_{\Omega} h^2 d\mu, \tag{11}$$

and all the quantities are finite. In fact any $h \in L^{\rho}(\Sigma) \cap L^{\infty} \subset L^{\rho'}(\Sigma)$, $\int_{\Omega} h^2 d\mu \leq \rho(h)\rho'(h) < \infty$ so that $L^{\rho} \cap L^{\infty} \subset L^2$ as well, and $f_o \in L^{\rho}(\Sigma) \cap L^{\rho'}(\Sigma) \cap L^2(\Sigma) \cap L^{\infty}(\Sigma)$. Thus (11) implies that U is an isometry in the L^2-norm on all the bounded functions $\mathfrak{F}$ of L^{ρ}. If $\mathcal{G}$ is the L^2-closure of $\mathfrak{F}$, then U can be extended to $\tilde{U}$ on $L^2(\Omega,\Sigma,\mu)$ by defining it to be identity on $\mathcal{G}^{\perp}$ so that $\tilde{U}$ is an isometry on all of $L^2(\Sigma)$. Actually the result of ([15], Thm. 21) implies that the σ-field generated by $\mathcal{G}$ (when completed for μ) is Σ so that $\mathcal{G}^{\perp} = \{0\}$. It now follows that R is defined and continuous in the L^2-norm also, on $\mathcal{G}$ $(= L^2(\Sigma))$.

The operator $\tilde{U}$ can be used to obtain various properties of R. Applying the mean ergodic theorem to $\tilde{U}$ on $L^2(\Sigma)$, it follows that $\frac{1}{n}\sum_{i=0}^{n-1} \tilde{U}^i$ converges strongly to a projection P_1 onto the fix points of $\tilde{U}$ in $L^2(\Sigma)$, and $Q_1 = I - P_1$ has its range as the closure of $(I-\tilde{U})(L^2(\Sigma))$ which is immediately seen to be the L^2-closure of $2R(\mathcal{G}) = \mathcal{R}$, say. Then Q_1 and $\tilde{U}$, and hence Q_1 and R, commute on $\mathcal{R}$. Since $Rf_o = f_o \in \mathcal{G} \subset \mathcal{R}$, it follows, using the by now familiar argument, that $\mathcal{R} = L^2(\mathcal{B}_2)$ and $Q_1 = E^{\mathcal{B}_2}$ for a sub σ-field $\mathcal{B}_2$ of Σ with $\mu|\mathcal{B}_2$ being σ-finite. It is now clear that R is defined and continuous on all of $L^2(\Sigma)$. Since $\mathcal{R}$ is the L^2-closure of the range of R and $\mathfrak{M}$ is the L^{ρ}-closure of the range of R on the respective spaces, it follows by the result of [15], noted above, that $\mathcal{B} = \mathcal{B}_2$. Thus $P (= E^{\mathcal{B}} = E^{\mathcal{B}_2})$ and R commute on $\mathfrak{M} = L^{\rho}(\mathcal{B})$. This proves the second statement promised earlier as well as parts (i), (ii) and (a), (b) of the theorem. The crucial (iii) can now be concluded with [22], and only a very brief account need be recalled here.

The above work shows that R is a contractive Reynold's operator on $L^2(\Sigma)$ also. If $D = I-R^{-1}$ on $\mathfrak{M}$, which reduces R, then D is a closed (densely defined and unbounded) operator on $\mathfrak{M}$ whose spectrum lies in the lower half of the complex plane and by the work of [22], it is the infinitesimal generator of a strongly continuous semi-group $\{V(t), t \geq 0\}$ induced by a measure-preserving transformation on Σ, and the resolvent is given (due to the Hille-Yosida theorem) by the Bochner integral

$$R(\lambda, D) f = \int_0^{\infty} e^{-\lambda t} V(t) f dt, \quad f \in L^{\rho}(\mathcal{B}), \ \lambda > 0, \tag{12}$$

since $R(1,D) = R$, one obtains (5) from (12) at once, since $E^{\mathcal{B}}(L^{\rho}(\Sigma)) = L^{\rho}(\mathcal{B})$. This concludes the proof.

<u>Remark</u>. The above proof shows that the hypothesis (2) of the theorem may be replaced by: (2') R is positive. Here the lattice part of the proposition can be used, and the result is seen to be valid in this case also.

Since a bounded operator in any reflexive Banach space is weakly compact ([5], p. 483), the following result is a consequence of the theorem (and the above remark).

<u>Corollary</u> 3. Let $L^{\rho}(\Sigma)$ be a reflexive space on (Ω, Σ, μ) and $f_0 \in L^{\rho} \cap L^{\rho'}$ be a weak unit. If R is any contractive Reynold's

operator in $L^\rho(\Sigma)$ such that $Rf_o = f_o$ and either $R(L^\rho \cap L^\infty) \subset L^\rho \cap L^\infty$, or R is positive, then R admits the representation (5) of the theorem.

This is Rota's result with $L^\rho = L^2$. It is of interest to note that if R is any positive contraction in L^1 and L^Φ, with $\varphi(x) = x \log^+ x$ (or more generally any strictly convex Young's function) then R is also a contraction on all L^p, $1 \leq p \leq \infty$, so that, in particular, it maps bounded functions into bounded functions. This was first proved in [1] if $\Phi(x) = |x|^p$, $p > 1$, and in the above form in [14]. In this alternate form, the weak compactness hypothesis of R can be dropped, since it can be shown first to have an extension to L^∞ so as to be a contraction. This form was discussed in [14]. The proof can be simplified and the result slightly extended, if the hypothesis is taken to be: $Rf_o = f_o$ and $R^* f_o = f_o$. However, this will not be a satisfactory extension as long as R^* comes explicitly into the hypothesis.

This representation theory is now applied to prove the ergodic-martingale theorems of this paper in the next section.

4. <u>Convergence</u>. As noted earlier, the convergence theory of generalized martingales uses crucially the representation of the Reynold's operators of the preceding section. Consequently, it depends also on the properties of the semi-group $\{V(t), t \geq 0\}$. For this purpose some results of E. Hille on the behavior of $V(t)$, as specialized to the L^ρ-spaces, will be needed and so they will be sketched below.

<u>Definition</u>. Let $\{T(t), t \geq 0\}$ be a strongly continuous positive contractive semi-group of operators on a Banach space X. If

$$\omega_o = \lim_{t\to\infty} \frac{\log\|T(t)\|}{t}$$

(which exists and $-\infty \leq \omega_o < \infty$), then the semi-group is termed of <u>class</u> (E) (or of ergodic class) whenever the following two conditions hold: (i) $X_o = \{x : \int_o^1 \|T(t)x\|dt < \infty\}$ is dense in X, and (ii) the operator $R(\lambda)$, defined by $R(\lambda)x = \int_o^{\infty} e^{-\lambda t}T(t)xdt$ (Bochner integral), is a mapping of $X_o \mapsto X_o$ and is bounded for each $\lambda > \omega_o$ and $x \in X_o$.

Note that if $T(t)$ is a contractive family, then $\omega_o \leq 0$, and this is true for the $\{V(t), t \geq 0\}$ of Theorem 1. The following result is a special case of a theorem of Hille ([8], p. 520).

<u>Proposition</u> 4. Let $\{T(t), t \geq 0\}$ be a strongly continuous positive contractive semi-group of operators of class (E) on $L^{\rho}(\Sigma) = L^{\rho}_a(E)$. If moreover, $\|T(t)f\|_{\infty} \leq \|f\|_{\infty}$ for each $f \in L^{\rho} \cap L^{\infty}$, then (i) $\lim_{\lambda\to 0^+} \lambda R(\lambda)$ exists, (ii) $\lim_{\lambda\to\infty} \lambda R(\lambda)$ exists, both in the strong operator topology, where $R(\lambda)$ is given in the above definition. In case L^{ρ} is reflexive, then the same conclusions hold for any strongly continuous contractive semi-group of class (E) on L^{ρ}.

<u>Proof</u>. The result is a consequence of ([8], 18.7.1 and 18.7.3) if it is shown that, for each $f \in L^{\rho}(\Sigma) \cap L^{\infty}(\Sigma)$, the sets

(i) $\{\lambda R(\lambda)f, 0 < \lambda < \omega\}$ for some $\omega > 0$, and

(ii) $\{\lambda R(\lambda)f, \omega < \lambda < \infty\}$, for some $\omega \geq 0$,

are conditionally weakly sequentially compact, since bounded functions in L^{ρ} are dense under the present hypothesis.

Since $\|\lambda R(\lambda)\| \leq 1$ for all $\lambda > 0$, let $f_o \in L^{\rho} \cap L^{\infty}$ be arbitrary. Let $B = \{\lambda R(\lambda)f_o, 0 < \lambda < \omega\}$. Then $B \subset L^{\rho}$ is bounded. Now the conditional weak sequential compactness of B follows from ([12], Thm. 5.1) if for each $g \in L^{\rho'}$ the following two conditions are verified:

(a) $N(g) = \sup\{\int_{\Omega} |fg| d\mu : f \in B\} < \infty$

(b) $N(g\chi_{E_n}) \downarrow 0$ for any $E_n \in \Sigma$, $E_n \downarrow \emptyset$.

By the Hölder inequality $N(g) \leq \rho(f)\rho'(g) \leq \rho(f_o)\rho'(g) < \infty$, and (a) holds. Only for (b) the additional hypothesis is needed. Thus

$$N(g\chi_{E_n}) = \sup\{\int_\Omega |g\chi_{E_n} f|d\mu, f = \lambda R(\lambda)f_o \in B\}$$

$$= \sup\{\int_\Omega |\chi_{E_n} g\lambda\int_o^\infty e^{-\lambda t}T(t)f_o dt|d\mu, 0 < \lambda < \omega\}$$

$$\leq \sup\{\int_o^\infty \lambda e^{-\lambda t}\int_\Omega |g\chi_{E_n} T(t)f_o|d\mu dt, 0 < \lambda < \omega\}$$

by the Fubini theorem ([8], or [5]). But by the positivity of $T(t)$, and of its contraction on $L^\rho \cap L^\infty$ in L^∞-norm imply $|T(t)f_o| \leq |f_o|$, a.e., and hence the above inequality becomes

$$N(g\chi_{E_n}) \leq \sup\{\int_o^\infty \lambda e^{-\lambda t}\int_\Omega |g\chi_{E_n}||f_o|d\mu dt, 0 < \lambda < \omega\}$$

$$\leq \sup\{\int_o^\infty \lambda e^{-\lambda t}dt \cdot \rho(f_o\chi_{E_n})\cdot\rho'(g), 0 < \lambda < \omega\}$$

$$= \rho'(g)\rho(f_o\chi_{E_n}), \tag{13}$$

where the Hölder inequality is used in (13). Since ρ is an a.c.n., $\rho(f_o\chi_{E_n}) \downarrow 0$ as $n \to \infty$ and hence $N(g\chi_{E_n}) \downarrow 0$. This proves the result for (i). The computation for (ii) is identical. Thus the result holds in this case. In the reflexive case the sets (i) and (ii) are bounded and hence are automatically weakly compact. This completes the proof of the proposition.

The main result on the norm convergence is as follows.

<u>Theorem</u> 5. Let $L^\rho(\Sigma) = L^\rho_a(\Sigma)$ be the Banach function space, and let $f_o \in L^\rho(\Sigma) \cap L^{\rho'}(\Sigma)$ be a weak unit. Suppose $\{R_t, t > 0\}$ is a

generalized martingale on L^{ρ} such that for each t the following three conditions hold: (i) $R_t f_o = f_o$, (ii) $R_t(L^{\rho} \cap L^{\infty}) \subset (L^{\rho} \cap L^{\infty})$, and (iii) R_t is a weakly compact contractive operator on L^{ρ}. Then for each $f \in L^{\rho}$, $\lim_{t \to 0^+} R_t f$ and $\lim_{t \to \infty} R_t f$ exist in norm.

Remark. In [14] a specialized case of the above result for certain L^{Φ}-spaces on a finite measure space was proved. In [20] Rota gave a similar result for L^p, $1 < p < \infty$, spaces, also on a finite measure space. The above theorem now includes the corresponding results of [10] for martingales, on σ-finite spaces. In the above theorem, the weak compactness hypothesis may not be dropped. In fact, if $L^{\rho} = L^1$, $R_t = E^{\mathcal{B}_t}$, then $\lim_{t \to 0^+} R_t f$ need not exist as asserted, when $\mu(\Omega) = \infty$. For a simple counterexample see ([10], p. 539).

Proof of theorem. By the representation (5), every (weakly compact) Reynold's operator is positive on L^{ρ} and is also defined on L^p, $1 \leq p < \infty$. First suppose that the generalized martingales $\{R_t, t>0\}$ actually verifies the slightly stronger equation:

$$(sR_t - tR_s)f = (s-t)R_t R_s f, \quad 0 < t < s, \ f \in L^{\rho}. \tag{14}$$

After proving the result in this case, the general case of R_t satisfying (4) will be deduced. But (14) can be written as

$$\left(\frac{R_t}{t} - \frac{R_s}{s}\right) f = (s-t) \frac{R_t}{t} \cdot \frac{R_s}{s} f, \quad 0 < t < s, \ f \in L^{\rho}. \tag{15}$$

If $A_t = \frac{R_t}{t}$, then A_t satisfies the resolvent equation (15) and $A_t : L^{\rho} \mapsto L^{\rho}$ is a bounded operator for each t. Moreover, A_1^{-1} exists as a closed operator on $L^{\rho}(\mathcal{B}_1)$, and hence by ([23], p. 259, and [8], p. 185) the operator $D = t - A_t^{-1}$ is closed with domain (dense) in $L^{\rho}(\mathcal{B}_1)$ and does not involve t. By Theorem 1,

$$R_t f = tA_t f = t \int_0^\infty e^{-tu} V(u) f du, \quad f \in L^\rho(\mathcal{B}_1), \tag{16}$$

where $\{V(u), u \geq 0\}$ is the (strongly-continuous) semi-group induced by the measure preserving transformation and, what is more important, its infinitesimal generator is D. It is clear that $\{V(u), u \geq 0\}$ satisfies the hypothesis of Proposition 4, so that $\lim_{t \to 0^+} R_t f$ exists in norm, for each $f \in L^\rho(\mathcal{B}_1)$.

For the general case, note that (4) implies the ranges of R_t are increasing as $t \to 0^+$. This again implies, by (5), that $\mathcal{B}_t \supset \mathcal{B}_{t'}$ for $0 < t < t'$. If $\mathcal{B}_o = \sigma(\bigcup_{t>0} \mathcal{B}_t)$, the smallest σ-field containing $\bigcup \mathcal{B}_t$, then $L^\rho(\mathcal{B}_o)$ is generated by $\bigcup_{t>0} L^\rho(\mathcal{B}_t)$ and hence if $f \in L^\rho(\mathcal{B}_{t_o})$, then $f \in L^\rho(\mathcal{B}_{t_o})$ for some $t_o > 0$. But then A_1 can be replaced by A_{t_o} in the above and the result is that $\lim_{t \to 0^+} R_t f$ exists in norm for $f \in L^\rho(\mathcal{B}_{t_o})$. This implies the result at once for each $f \in L^\rho(\mathcal{B}_o)$. Since for any $f \in L^\rho$ $E^{\mathcal{B}_o}(f) \in L^\rho(\mathcal{B}_o)$, it follows that $\lim_{t \to 0^+} R_t f$ exists in norm for each $f \in L^\rho$. An exactly similar argument yields the result for the case $t \to \infty$ also. This completes the proof of the theorem.

A natural question now is to consider the pointwise convergence. The following result holds.

<u>Theorem</u> 6. Under the hypothesis of Theorem 5, $\lim_{t \to 0^+} R_t f$ exists a.e., for each $f \in L^\rho(\Sigma)$, as well as $\lim_{t \to \infty} R_t f$ exists a.e.

This result is proved on using the norm convergence of the above theorem in the manner of the pointwise convergence of Cesáro limits of [5]. The needed maximal theorem for the Abel limits, which are of the main concern here, for the discrete parameter case is available [21]. The standard reduction of the continuous parameter case to the discrete parameter can then be effected and the general statements as stated will then follow. However, the computations are not entirely simple, and the details have to be written up with some care. For a corresponding result on Cesáro limits, involving a semi-group of operators, see [11]. Consequently the complete details of proof of this result and the deduction of certain Cesáro limits will be considered later.

5. Extensions. The work of the preceding section shows clearly that the crucial step in the convergence statements is the structure of the Reynold's operators. A natural generalization of the problem is to consider directly operators R_λ defined by

$$R_\lambda = \lambda\int_0^\infty e^{-\lambda t}T(t)\,dt, \quad \lambda > 0, \tag{17}$$

where the integrals are taken in Bochner's sense and where $\{T(t), t \geq 0\}$ is a strongly continuous contraction semi-group on an appropriate Banach space L^ρ. One may go further and replace the range of t ($\in \mathbb{R}^+$) by a locally compact semi-group $\mathcal{S}$ and $\frac{e^{-\lambda t}}{t}$ by a "normalized" real character χ of $\mathcal{S}$, replacing dt by a Haar measure, $d\mu$. Then (18) reads formally

$$R_\chi = \frac{1}{\mu(\chi)}\int_{\mathcal{S}} \chi(t)T(t)\,d\mu(t), \quad \mu(\chi) = \int_{\mathcal{S}} |\chi(t)|\,d\mu(t). \tag{18}$$

Since many special properties of the semi-group of operators determined by a measure preserving transformation are not now avaialbe, several restrictions on $\{T(t), t\in \mathbb{R}^+\}$ need be imposed. Even in this case, the R_λ defined by (17) (and hence also (18)) does not satisfy the Reynold's identity (2), in general. The needed restrictions and the corresponding mean convergence problem were considered for the operators given by (18), by Bray [2]. Since in general the R_λ defined by (17) need not be the resolvent of an infinitesimal generator of a strongly continuous semi-group (cf. [8], p. 510), the proof of Theorem 5, breaks down and the theory runs into real difficulties. The fact that R_λ does not satisfy (2) implies that conditional expectation operators, and hence the martingale theory, are not easily included in such generalizations. An entirely different generalization of martingales is recently given in [3], under the title of "generalized martingales", for a family of "c-projections", on certain inductive limit spaces of Hilbert spaces.

As briefly noted in Section 2, the martingale formulation of ergodic theorems (cf. [10]) is quite interesting. Except for a special problem considered for such martingales in [10], on a finite measure space, these new martingales almost always are about decreasing indexed (non-integrable!) sequences on σ-finite spaces. To obtain new results on ergodic theory, it will be necessary to prove, using the existing ergodic theorems of the Hopf-Dunford-Schwartz type as guidance, new martingale convergence theorems for a decreasing index. (For the increasing index, many such results are known [4].) This should be the next item in investigations of the classical martingale theory.

Finally the result of Theorem 1 can be considered, with the representation theory of Gretsky's [6]. This says that an R_λ admits a representation

$$R_\lambda f = \int_\Omega f d\nu_\lambda, \quad f \in L^\rho \tag{19}$$

where $\nu_\lambda : \Sigma \mapsto L^{\rho'}(\Sigma)$ is a vector measure of "ρ'-bounded variation". Thus ν_λ can be "disintegrated". This leads to a study of disintegration of vector measures which, as yet, has not received much attention. The present work may provide some motivation for this study as well.

References

1. M. A. Akcoglu and R. V. Chacón, "A convexity theorem for positive operators", Z. Wahrscheinlichkeitstheorie verw. Geb., 3(1965), 328-332.

2. G. Bray, "Théorèmes ergodiques de convergence en moyenne", J. Math. Anal. Applic., 25(1969), 471-502.

3. E. Briem, A. Guichardet et Nguyen-Xuan-Loc, "Les martingales généralisées", C.R. Acad. Sci., Ser. A, 270(1970), 373-375.

4. Y. S. Chow, "Martingales in a σ-finite measure space indexed by directed sets", Trans. Amer. Math. Soc., 97(1960), 254-285.

5. N. Dunford and J. T. Schwartz, Linear Operators, Part I: General Theory, Interscience, New York, 1958.

6. N. E. Gretsky, "Representation theorems on Banach function spaces", Amer. Math. Soc. Memoirs #84(1968), 52 pp.

7. P. R. Halmos, Lectures on Ergodic Theory, Publication of the Math. Soc. Japan #3(1956).

8. E. Hille and R. S. Phillips, Functional Analysis and Semi-Groups, Amer. Math. Soc. Colloq. Pub. #31(1957).

9. A. and C. Ionescu Tulcea, "Abstract ergodic theorems", Trans. Amer. Math. Soc., 107(1963), 107-124.

10. M. Jerison, "Martingale formulation of ergodic theorems", Proc. Amer. Math. Soc., 10(1959), 531-539.

11. U. Krengel, "A local ergodic theorem", Invent. Math., 6(1969), 324-333.

12. W.A.J. Luxemburg and A. C. Zaanen, "Compactness of integral operators in Banach function spaces", Math. Ann., 149(1963), 150-180.

13. M. M. Rao, "Linear functionals on Orlicz spaces", Nieuw Arkiv v. Wisk (3), 12(1964), 77-98.

14. M. M. Rao, "Interpolation, ergodicity, and martingales", J. Math. Mech., 16(1966), 543-568.

15. M. M. Rao, "Stone-Weierstrass theorems for function spaces", J. Math. Anal. Applic., 25(1969), 362-371.

16. M. M. Rao, "Contractive projections and prediction operators", Bull. Amer. Math. Soc., 75(1969), 1369-1373.

17. M. M. Rao, "Operateurs de moyennes et moyennes conditionnelles", C.R. Acad. Sci., Ser. A, 268(1969), 795-797.

18. M. M. Rao, "Inference in stochastic processes-IV", (to appear).

19. M. M. Rao, "Conditional expectations, Reynold's operators, and vector measures", Bull. Amer. Math. Soc., 76(1970), (to appear).

20. G.-C. Rota, "Une théorie unifiée des martingales et des moyennes ergodiques", C.R. Acad. Sci., Ser. A, 252(1961), 2064-2066.

21. G.-C. Rota, "On the maximal ergodic theorem for Abel-limits", Proc. Amer. Math. Soc., 14(1963), 722-723.

22. G.-C. Rota, "Reynold's operators", Proc. Symp. Appl. Math., Amer. Math. Soc., 16(1964), 70-83.

23. A. E. Taylor, Introduction to Functional Analysis, Wiley, New York, 1958.

24. J. J. Uhl, Jr., "Orlicz spaces of finitely additive set functions", Studia Math., 29(1967), 19-58.

25. A. C. Zaanen, Integration, North-Holland Publishing Company, 1967.

LOCAL ERGODIC THEOREMS FOR N-PARAMETER SEMIGROUPS OF OPERATORS

by

Thomas R. Terrell*

SUMMARY

The main purpose of this paper is to prove the following local ergodic theorem. If $\{T(t_1,\ldots,t_N): t_i \geq 0, i = 1,\ldots,N\}$ is an N-parameter strongly continuous semigroup of positive contraction operators on $L_1(\Omega,\mathfrak{F},\mu)$, then for all $f \in L_1(\Omega)$ $M(\epsilon)f = \frac{1}{\epsilon^N}\int_0^\epsilon \ldots \int_0^\epsilon T(t_1,\ldots,t_N)f\, dt_1 \ldots dt_N$ converges almost everywhere as $\epsilon \to 0+$. The theorem will also be proved for semigroups of non-positive L_1 contractions which are also L_∞ contracting. Examples are given to show that the maximal ergodic lemmas which are used to prove the one parameter case of the above results do not extend to the N-parameter case. The N-parameter case is proved by successive reduction of the number of parameters.

---

*The results of this paper are to appear in the author's Ph.D. thesis, which is being written under the direction of Professor U. Krengel.

Part of this work has been supported through N.S.F. grant GP 9354.

Introduction

In this paper I will present several local ergodic theorems for N-parameter semigroups of contraction operators. Throughout the paper $(\Omega,\mathfrak{F},\mu)$ will represent a σ-finite measure space and $L_1(\Omega,\mathfrak{F},\mu)$ will represent the Banach space of equivalence classes of integrable functions. The N-parameter semigroup of contraction operators an $L_1(\Omega,\mathfrak{F},\mu)$, $\{T(t_1,\ldots,t_N): t_i \geq 0,\ i = 1,\ldots,N\}$, is said to be strongly continuous if $\|T(t_1,\ldots,t_N)f - T(s_1,\ldots,s_N)f\|_1 \to 0$ as $(t_1,\ldots,t_N) \to (s_1,\ldots,s_N)$ holds for all $(s_1,\ldots,s_N)$, $s_i \geq 0$ and all $f \in L_1(\Omega,\mathfrak{F},\mu)$. For such strongly continuous semigroups we shall consider the operator averages

$$(1)\quad M(\epsilon)\, f(\omega) = \frac{1}{\epsilon^N} \int_0^\epsilon \cdots \int_0^\epsilon T(t_1,\ldots,t_N) f(\omega)\, dt_1 \ldots dt_N .$$

The local ergodic theorems concern the almost everywhere convergence of these averages as $\epsilon \to 0+$.

Remark: The strong continuity of the semigroup is a sufficient condition for choosing $T(t_1,\ldots,t_N)f$ from its equivalence class in such a way that for almost every $\omega \in \Omega$ $T(t_1,\ldots,t_N)f(\omega)$ is Lebesgue measurable in $(t_1,\ldots,t_N)$. This then justifies the validity of the averages. For further details see Dunford and Schwartz [3, p. 150] and Ornstein [proposition 4.1, 5].

The two primary results I will present are the following:

Theorem 1: If $\{T(t_1,\ldots,t_N): t_i \geq 0,\ i = 1,\ldots,N\}$ is a strongly continuous N-parameter semigroup of positive contraction operators on $L_1(\Omega,\mathfrak{F},\mu)$, then for all $f \in L_1(\Omega,\mathfrak{F},\mu)$

$$\lim_{\epsilon\to 0+} M(\epsilon)f = T(0,\ldots,0)f$$

almost everywhere.

Theorem 2: If $\{T(t_1,\ldots,t_N): t_i \geq 0,\ i = 1,\ldots,N\}$ is a strongly continuous N-parameter semigroup of contraction operators (not necessarily positive) on $L_1(\Omega,\mathfrak{F},\mu)$ which also satisfies

(*) $\operatorname{ess\,sup}|T(t_1,\ldots,t_N)f| \leq \operatorname{ess\,sup}|f|$ for all $f \in L_1(\Omega) \cap L_\infty(\Omega)$ and all $(t_1,\ldots,t_N)$, $t_i > 0$, then for all $f \in L_1(\Omega,\mathfrak{F},\mu)$

$$\lim_{\epsilon\to 0+} M(\epsilon)f = T(0,\ldots,0)f$$

almost everywhere.

Theorems of this type were considered by N. Wiener [6], who established similar theorems for groups of point transformations. Then later N. Dunford and J. Schwartz [3] generalized several of Wiener's theorems to the operator case. However, they only considered the limit of the operator averages as $\epsilon \to \infty$. Then in 1968 the following one parameter version of the local ergodic theorem was proved by U. Krengel [4] and independently by D. Ornstein [5].

Theorem [4], [5] If $\{T(t): t \geq 0\}$ is a strongly continuous one parameter semi-group of positive contraction operators on $L_1(\Omega,\mathfrak{F},\mu)$, then for all $f \in L_1(\Omega)$

$$\lim_{\epsilon\to 0+} \frac{1}{\epsilon}\int_0^\epsilon T(t)f\,dt = T(0)f \qquad \text{a.e.}$$

In section 1 I will prove theorem 2. I will show that the methods used to prove the one-parameter local ergodic theorem do not carry directly over to the N-parameter case. I will also discuss the necessity of condition (*) in Theorem 2.

In section 2 Theorem 1 will be proved by induction based on the known one parameter result. Then in section 3 I will consider the case where the averages are taken over N-dimensional rectangles, that is, averages of the form

$$\frac{1}{\epsilon_1\cdots\epsilon_N}\int_0^{\epsilon}\cdots\int_0^{\epsilon_N} T(t_1,\ldots,t_N)f\,dt_1\cdots dt_N .$$

I will prove a theorem and give a short discussion on the almost everywhere convergence of this type of average. Finally in section 4 I will mention some remaining problems.

Section 1

In most of the earlier results the general method of proof was to establish the result for a dense subclass of functions and then to apply a maximal type lemma or inequality. For example, Krengel's proof was based on the following continuous time version of Hopf's Maximal Ergodic Theorem.

Lemma [4] If $\{T(t): t \geq 0\}$ is a strongly continuous one-parameter semigroup of positive contraction operators on $L_1(\Omega,\mathfrak{F},\mu)$, then for any $f \in L_1(\Omega,\mathfrak{F},\mu)$

$$\int_A T(0)f\,d\mu \geq 0$$

where $$A = \{\omega : \sup_{\epsilon>0} \int_0^\epsilon T(t)\, f(\omega)\, dt > 0\} .$$

One might expect that the methods used in the proof of the one-parameter case could be directly extended to the N-parameter case. However, this could not be done since this maximal ergodic lemma does not extend to the N-parameter case. To be more precise, to use Krengel's technique of proof we would need to have that if $\{T(t_1 \ldots t_N): t_i \geq 0 \ \ i = 1 \ldots N\}$ is as in Theorem 1, then

$$\int_A T(0 \ldots 0) f \, d\mu \geq 0$$

where

$$A = \{\omega : \sup_{\epsilon>0} \int_0^\epsilon \cdots \int_0^\epsilon T(t_1 \ldots t_N) f(\omega)\, dt_1 \ldots dt_N > 0\} .$$

But we can easily show this to be a false statement. Consider the following simple counter-example. Let $\Omega = \mathbb{R}^2$, $\mathfrak{F}$ = Borel σ-field of $\mathbb{R}^2$, μ = Lebesgue measure on $\mathbb{R}^2$. Then let $\{T(t_1, t_2): t_i \geq 0 \ \ i = 1,2\}$ be the semigroup of two dimensional translations. Then define

$$f(x,y) = \begin{cases} 3 & \text{on } [0,1) \times [0,1) \\ -2 & \text{on } [1,2) \times [0,1) \\ -2 & \text{on } [0,1) \times [1,2) \\ 0 & \text{otherwise} . \end{cases}$$

Then $f \in L_1(\Omega, \mathfrak{F}, \mu)$. However, for all $(x,y) \in \{[0,1) \times [1,2)\} \cup \{[1,2) \times [0,1)\}$

$$\int_0^2 \int_0^2 T(t_1, t_2)\, f(x,y)\, dt_1\, dt_2 > 0 .$$

Hence,

$$A = \{(x,y): \sup_{\epsilon>0} \int_0^\epsilon \int_0^\epsilon T(t_1, t_2) f(x,y) dt_1\, dt_2 > 0\}$$

$$\supseteq \{[0,1) \times [0,1)\} \cup \{[0,1) \times [1,2)\} \cup \{[1,2) \times [0,1)\} ,$$

and thus

$$\int_A f\, d\mu = \int_A T(0,0) f\, d\mu = -1 < 0 .$$

Since Krengel's method does not extend to N-parameter semigroups, one might look for other maximal ergodic type inequalities which do hold for N-parameter semigroups. In Wiener's paper there appears such a lemma for point transformations [Theorem IV', 6] which Dunford and Schwartz generalized to the operator case [lemma 11, 3]. Their lemma is as follows:

<u>Lemma 1.1</u>: [3] Let $\{T(t_1, \ldots, t_N): t_i \geq 0 \ i = 1, \ldots, N\}$ be a strongly continuous,

semigroup of contraction operators on $L_1(\Omega,\mathfrak{F},\mu)$ which also satisfies

(*) $\text{ess sup}|T(t_1,\dots,t_N)f| \leq \text{ess sup}\ |f|$ for all $f \in L_1 \cap L_\infty$ and all $t_i > 0$,

then there exists an absolute constant $c_N > 0$ such that for all $f \in L_1(\Omega)$ and all

$$\beta > 0 \quad \mu\{\omega: \sup_{\epsilon>0} : \frac{1}{\epsilon^N}\int_0^\epsilon \cdots \int_0^\epsilon T(t_1,\dots,t_N)\ f(\omega)\ dt_1\dots dt_N| > \beta\} \leq \frac{1}{\beta c_n}\int_{\{\omega:|f|\geq\beta c_n\}} |f|\ d\mu \ .$$

It is with this lemma that I am able to prove theorem 2. But before giving the proof of theorem 2 I will prove another lemma which is necessary in both the proof of theorem 2 and of theorem 1.

<u>Lemma 1.2</u>: If $\{T(t_1,\dots,t_N): t_i \geq 0,\ i = 1,\dots N\}$ is as in the statement of theorem 1 or theorem 2, then the set of functions

$$\mathfrak{M} = \{M(\alpha)f: 0 < \alpha < 1 \ \ f \in L_1(\Omega)\}$$

is dense in $T(0,\dots,0)L_1(\Omega)$ and all functions in $\mathfrak{M}$ satisfy the conclusion of the theorem.

<u>Proof</u>: Since each $M(\alpha)\,f$ can be written as the limit of Riemann sums in the norm topology we have that $T(t_1,\dots,t_N)M(\alpha)f = M(\alpha)(T(t_1\dots t_N)f)$. Also we have that $M(\alpha)(T(0,\dots,0)f) = M(\alpha)f$. Thus $T(0,\dots,0)M(\alpha)f = M(\alpha)(T(0,\dots,0)f) = M(\alpha)f$. So all $M(\alpha)f \in T(0,\dots,0)L_1(\Omega)$.

The denseness of $\mathfrak{M}$ in $T(0,\dots,0)L_1(\Omega)$ results from the strong continuity of the semigroup at zero. By an application of Fubini's Theorem we have

$$\|M(\alpha)f - T(0,\dots,0)f\|_1 \leq \frac{1}{\alpha^N}\int_0^\alpha \cdots \int_0^\alpha \|T(t_1,\dots,t_N)f - T(0,\dots,0)f\|_1\ dt_1\dots dt_N$$

which converges to zero as $\alpha \to 0+$.

To show that all $M(\alpha)f$ satisfy the conclusion of the theorem we have the following:

$$|\frac{1}{\epsilon^N}\int_0^\epsilon \cdots \int_0^\epsilon T(t_1,\dots,t_N)\ M(\alpha)f\ dt_1\dots dt_N - M(\alpha)f|$$

$$= |\frac{1}{\epsilon^N}\frac{1}{\alpha^N}\int_0^\epsilon \cdots \int_0^\epsilon \int_0^\alpha \cdots \int_0^\alpha T(t_1+s_1,\dots,t_N+s_N)f\ ds_1\dots ds_N\ dt_1\dots dt_N$$

$$- \frac{1}{\epsilon^N}\frac{1}{\alpha^N}\int_0^\epsilon \cdots \int_0^\epsilon \int_0^\alpha \cdots \int_0^\alpha T(s_1,\dots,s_N)f\ ds_1\dots ds_N\ dt_1\dots dt_N|$$

$$= |\frac{1}{\epsilon^N}\frac{1}{\alpha^N}\int_0^\epsilon \cdots \int_0^\epsilon \int_{t_1}^{\alpha+t_1} \cdots \int_{t_N}^{\alpha+t_N} T(\tau_1,\dots,\tau_N)f\ d\tau_1\dots d\tau_N\ dt_1\dots dt_N$$

$$- \frac{1}{\epsilon^N} \frac{1}{\alpha^N} \int_0^\epsilon \cdots \int_0^\epsilon \int_0^\alpha \cdots \int_0^\alpha T(\tau_1,\ldots,\tau_N)f \, d\tau_1 \ldots d\tau_N \, dt_1 \ldots dt_N \Big|$$

$$\leq \frac{1}{\epsilon^N} \frac{1}{\alpha^N} \int_0^\epsilon \cdots \int_0^\epsilon \Big\{ \int_\alpha^{\alpha+t_1} \cdots \int_\alpha^{\alpha+t_N} | T(\tau_1,\ldots,\tau_N)f | d\tau_1 \ldots d\tau_N$$

$$+ \int_0^{t_1} \cdots \int_0^{t_N} |T(\tau_1,\ldots,\tau_N)f| d\tau_1 \ldots d\tau_N \Big\} \, dt_1 \ldots dt_N$$

which converges to zero almost everywhere as $\epsilon \to 0+$, since by the integrability of $T(\tau_1,\ldots,\tau_N)f$

$$\int_{t_1}^{\alpha+t_1} \cdots \int_{t_N}^{\alpha+t_N} |T(\tau_1,\ldots,\tau_N)f| d\tau_1 \ldots d\tau_N \to 0 \quad \text{a.e.}$$

$$\int_0^{t_1} \cdots \int_0^{t_N} |T(\tau_1 \ldots \tau_N)f| d\tau_1 \ldots d\tau_N \to 0 \quad \text{a.e.}$$

as $t_i \to 0 \quad i = 1,\ldots,N$. □

Proof of Theorem 2: Suppose the theorem would not hold. Then there would exist an $f \in L_1(\Omega)$ such that $\mu\{\limsup_{\epsilon\to 0+} M(\epsilon)f > T(0\ldots0)f\} > 0$. And so there would also be some $b > 0$ such that $\mu\{\limsup_{\epsilon\to 0+} M(\epsilon)f > b + T(0\ldots0)f\} = \delta > 0$. Then choose an $f_o \in \mathcal{M}$ such that

(1) $\|T(0\ldots0)f - f_o\|_1 < \min\left(\frac{\delta b c_N}{8}, \frac{\delta b}{4}\right)$ where c_N is as in lemma 1. Then from

(1) it follows that

(2) $\mu\{|T(0\ldots0)f - f_o| \geq \frac{b}{2}\} < \frac{\delta}{2}$ and

(3) $\|T(0\ldots0)f - f_o\|_1 < \frac{\delta b c_N}{8}$.

By lemma 1 we have that

(4) $\mu\{\limsup_{\epsilon\to 0+} M(\epsilon)(f-f_o) > \frac{b}{2}\} \leq \mu\{\sup_{\epsilon>0} M(\epsilon)(f-f_o) > \frac{b}{2}\}$

$$\leq \frac{2}{bc_n} \| T(0\ldots0)f - f_o\|_1 < \frac{\delta}{4}.$$

But by (2), (3) and the properties of f_o we have that

(5) $\mu\{\limsup_{\epsilon\to 0+} M(\epsilon)(f-f_o) > \frac{b}{2}\} = \mu\{\limsup_{\epsilon\to 0+} M(\epsilon)f > \frac{b}{2} + f_o\}$

$$\geq \mu\{\limsup_{\epsilon\to 0+} M(\epsilon)f > b + T(0\ldots0)f\} - \mu\{T(0\ldots0)f - f_o \geq \frac{b}{2}\}$$

$$> \delta - \frac{\delta}{2} = \frac{\delta}{2}.$$

But (5) and (4) yield a contradiction, thus proving the theorem. □

Although theorem 2 does not require the operators to be positive, it does require the condition (*), which seems to be a very restrictive condition. Thus it would be desirable to remove or lessen the restriction (*). However, even with the assumption that the operators are positive lemma 1.1 is false without condition (*). In fact I will give an example of a strongly continuous semigroup of positive contraction which does not have property (*) and for which NOT even the following inequality holds;

(6) $\mu\{\sup_{\epsilon>0} M(\epsilon)f > \beta\} \leq \frac{1}{\beta c} \|f\|_1$.

Note that condition (6) was the key inequality necessary for the proof of theorem 2. My example is the following:

Let $\Omega = [0,\infty)$, $\mathfrak{F}$ = Borel sets on $[0,\infty)$ and let μ be Lebesgue measure with the density $d(x)$ where $d(x) = \frac{1}{n+1}$ on $[n,n+1)$. Then define $\{T(t):t \geq 0\}$ on $L_1(\Omega,\mathfrak{F},\mu)$ by

$$T(t)\, f(x) = \begin{cases} 0 & 0 \leq x < t \\ f(x-t)\,\dfrac{d(x-t)}{d(x)} & x \geq t\,. \end{cases}$$

Then $\{T(t):\, t \geq 0\}$ is a strongly continuous semigroup of positive contractions on $L_1(\Omega,\mathfrak{F},\mu)$. Then let $f(x) = 1_{[0,1)}(x)$. Thus $\|f\|_1 = 1$ and for any $n \leq x \leq n+1$

$$\frac{1}{x}\int_0^x T(t)\, f(x)\, dt \geq \frac{1}{x} \cdot \frac{1}{d(x)} = \frac{1}{x}\,(n+1) \geq 1\,.$$

Thus,

$$\mu\{\sup_{\epsilon>0} \frac{1}{\epsilon}\int_0^\epsilon T(t)f\, dt \geq 1\} = \mu[0,\infty) = \infty > \frac{1}{c}\|f\|_1$$

for all finite values of c .

So it does not appear that the techniques used to prove theorem 2 can be used for theorem 1 without adding the condition (*) . In the next section I shall give a quite different proof for theorem 1.

Section 2

As I pointed out in section 1, Dunford and Schwartz's lemma cannot be used to prove theorem 1. However, I discovered that by modifying a technique they used in their proof I could develop a method for proving theorem 1 by induction. The basic idea is to be able to reduce a 2N-parameter semigroup to an N-parameter semigroup in some useful manner.

I will first need to prove some lemmas to set up the machinery for this induction argument.

Lemma 2.1 For each $u > 0$ define the function

$$\varphi_u(x) = \begin{cases} \dfrac{u}{2\sqrt{\pi}} x^{-\frac{3}{2}} e^{-\frac{u^2}{4x}} & \text{if } x > 0 \\ 0 & \text{if } x \leq 0 \end{cases}$$

Then $\{\varphi_u : u > 0\}$ has the following properties:

(i) $\varphi_u(x) \geq 0 \quad \forall x$ and $\forall u > 0$;

(ii) $\int_{-\infty}^{\infty} \varphi_u(x)\, dx = 1 \quad \forall u > 0$;

(iii) $\{\varphi_u : u > 0\}$ is a semigroup under convolution ;

(iv) for all $s > 0$ $\lim_{u \to 0} \int_s^{\infty} \varphi_u(x)\, dx = 0$.

Proof: This is essentially Dunford and Schwartz's lemma 12 [3,p.160]. In their proof they verify (i), (ii) and (iii), so I will just prove condition (iv).

For $s > 0$ fixed, if $u \leq 1$ then

$$0 \leq \int_s^{\infty} \varphi_u(x)\, dx = \frac{u}{2\sqrt{\pi}} \int_s^{\infty} x^{-\frac{3}{2}} e^{-\frac{u^2}{4x}}\, dx \leq \frac{u}{2\sqrt{\pi}} \int_s^{\infty} x^{-\frac{3}{2}} e^{-\frac{1}{4x}}\, dx \ .$$

But $\int_s^{\infty} x^{-\frac{3}{2}} e^{-\frac{1}{4x}}\, dx < \infty$ so

$$\frac{u}{2\sqrt{\pi}} \int_s^{\infty} x^{-\frac{3}{2}} e^{-\frac{1}{4x}}\, dx \to 0 \qquad \text{as } (u \to 0) \ .$$

□

For technical reasons arising in the proof of theorem 1 I will revise the requirements on "strongly continuous semigroups".

Definition 2.1 $\{T(t_1,\ldots,t_N),\ T(0):\ t_i \geqq 0 \quad i = 1,\ldots,N\}$ will be called a strongly continuous N-parameter semigroup of positive contractions on $L_1(\Omega,\mathcal{F},\mu)$ if

(i) $\{T(t_1,\ldots,t_N):\ t_i \geqq 0,\ i = 1,\ldots,N\}$ is a strongly continuous semigroup of positive contractions,

(ii) $T(0)$ is a positive contraction on $L_1(\Omega)$ commuting with all $T(t_1 \dots t_N)$

and

(iii) $\forall\, f \in L_1(\Omega), \|T(t_1 \dots t_N)\, f - T(0)\, f\|_1 \to 0$ as $(t_1 \dots t_N) \to (0, \dots, 0) +$.

Clearly the semigroup stated in theorem 1 meets the requirements of definition 2.1 (in which case $T(0) \equiv T(0, \dots, 0))$. So I will now work with semigroups of the type just defined.

<u>Lemma 2.2</u>: Let $\{\varphi_u : u > 0\}$ be as in lemma 2.1, and $\{T(t_1, \dots, t_{2N}), T(0): t_i > 0 \;\; i = 1, \dots, 2N\}$ a strongly continuous 2N-parameter semigroup of positive contractions on $L_1(\Omega, \mathfrak{F}, \mu)$. Then for $x_i > 0 \;\; (i = 1, \dots, N)$ define the operators

$$S(x_1, \dots, x_N)f = \int_0^\infty \dots \int_0^\infty \varphi_{x_1}(t_1)\varphi_{x_1}(t_2)\, \varphi_{x_2}(t_3)\, \varphi_{x_2}(t_4) \dots \varphi_{x_N}(t_{2N-1})\, \varphi_{x_N}(t_{2N})\, T(t_1, \dots, t_{2N}) f \, dt_1 \dots dt_{2N}.$$

Then $\{S(x_1, \dots, x_N), T(0): x_i > 0, i = 1, \dots, N\}$ is a strongly continuous N-parameter semigroup of positive contractions on $L_1(\Omega, \mathfrak{F}, \mu)$.

<u>Proof</u>: The operators are positive since the $T(t_1, \dots, t_{2N})$ are positive and $\varphi_x(t) \geq 0 \quad \forall\, t \geq 0, x > 0$. They are contractions since $\forall\, f \in L_1(\Omega)$

$$\|S(x_1, \dots, x_{2N})f\|_1 = \left\| \int_0^\infty \dots \int_0^\infty \varphi_{x_1}(t_1)\, \varphi_{x_1}(t_2) \dots \varphi_{x_N}(t_{2N-1})\, \varphi_{x_N}(t_{2N})\, T(t_1 \dots t_{2N}) f \, dt_1 \dots dt_{2N} \right\|_1$$

$$\leq \int_0^\infty \dots \int_0^\infty \varphi_{x_1}(t_1)\, \varphi_{x_1}(t_2) \dots \varphi_{x_N}(t_{2n-1})\, \varphi_{x_N}(t_{2N}) \|T(t_1, \dots, t_{2N})f\|_1 \, dt_1 \dots dt_{2N}$$

$$\leq \|f\|_1 \left(\int_0^\infty \varphi_x(t)\, dt \right)^{2N} = \|f\|_1 .$$

To show that they form a semigroup, we first observe that since $S(y_1, \dots, y_N)f$ can be written as the limit of Riemann sums in the norm topology it follows that $T(t_1, \dots, t_{2N})\, S(y_1, \dots, y_N)f = S(y_1, \dots, y_N)\, (T(t_1, \dots, t_{2N})f)$.

Using this we obtain

$$S(x_1, \dots, x_N)\, S(y_1, \dots, y_N)\, f$$

$$= \int_0^\infty \dots \int_0^\infty \varphi_{x_1}(t_1)\, \varphi_{x_1}(t_2) \dots \varphi_{x_N}(t_{2N-1})\, \varphi_{x_N}(t_{2N})\, \varphi_{y_1}(s_1)\, \varphi_{y_1}(s_2) \dots \varphi_{y_N}(s_{2N-1})\, \varphi_{y_N}(s_{2N})$$

$$T(t_1 + s_1, \dots, t_{2N} + s_{2N}) f \, ds_1 \dots ds_{2N} \, dt_1 \dots dt_{2N}$$

$$= \int_{-\infty}^{\infty} \cdots \int_{-\infty}^{\infty} \varphi_{x_1}(v_1 - w_1)\, \varphi_{y_1}(w_1)\, \varphi_{x_1}(v_2 - w_2)\, \varphi_{y_1}(w_2) \cdots$$

$$\varphi_{x_N}(v_{2N} - w_{2N})\, \varphi_{y_N}(w_{2N})\, T(v_1, \ldots, v_{2N}) f\, dv_1 \ldots dv_{2N}\, dw_1 \ldots dw_{2N}$$

$$= \int_{-\infty}^{\infty} \cdots \int_{-\infty}^{\infty} \varphi_{x_1+y_1}(v_1)\, \varphi_{x_1+y_1}(v_2) \cdots \varphi_{x_N+y_N}(v_{2N-1})\, \varphi_{x_N+y_N}(v_{2N})\, T(v_1, \ldots, v_{2N}) f\, dv_1 \ldots dv_{2N}$$

$$= S(x_1+y_1, \ldots, x_N+y_N) f \quad .$$

To prove the strong continuity of the semigroup we distinguish two cases. First let $y_i > 0$, $i = 1, \ldots, N$. Then for $f \in L_1(\Omega)$

$$\|S(x_1, \ldots, x_N) f - S(y_1, \ldots, y_N) f\|_1$$

$$= \left\| \int_0^{\infty} \cdots \int_0^{\infty} \{\varphi_{x_1}(t_1) \cdots \varphi_{x_N}(t_{2N}) - \varphi_{y_1}(t_1) \cdots \varphi_{y_N}(t_{2N})\}\, T(t_1, \ldots, t_{2N}) f\, dt_1 \ldots dt_{2N} \right\|_1$$

$$\leq \|f\|_1 \int_0^{\infty} \cdots \int_0^{\infty} |\varphi_{x_1}(t_1) \cdots \varphi_{x_N}(t_{2N}) - \varphi_{y_1}(t_1) \cdots \varphi_{y_N}(t_{2N})|\, dt_1 \ldots dt_{2N} \quad .$$

But since each $y_i > 0$, $\varphi_{x_i}(t) \to \varphi_{y_i}(t)$ as $(x_i \to y_i)$ uniformly in t and for each y_i given $\epsilon > 0$ there always exists an $N > 0$ such that $\int_N^{\infty} \varphi_{y_i}(t)dt < \epsilon$. This is sufficient to give

$$\int_0^{\infty} \cdots \int_0^{\infty} |\varphi_{x_1}(t_1) \cdots \varphi_{x_N}(t_{2N}) - \varphi_{y_1}(t_1) \cdots \varphi_{y_N}(t_{2N})|\, dt_1 \ldots dt_{2N}$$

converges to zero as $(x_1, \ldots, x_N) \to (y_1, \ldots, y_N)$.

Thus $\|S(x_1, \ldots, x_N) f - S(y_1, \ldots, y_N) f\|_1 \to 0$ as $(x_1, \ldots, x_N) \to (y_1, \ldots, y_N)$.

Finally we must show strong continuity at zero. So let $f \in L_1(\Omega)$. Then for $\epsilon > 0$ there exists $s > 0$ such that $0 < t_i < s$, $i = 1, \ldots, 2N \Rightarrow$

(7) $\|T(t_1, \ldots, t_{2N}) f - T(0) f\|_1 < \frac{\epsilon}{2}$.

By lemma 2.1 $\int_s^{\infty} \varphi_x(t)dt \to 0$ as $(x \to 0)$, so there exists $r > 0$ such that $x_i < r \Rightarrow$

(8) $$\int_s^{\infty} \varphi_{x_i}(t)dt < \frac{\epsilon}{8N\|f\|_1} \cdot$$

Thus for $0 < x_i < r$, $i = 1, \ldots, N$ we have that $\|S(x_1, \ldots, x_N) f - T(0) f\|_1$

$$= \left\| \int_0^{\infty} \cdots \int_0^{\infty} \varphi_{x_1}(t_1) \cdots \varphi_{x_N}(t_{2N})\, T(t_1, \ldots, t_{2N}) f\, dt_1 \ldots dt_{2N} \right.$$

$$\left. - \int_0^{\infty} \cdots \int_0^{\infty} \varphi_{x_1}(t_1) \cdots \varphi_{x_N}(t_{2N})\, t(0) f\, dt_1 \ldots dt_{2N} \right\|_1$$

$$\leq \int_0^\infty \cdots \int_0^\infty \varphi_{x_1}(t_1)\cdots\varphi_{x_N}(t_{2N}) \|T(t_1,\dots,t_{2N})f - T(0)f\|_1 \, dt_1\cdots dt_{2N}$$

$$\leq \frac{\epsilon}{2} \int_0^s \cdots \int_0^s \varphi_{x_1}(t_1)\cdots\varphi_{x_N}(t_{2N}) dt_1\cdots dt_{2N}$$

$$+ 2\|f\|_1 \Big\{ \int_0^\infty \cdots \int_0^\infty \int_s^\infty \varphi_{x_1}(t_1)\cdots\varphi_{x_N}(t_{2N}) dt_1\cdots dt_{2N}$$

$$+ \int_0^\infty \cdots \int_s^\infty \int_0^s \varphi_{x_1}(t_1)\cdots\varphi_{x_N}(t_{2N}) dt_1\cdots dt_{2N} + \cdots +$$

$$\int_s^\infty \cdots \int_0^s \int_0^s \varphi_{x_1}(t_1)\cdots\varphi_{x_N}(t_{2N}) \, dt_1\cdots dt_{2N} \Big\}$$

$$\leq \frac{\epsilon}{2} + 2\|f\|_1 \Big(2N \frac{\epsilon}{8N\|f\|_1}\Big) = \epsilon \, .$$

The last inequalities follow from (7) and (8) . Hence we have that

$$\|S(x_1,\dots,x_N)f - T(0)f\|_1 \to 0 \qquad \text{as} \quad (x_1,\dots,x_N) \to (0,\dots,0)+ \, .$$

□

The next lemma gives us the important relationship between the original semigroup and the derived semigroup. Although this lemma does not appear explictly in Dunford and Schwartz [3], the idea is essentially contained in the proof of their lemma 13 [3, p. 161].

<u>Lemma 2.3</u> Let $\{T(t_1,\dots,t_{2N}),\ T(0):\ t_i > 0,\ i = 1\dots 2N\}$ and $\{S(x_1,\dots,x_N),\ T(0):\ x_i > 0\ \ i = 1\dots N\}$ be as in lemma 2.2 . Then there exists an absolute constant $d > 0$, which depends only on the size of N, such that for all $f \in L_1^+(\Omega) = \{f \in L_1(\Omega):\ f \geq 0 \ \text{a.e.}\}$ and for all $\epsilon > 0$ we have that

$$(9) \quad \frac{1}{(\sqrt{\epsilon})^N} \int_0^{\sqrt{\epsilon}} \cdots \int_0^{\sqrt{\epsilon}} S(x_1,\dots,x_N)f \, dx_1\cdots dx_N$$

$$\geq d \, \frac{1}{\epsilon^{2N}} \int_0^\epsilon \cdots \int_0^\epsilon T(t_1,\dots,t_{2N})f \, dt_1\cdots dt_{2N} \qquad \text{a.e.}$$

<u>Proof:</u> $$\frac{1}{(\sqrt{\epsilon})^N} \int_0^{\sqrt{\epsilon}} \cdots \int_0^{\sqrt{\epsilon}} S(x_1,\dots,x_N)f \, dx_1\cdots dx_N$$

$$= \frac{1}{(4\pi)^N} \int_0^\infty \cdots \int_0^\infty h(\sqrt{\epsilon}, t_1, t_2)\cdots h(\sqrt{\epsilon}, t_{2N-1}, t_{2N}) \, T(t_1,\dots,t_{2N})f \, dt_1\cdots dt_{2N}$$

where

$$h(\sqrt{\epsilon}, t_i, t_{i+1}) = \frac{4\pi}{\sqrt{\epsilon}} \int_0^{\sqrt{\epsilon}} \varphi_u(t_i)\, \varphi_u(t_{i+1}) du$$

$$= \frac{1}{\sqrt{\epsilon}} (t_i t_{i+1})^{-3/2} \int_0^{\sqrt{\epsilon}} u^2 e^{-u^2\left(\frac{1}{4t_i} + \frac{1}{4t_{i+1}}\right)} du$$

I shall show that there exists $\delta > 0$ such that

(10) $h(\sqrt{\epsilon}, t_i, t_{i+1}) > \frac{\delta}{\epsilon^2}$ for $0 < t_i, t_{i+1} < \epsilon$.

It is sufficient to work with the case $t_i = t_1$ $t_{i+1} = t_2$. By making the change of variables

$$u = \sqrt{\epsilon}\ v,\ t_1 = \sqrt{\epsilon}\ s_1,\ t_2 = \sqrt{\epsilon}\ s_2$$

showing (10) is equivalent to showing

(11) $(s_1\, s_2)^{-3/2} \int_0^1 v^2 e^{-v^2\left(\frac{1}{4s_1} + \frac{1}{4s_2}\right)} dv > \delta$ for $0 < s_1, s_2 \leq 1$.

Let $H(a) = \int_0^1 v^2 e^{-v^2 a} dv$. Then what we are trying to show is that

$$(s_1\, s_2)^{-3/2}\ H\left(\frac{1}{4s_1} + \frac{1}{4s_2}\right) > \delta \qquad \text{for} \qquad 0 < s_1, s_2 \leq 1$$

Now $H(a)$ is positive and continuous, so if s_1, s_2 are bounded away from 0, then so is $H\left(\frac{1}{4s_1} + \frac{1}{4s_2}\right)$. So our only problem occurs when s_1 or s_2 is close to 0 . But

$$H(a) = \int_0^1 v^2 e^{-v^2 a} dv = \frac{a^{-3/2}}{2} \int_0^a v^{1/2} e^{-v} dv .$$

Choose $b > 0$ such that $\forall\, a > b$

$$0 < \frac{\Gamma(3/2)}{2} \leq \int_0^a v^{1/2} e^{-v} dv \leq \Gamma(3/2) .$$

Then for all $a > b$

$$H(a) \geq M\, a^{-3/2} \qquad \text{where} \quad M = \frac{\Gamma(3/2)}{4} .$$

Therefore, for $\frac{1}{4s_1} + \frac{1}{4s_2} > b$

$$(s_1 s_2)^{-\frac{3}{2}}\ H\left(\frac{1}{4s_1} + \frac{1}{4s_2}\right) \geq 8M(s_1 + s_2)^{-\frac{3}{2}}$$

which is bounded away from 0 if s_1 or s_2 is close to 0 . So the existence of

δ is clear, in fact we could use $\delta = \min\left(\frac{\Gamma(3/2)}{2}, \frac{1}{2b^3}\int_0^{1/2} v^{1/2} e^{-v}\, dv\right)$.

Now we have that

$$\frac{1}{(\sqrt{\epsilon})^N}\int_0^{\sqrt{\epsilon}}\cdots\int_0^{\sqrt{\epsilon}} S(x_1,\ldots,x_N)f\, dx_1\cdots dx_N$$

$$= (4\pi)^{-N}\int_0^{\infty}\cdots\int_0^{\infty} h(\sqrt{\epsilon},t_1,t_2)\cdots h(\sqrt{\epsilon},t_{2N-1},t_{2N})T(t_1,\ldots,t_{2N})f\, dt_1\cdots dt_{2N}$$

$$\geq (4\pi)^{-N}\int_0^{\epsilon}\cdots\int_0^{\epsilon} h(\sqrt{\epsilon},t_1,t_2)\cdots h(\sqrt{\epsilon},t_{2N-1},t_{2N})T(t_1\cdots t_{2N})f\, dt_1\cdots dt_{2N}$$

$$\geq \left(\frac{\delta}{4\pi}\right)^N \frac{1}{\epsilon^{2N}}\int_0^{\epsilon}\cdots\int_0^{\epsilon} T(t_1,\ldots,t_{2N})f\, dt_1\cdots dt_{2N}\ .$$

Thus the lemma is completed with $d = \left(\frac{\delta}{4\pi}\right)^N$.

□

We are now ready to prove theorem 1. Again $\mathcal{M}$ will refer to the class of functions in lemma 1.2.

Proof of Theorem 1: First notice that if $\{T(t_1,\ldots,t_k),\ T(0): t_i > 0\}$ is as in the statement of theorem 1. and $1 \leq k \leq m$ and $P(t_1,\ldots,t_m) = T(t_1,\ldots,t_k)$ then $\{P(t_1,\ldots,t_m),\ T(0): t_i > 0\}$ also satisfies the hypotheses of the theorem, and furthermore

$$\frac{1}{\epsilon^m}\int_0^{\epsilon}\cdots\int_0^{\epsilon} P(t_1,\ldots,t_m)dt_1\cdots dt_m = \frac{1}{\epsilon^k}\int_0^{\epsilon}\cdots\int_0^{\epsilon} T(t_1,\ldots,t_k)dt_1\cdots dt_k\ .$$

So if the theorem is known to hold for an integer m, then it also holds for all integers $1 \leq k \leq m$. Therefore, it will suffice to show the theorem holds for all integers of the form $N = 2^k$, $k > 0$.

I now proceed by induction. The theorem is known to hold for $N = 1$. So suppose it holds for $N = 2^k$. Then I shall show it holds for N replaced by $2N$.

Let $\{T(t_1,\ldots,t_{2N}),\ T(0): t_i > 0\}$ be a $2N$-parameter semigroup satisfying the hypotheses of the theorem. Then construct $\{S(x_1,\ldots,x_N),\ T(0): x_i > 0\}$ as in lemma 2.2. Then by lemma 2.3 and the induction assumption we have for all $f \in L_1^+(\Omega)$

$$(12)\quad T(0)f = \lim_{\epsilon\to 0+}\frac{1}{\epsilon^N}\int_0^{\epsilon}\cdots\int_0^{\epsilon} S(x_1,\ldots,x_N)f\, dx_1\cdots dx_N$$

$$\geq d \limsup_{\epsilon\to 0+} \frac{1}{\epsilon^{2N}} \int_0^\epsilon \cdots \int_0^\epsilon T(t_1,\ldots,t_{2N}) f \, dt_1 \ldots dt_{2N}$$

$$= d \limsup_{\epsilon\to 0+} M(\epsilon) f \quad .$$

Thus for all $f \in L_1^+ (\Omega)$ we must have

(13) $\mu\{\limsup_{\epsilon\to 0+} M(\epsilon)f > d^{-1}T(0)f\} = 0$.

Suppose then that the result does not hold. Then there would exist some $f \in L_1(\Omega)$ such that

$$\mu\{\limsup_{\epsilon\to 0+} M(\epsilon)f > T(0)f\} > 0 .$$

Hence, we could find $\alpha > 0$ such that

$$\mu\{\limsup_{\epsilon\to 0+} M(\epsilon)f > \alpha + T(0)f\} = b > 0 .$$

Let $\delta > 0$ and choose $f_o \in \mathcal{M}$ such that

(14) $\|T(0)f - f_o\|_1 < \min\left(\frac{\delta b}{4}, \frac{\alpha b}{8}\right)$.

Since $T(0)$ is a contraction we would then also have

(15) $\|T(0)|T(0)f - f_o|\| < \frac{\delta b}{4}$.

(14) and (15) imply that

(16) $\mu\{T(0)|T(0)f - f_o| > \frac{\delta}{2}\} < \frac{b}{4}$ and

(17) $\mu\{|T(0)f - f_o| > \frac{\alpha}{2}\} < \frac{b}{4}$.

Therefore, there must exist a set $A \subset B$, $\mu(A) \geq \frac{b}{2}$ such that on A

(18) $T(0)|T(0)f - f_o| < \delta$ and

(19) $|T(0)f - f_o| < \frac{\alpha}{2}$.

Now by the properties of f_o we have that for a.e. $\omega \in A$

$$\limsup_{\epsilon\to 0+} M(\epsilon)|T(0)f-f_o| \geq |\limsup_{\epsilon\to 0+} M(\epsilon)\,(T(0)f - f_o)|$$

$$= |\limsup_{\epsilon\to 0+} M(\epsilon)f - f_o|$$

$$> (T(0)f + \alpha) - (T(0)f - \frac{\alpha}{2}) = \frac{\alpha}{2} .$$

But if δ was choosen such that $\frac{\alpha}{2} > \frac{\delta}{d}$, then we would have that a.e. on A,

$$\limsup_{\epsilon \to 0+} M(\epsilon)|T(0)f - f_0| > \frac{\alpha}{2} > \frac{\delta}{d} > d^{-1} T(0)|T(0)f - f_0|$$

thus giving us a contradiction to (13). Hence our induction is completed and the theorem proved. □

Section 3.

Although the main objectives of the paper have been completed, I should still point out that the method of averaging can be generalized somewhat. That is, instead of considering the averages as in theorems 1 and 2 we might consider the following types of averages

$$(20) \quad \frac{1}{\epsilon_1 \cdots \epsilon_N} \int_0^{\epsilon_1} \cdots \int_0^{\epsilon_N} T(t_1, \ldots, t_N) f \, dt_1 \ldots dt_N .$$

We cannot hope that the limit exists a.e. as the $\epsilon_i \to 0+$ independently, for it has long been known that if $(\Omega, \mathfrak{F}, \mu)$ is two-dimensional Lebesgue space and $\{T(t_1,t_2): t_1 \geq 0\}$ two-dimensional translations the convergence of (20) can fail if the $\epsilon_i \to 0+$ independently (see Busemann and Feller, [2]). However, it was shown by Busemann and Feller that if a slight regularity condition is placed on the convergence of the ϵ_i then convergence can be proved for the case of translation semigroups on $\mathbb{R}^N$. I should remark that Busemann and Feller were not considering semigroup of translations, but rather the problem of the differentiability of N-dimensional indefinite Lebesgue integrals. However, the study of translation semigroups on $\mathbb{R}^N$ encompasses their study.

The regularity condition required by Busemann and Feller was that the $\epsilon_i \to 0+$ in such a way that the ratios of the ϵ_i were bounded above and below. I shall now show that this condition is sufficient for the convergence a.e. of the averages of type (20).

Definition 3.1 Let us say that $(\epsilon_i, \ldots, \epsilon_N) \underset{B}{\to} (0, \ldots, 0)$ if $\epsilon_i \to 0+$ and we always have $\frac{\epsilon_i}{\epsilon_j} < B$ for $i = 1, \ldots, N$, $j = 1, \ldots, N$.

Theorem 3: If $\{T(t_1,\ldots,t_N): t_i \geq 0\}$ is a strongly continuous N-parameter semi-group of positive contractions on $L_1(\Omega,\mathfrak{F},\mu)$, then for all $f \in L_1(\Omega)$

$$\lim_{(\epsilon_1,\ldots,\epsilon_N) \underset{B}{\rightarrow} (0,\ldots,0)} \frac{1}{\epsilon_1\cdots\epsilon_N}\int_0^{\epsilon_1}\cdots\int_0^{\epsilon_N} T(t_1,\ldots,t_N)f\,dt_1\ldots dt_N$$

$$= T(0,\ldots,0)f \qquad \text{a.e.}$$

Sketch of proof

I shall use the notation

$$M(\epsilon_1,\ldots,\epsilon_N)f = \frac{1}{\epsilon_1\cdots\epsilon_N}\int_0^{\epsilon_1}\cdots\int_0^{\epsilon_N} T(t_1\ldots t_N)f\,dt_1\ldots dt_N \,.$$

Let $\mathcal{M}$ be the class of functions defined in lemma 2. The proof of lemma 2 easily carries over to the type of convergence in this theorem. So each $f \in \mathcal{M}$ also satisfies the conclusion of this theorem.

Now for all $(\epsilon_1,\ldots,\epsilon_N)$ such that $\frac{\epsilon_i}{\epsilon_j} < B$ $i = 1,\ldots,N$, $j = 1,\ldots,N$ we have that if $\epsilon^* = \max(\epsilon_1,\ldots,\epsilon_N)$ then $M(\epsilon_1,\ldots,\epsilon_N)f \leq B^{N-1}\frac{1}{\epsilon^{*N}}\int_0^{\epsilon^*}\cdots\int_0^{\epsilon^*} T(t_1,\ldots,t_N)f\,dt_1\ldots dt_N$ holds a.e. for all $f \in L_1^+(\Omega)$. Thus as a result of Theorem 1 we have

$$(21)\quad \limsup_{(\epsilon_1,\ldots,\epsilon_N) \underset{M}{\rightarrow} (0,\ldots,0)} M(\epsilon_1,\ldots,\epsilon_N)f \leq B^{N-1}\, T(0\ldots0)f \qquad \text{a.e.}$$

But (21) is exactly the same type of inequality as was (12). Thus the last part of the proof of theorem 1 carries over identically to this case and thus proving theorem 3.

□

Section 4:

There exist several possibilities for extensions of theorems 1 and 2. I am still considering the validity of theorem 2 for non-positive operators but with the removal or weakening of condition (*). Of course, as pointed out in section 1, this will require abandoning the use of lemma 1.1.

The other possibility is proving theorem 1 for semigroups which are not strongly continuous at zero. Akcoglu and Chacon [1] pointed out that there exist strongly continuous semigroups $\{T(t): t > 0\}$ which cannot be completed at 0 in the strong operator topology. They, however, have proved the one parameter local ergodic theorem for semigroups not continuous at 0 .

Remark: It was pointed out to me after this paper was written that a one-parameter version of Theorem 2 (with a different proof) will appear in Ornstein's paper [5].

References

1. Akcoglu, M. A. and R. V. Chacon: A Local Ration Theorem. to appear.

2. Busemann, H. and W. Feller: Zur Differentiation der Lebesgueshen Integrale. Fund. Math. 22, 226-256 (1934).

3. Dunford, N. and J. T. Schwartz: Convergence almost everywhere of operator averages. J. Rational Mech. and Anal. 5, 129-178 (1956).

4. Krengel, U.: A Local Ergodic Theorem. Inventiones Math. 6, 329-333 (1969).

5. Ornstein, D.: The Sums of Iterates of a Positive Operator. to appear.

6. Wiener, N.: The Ergodic Theorem. Duke Math. J. 5, 1-18 (1939).

Lecture Notes in Mathematics

Bisher erschienen/Already published

Vol. 1: J. Wermer, Seminar über Funktionen-Algebren. IV, 30 Seiten. 1964. DM 3,80 / $ 1.10

Vol. 2: A. Borel, Cohomologie des espaces localement compacts d'après. J. Leray. IV, 93 pages. 1964. DM 9,– / $ 2.60

Vol. 3: J. F. Adams, Stable Homotopy Theory. Third edition. IV, 78 pages. 1969. DM 8,– / $ 2.20

Vol. 4: M. Arkowitz and C. R. Curjel, Groups of Homotopy Classes. 2nd. revised edition. IV, 36 pages. 1967. DM 4,80 / $ 1.40

Vol. 5: J.-P. Serre, Cohomologie Galoisienne. Troisième édition. VIII, 214 pages. 1965. DM 18,– / $ 5.00

Vol. 6: H. Hermes, Term Logic with Choise Operator. III, 55 pages. 1970. DM 6,– / $ 1.70

Vol. 7: Ph. Tondeur, Introduction to Lie Groups and Transformation Groups. Second edition. VIII, 176 pages. 1969. DM 14,– / $ 3.80

Vol. 8: G. Fichera, Linear Elliptic Differential Systems and Eigenvalue Problems. IV, 176 pages. 1965. DM 13,50 / $ 3.80

Vol. 9: P. L. Ivănescu, Pseudo-Boolean Programming and Applications. IV, 50 pages. 1965. DM 4,80 / $ 1.40

Vol. 10: H. Lüneburg, Die Suzukigruppen und ihre Geometrien. VI, 111 Seiten. 1965. DM 8,– / $ 2.20

Vol. 11: J.-P. Serre, Algèbre Locale. Multiplicités. Rédigé par P. Gabriel. Seconde édition. VIII, 192 pages. 1965. DM 12,– / $ 3.30

Vol. 12: A. Dold, Halbexakte Homotopiefunktoren. II, 157 Seiten. 1966. DM 12,– / $ 3.30

Vol. 13: E. Thomas, Seminar on Fiber Spaces. IV, 45 pages. 1966. DM 4,80 / $ 1.40

Vol. 14: H. Werner, Vorlesung über Approximationstheorie. IV, 184 Seiten und 12 Seiten Anhang. 1966. DM 14,– / $ 3.90

Vol. 15: F. Oort, Commutative Group Schemes. VI, 133 pages. 1966. DM 9,80 / $ 2.70

Vol. 16: J. Pfanzagl and W. Pierlo, Compact Systems of Sets. IV, 48 pages. 1966. DM 5,80 / $ 1.60

Vol. 17: C. Müller, Spherical Harmonics. IV, 46 pages. 1966. DM 5,– / $ 1.40

Vol. 18: H.-B. Brinkmann und D. Puppe, Kategorien und Funktoren. XII, 107 Seiten, 1966. DM 8,– / $ 2.20

Vol. 19: G. Stolzenberg, Volumes, Limits and Extensions of Analytic Varieties. IV, 45 pages. 1966. DM 5,40 / $ 1.50

Vol. 20: R. Hartshorne, Residues and Duality. VIII, 423 pages. 1966. DM 20,– / $ 5.50

Vol. 21: Seminar on Complex Multiplication. By A. Borel, S. Chowla, C. S. Herz, K. Iwasawa, J.-P. Serre. IV, 102 pages. 1966. DM 8,– / $ 2.20

Vol. 22: H. Bauer, Harmonische Räume und ihre Potentialtheorie. IV, 175 Seiten. 1966. DM 14,– / $ 3.90

Vol. 23: P. L. Ivănescu and S. Rudeanu, Pseudo-Boolean Methods for Bivalent Programming. 120 pages. 1966. DM 10,– / $ 2.80

Vol. 24: J. Lambek, Completions of Categories. IV, 69 pages. 1966. DM 6,80 / $ 1.90

Vol. 25: R. Narasimhan, Introduction to the Theory of Analytic Spaces. IV, 143 pages. 1966. DM 10,– / $ 2.80

Vol. 26: P.-A. Meyer, Processus de Markov. IV, 190 pages. 1967. DM 15,– / $ 4.20

Vol. 27: H. P. Künzi und S. T. Tan, Lineare Optimierung großer Systeme. VI, 121 Seiten. 1966. DM 12,– / $ 3.30

Vol. 28: P. E. Conner and E. E. Floyd, The Relation of Cobordism to K-Theories. VIII, 112 pages. 1966. DM 9,80 / $ 2.70

Vol. 29: K. Chandrasekharan, Einführung in die Analytische Zahlentheorie. VI, 199 Seiten. 1966. DM 16,80 / $ 4.70

Vol. 30: A. Frölicher and W. Bucher, Calculus in Vector Spaces without Norm. X, 146 pages. 1966. DM 12,– / $ 3.30

Vol. 31: Symposium on Probability Methods in Analysis. Chairman. D. A. Kappos.IV, 329 pages. 1967. DM 20,– / $ 5.50

Vol. 32: M. André, Méthode Simpliciale en Algèbre Homologique et Algèbre Commutative. IV, 122 pages. 1967. DM 12,– / $ 3.30

Vol. 33: G. I. Targonski, Seminar on Functional Operators and Equations. IV, 110 pages. 1967. DM 10,– / $ 2.80

Vol. 34: G. E. Bredon, Equivariant Cohomology Theories. VI, 64 pages. 1967. DM 6,80 / $ 1.90

Vol. 35: N. P. Bhatia and G. P. Szegö, Dynamical Systems. Stability Theory and Applications. VI, 416 pages. 1967. DM 24,– / $ 6.60

Vol. 36: A. Borel, Topics in the Homology Theory of Fibre Bundles. VI, 95 pages. 1967. DM 9,– / $ 2.50

Vol. 37: R. B. Jensen, Modelle der Mengenlehre. X, 176 Seiten. 1967. DM 14,– / $ 3.90

Vol. 38: R. Berger, R. Kiehl, E. Kunz und H.-J. Nastold, Differentialrechnung in der analytischen Geometrie IV, 134 Seiten. 1967 DM 12,– / $ 3.30

Vol. 39: Séminaire de Probabilités I. II, 189 pages. 1967. DM 14,– / $ 3.90

Vol. 40: J. Tits, Tabellen zu den einfachen Lie Gruppen und ihren Darstellungen. VI, 53 Seiten. 1967. DM 6.80 / $ 1.90

Vol. 41: A. Grothendieck, Local Cohomology. VI, 106 pages. 1967. DM 10,– / $ 2.80

Vol. 42: J. F. Berglund and K. H. Hofmann, Compact Semitopological Semigroups and Weakly Almost Periodic Functions. VI, 160 pages. 1967. DM 12,– / $ 3.30

Vol. 43: D. G. Quillen, Homotopical Algebra. VI, 157 pages. 1967. DM 14,– / $ 3.90

Vol. 44: K. Urbanik, Lectures on Prediction Theory. IV, 50 pages. 1967. DM 5,80 / $ 1.60

Vol. 45: A. Wilansky, Topics in Functional Analysis. VI, 102 pages. 1967. DM 9,60 / $ 2.70

Vol. 46: P. E. Conner, Seminar on Periodic Maps. IV, 116 pages. 1967. DM 10,60 / $ 3.00

Vol. 47: Reports of the Midwest Category Seminar I. IV, 181 pages. 1967. DM 14,80 / $ 4.10

Vol. 48: G. de Rham, S. Maumary et M. A. Kervaire, Torsion et Type Simple d'Homotopie. IV, 101 pages. 1967. DM 9,60 / $ 2.70

Vol. 49: C. Faith, Lectures on Injective Modules and Quotient Rings. XVI, 140 pages. 1967. DM 12,80 / $ 3.60

Vol. 50: L. Zalcman, Analytic Capacity and Rational Approximation. VI, 155 pages. 1968. DM 13.20 / $ 3.70

Vol. 51: Séminaire de Probabilités II. IV, 199 pages. 1968. DM 14,– / $ 3.90

Vol. 52: D. J. Simms, Lie Groups and Quantum Mechanics. IV, 90 pages. 1968. DM 8,– / $ 2.20

Vol. 53: J. Cerf, Sur les difféomorphismes de la sphère de dimension trois ($\Gamma_4 = 0$). XII, 133 pages. 1968. DM 12,– / $ 3.30

Vol. 54: G. Shimura, Automorphic Functions and Number Theory. VI, 69 pages. 1968. DM 8,– / $ 2.20

Vol. 55: D. Gromoll, W. Klingenberg und W. Meyer, Riemannsche Geometrie im Großen. VI, 287 Seiten. 1968. DM 20,– / $ 5.50

Vol. 56: K. Floret und J. Wloka, Einführung in die Theorie der lokalkonvexen Räume. VIII, 194 Seiten. 1968. DM 16,– / $ 4.40

Vol. 57: F. Hirzebruch und K. H. Mayer, O (n)-Mannigfaltigkeiten, exotische Sphären und Singularitäten. IV, 132 Seiten. 1968. DM 10,80 / $ 3.00

Vol. 58: Kuramochi Boundaries of Riemann Surfaces. IV, 102 pages. 1968. DM 9,60 / $ 2.70

Vol. 59: K. Jänich, Differenzierbare G-Mannigfaltigkeiten. VI, 89 Seiten. 1968. DM 8,– / $ 2.20

Vol. 60: Seminar on Differential Equations and Dynamical Systems. Edited by G. S. Jones. VI, 106 pages. 1968. DM 9,60 / $ 2.70

Vol. 61: Reports of the Midwest Category Seminar II. IV, 91 pages. 1968. DM 9,60 / $ 2.70

Vol. 62: Harish-Chandra, Automorphic Forms on Semisimple Lie Groups X, 138 pages. 1968. DM 14,– / $ 3.90

Vol. 63: F. Albrecht, Topics in Control Theory. IV, 65 pages. 1968. DM 6,80 / $ 1.90

Vol. 64: H. Berens, Interpolationsmethoden zur Behandlung von Approximationsprozessen auf Banachräumen. VI, 90 Seiten. 1968. DM 8,– / $ 2.20

Vol. 65: D. Kölzow, Differentiation von Maßen. XII, 102 Seiten. 1968. DM 8,– / $ 2.20

Vol. 66: D. Ferus, Totale Absolutkrümmung in Differentialgeometrie und -topologie. VI, 85 Seiten. 1968. DM 8,– / $ 2.20

Vol. 67: F. Kamber and P. Tondeur, Flat Manifolds. IV, 53 pages. 1968. DM 5,80 / $ 1.60

Vol. 68: N. Boboc et P. Mustată, Espaces harmoniques associés aux opérateurs différentiels linéaires du second ordre de type elliptique. VI, 95 pages. 1968. DM 8,60 / $ 2.40

Vol. 69: Seminar über Potentialtheorie. Herausgegeben von H. Bauer. VI, 180 Seiten. 1968. DM 14,80 / $ 4.10

Vol. 70: Proceedings of the Summer School in Logic. Edited by M. H. Löb. IV, 331 pages. 1968. DM 20,– / $ 5.50

Vol. 71: Séminaire Pierre Lelong (Analyse), Année 1967 – 1968. VI, 19 pages. 1968. DM 14,– / $ 3.90

Bitte wenden / Continued

Beschaffenheit der Manuskripte

Die Manuskripte werden photomechanisch vervielfältigt; sie müssen daher in sauberer Schreibmaschinenschrift geschrieben sein. Handschriftliche Formeln bitte nur mit schwarzer Tusche eintragen. Notwendige Korrekturen sind bei dem bereits geschriebenen Text entweder durch Überkleben des alten Textes vorzunehmen oder aber müssen die zu korrigierenden Stellen mit weißem Korrekturlack abgedeckt werden. Falls das Manuskript oder Teile desselben neu geschrieben werden müssen, ist der Verlag bereit, dem Autor bei Erscheinen seines Bandes einen angemessenen Betrag zu zahlen. Die Autoren erhalten 75 Freiexemplare.

Zur Erreichung eines möglichst optimalen Reproduktionsergebnisses ist es erwünscht, daß bei der vorgesehenen Verkleinerung der Manuskripte der Text auf einer Seite in der Breite möglichst 18 cm und in der Höhe 26,5 cm nicht überschreitet. Entsprechende Satzspiegelvordrucke werden vom Verlag gern auf Anforderung zur Verfügung gestellt.

Manuskripte, in englischer, deutscher oder französischer Sprache abgefaßt, nimmt Prof. Dr. A. Dold, Mathematisches Institut der Universität Heidelberg, Tiergartenstraße oder Prof. Dr. B. Eckmann, Eidgenössische Technische Hochschule, Zürich, entgegen.

Cette série a pour but de donner des informations rapides, de niveau élevé, sur des développements récents en mathématiques, aussi bien dans la recherche que dans l'enseignement supérieur. On prévoit de publier

1. des versions préliminaires de travaux originaux et de monographies
2. des cours spéciaux portant sur un domaine nouveau ou sur des aspects nouveaux de domaines classiques
3. des rapports de séminaires
4. des conférences faites à des congrès ou à des colloquiums

En outre il est prévu de publier dans cette série, si la demande le justifie, des rapports de séminaires et des cours multicopiés ailleurs mais déjà épuisés.

Dans l'intérêt d'une diffusion rapide, les contributions auront souvent un caractère provisoire; le cas échéant, les démonstrations ne seront données que dans les grandes lignes. Les travaux présentés pourront également paraître ailleurs. Une réserve suffisante d'exemplaires sera toujours disponible. En permettant aux personnes intéressées d'être informées plus rapidement, les éditeurs Springer espèrent, par cette série de »prépublications«, rendre d'appréciables services aux instituts de mathématiques. Les annonces dans les revues spécialisées, les inscriptions aux catalogues et les copyrights rendront plus facile aux bibliothèques la tâche de réunir une documentation complète.

Présentation des manuscrits

Les manuscrits, étant reproduits par procédé photomécanique, doivent être soigneusement dactylographiés. Il est recommandé d'écrire à l'encre de Chine noire les formules non dactylographiées. Les corrections nécessaires doivent être effectuées soit par collage du nouveau texte sur l'ancien soit en recouvrant les endroits à corriger par du verni correcteur blanc.

S'il s'avère nécessaire d'écrire de nouveau le manuscrit, soit complètement, soit en partie, la maison d'édition se déclare prête à verser à l'auteur, lors de la parution du volume, le montant des frais correspondants. Les auteurs recoivent 75 exemplaires gratuits.

Pour obtenir une reproduction optimale il est désirable que le texte dactylographié sur une page ne dépasse pas 26,5 cm en hauteur et 18 cm en largeur. Sur demande la maison d'édition met à la disposition des auteurs du papier spécialement préparé.

Les manuscrits en anglais, allemand ou français peuvent être adressés au Prof. Dr. A. Dold, Mathematisches Institut der Universität Heidelberg, Tiergartenstraße ou au Prof. Dr. B. Eckmann, Eidgenössische Technische Hochschule, Zürich.